The Agricultural Handbook

The Agricultural Handbook

Martin Whitby
Peter Rowlinson
Michael Topham
Alan Younger

BSP PROFESSIONAL BOOKS

OXFORD LONDON EDINBURGH

BOSTON PALO ALTO MELBOURNE

First published 1988

ISBN 0–632–01821–6

BSP Professional Books
A division of Blackwell Scientific
   Publications Ltd
Editorial Offices:
Osney Mead, Oxford OX2 0EL
   (Orders: Tel. 0865 240201)
8 John Street, London WC1N 2ES
23 Ainslie Place, Edinburgh EH3 6AJ
3 Cambridge Center, Suite 208, Cambridge,
   MA 02142, USA
667 Lytton Avenue, Palo Alto, California
   94301, USA
107 Barry Street, Carlton, Victoria 3053,
   Australia

Printed and bound in Great Britain by
Mackays of Chatham PLC, Chatham, Kent

CONTENTS

INTRODUCTION

This book is aimed at the growing number of people who have a more than superficial interest in agriculture but who come from non-farming backgrounds. In a country such as the UK with less than 3% of the population working in agriculture the majority of readers probably have only slight acquaintance with this industry. Yet all consume food and the majority will have at least a recreational interest in agriculture. This broadening of interest has led to the introduction of many courses in schools, colleges and universities which require some knowledge of agriculture. The readership of this book is expected to come mainly from students on such courses.

Because the subject is extremely diverse, even elementary university and college level books have become longer, more specialised and more expensive. Yet, we believe there remains a demand for a short comprehensive introductory guide to the agricultural industry. That is what we have tried to provide.

The academically multi-disciplinary nature of our subject matter required authors with specialist knowledge. The separate areas for which we are individually responsible, in the order in which our names appear, are: economics, policies and institutions; animals and their products; management and accounting; crops and their products.

Having divided the contents amongst ourselves we have then chosen to present it in encyclopaedia format. This brings with it the particular advantage of ease of access for the reader, who may follow the cross-referencing of items to any depth required.

In selecting material to present we have chosen to avoid two particular types of information. First, we have not followed the opportunity to present a detailed guide to the rich vernacular language which pervades agriculture. We are well aware of the pleasures of ancient methods of counting sheep and labelling agricultural phenomena; but we are obliged to omit this material simply on the grounds of space. Secondly, we have resisted the temptation to include large numbers of illustrations and photographs. This is defended on the grounds of space and economy, but the reader who must have such material will find it copiously provided in the many farming journals which are regularly published.

How to use this book

The casual user who simply needs to discover the meaning of technical words may use this book like any other encyclopaedia. Those following specific courses in agriculture may find it useful to compile their own thesaurus of key words, which would guide them to the appropriate entries in sequence. Such a list could quickly be assembled by starting with one relevant entry and noting, and following up, the cross-references.

The reader will find that we have not made exhaustive use of cross-referencing. Instead we have limited ourselves to the main keywords which are printed thus *to direct the reader to the related entries*.

For reasons of space we have not tried to define all the general technical terms which are relevant to other industries as well as agriculture. For such words the reader may have to refer to a good dictionary or the appropriate text book.

Having spent many hours debating amongst ourselves as to the merits of including and excluding particular words, we are well aware of the breadth of choice. We also realise that some readers will not agree with the choices we have made. We shall be delighted to hear from anyone wishing to offer advice on the many aspects we have (or have not) covered in this volume.

Finally, we must acknowledge our debts. The most pressing of these are to our two typists, Julie Savage and Susan Gallagher who have laboured long and hard over the many drafts of the text we have produced. We are also grateful to Lionel Hubbard for carefully reading and commenting on two drafts of the book. Finally, we accept that any remaining errors are our own.

M.C. Whitby
P. Rowlinson
M.R. Topham
A. Younger
August 23, 1988

LIST OF ACRONYMS

We list below the most common acronyms used throughout the handbook. Readers will find many other acronyms with specific entries in the text.

ADAS   Agricultural Development and Advisory Service
AI   artificial insemination
DAFS   Department of Agriculture for Scotland
DANI   Department of Agriculture for Northern Ireland
EC   European (Economic) Community
Ecu   European currency unit
ha   hectare
HGCA   Home Grown Cereals Authority
kg   kilogram
MAFF   Ministry of Agriculture, Fisheries and Food
MLC   Meat and Livestock Commission
MMB   Milk Marketing Board

HANDBOOK

abattoir a place where animals are slaughtered and their *carcasses* undergo initial preparation for sale for human consumption. Also called *slaughterhouse.*

abdomen in vertebrate animals, the region of the body containing the viscera other than the heart and lungs which are in the thorax, which is anterior to the abdomen from which it is separated by the diaphragm. The intestine, liver and kidneys are all abdominal organs.

Aberdeen Angus a breed of *beef* cattle originating in E. Scotland. They are black, hornless and early maturing. Although there are limited numbers of purebreds they are used as a crossing sire on dairy cattle, particularly *heifers,* where their small size results in small calves and reduced calving problems.

aberrant an animal or plant showing some unusual difference in structure for the particular species under consideration. The aberrant shows characteristics not strictly in accordance with genetic type.

abomasum in ruminant animals the fourth or true stomach, the site of *enzymic* digestion.

abortion expulsion of the *foetus* from the *uterus* earlier than the usual duration of *pregnancy.* Abortion may be induced by man or may occur spontaneously perhaps as a result of a disease, e.g. *brucellosis.*

acariasis contagious skin disease caused by *mites* (acari).

accessory character a non-essential character of a species.

accessory chromosome see *sex chromosome.*

accessory sex glands various glands associated with the genitalia. The accessory sex glands of the male (e.g. the *prostate, seminal vesicles* and *Cowper's gland*) are important in the production of *semen.*

acclimatisation the process by which animals become accustomed to their environment. This may be by short-term behavioural and physiological adaptations or longer-term genetic changes. More specifically, sheep show acclimatisation when they are *hefted* and will not stray from a particular area of hill or upland unlike an imported flock.

accounting period the period for which accounts are drawn up, usually one year commonly chosen to coincide with the fiscal year or harvest year.

See also *trading and profit and loss account, balance sheet.*

accounting rate of return see *rate of return.*

accounts analysis a method of identifying financial strengths and weaknesses in a farm business, using survey data collected from farms of a similar type. Performance indicators are constructed and explanations sought for differences.

acetabulum in the skeleton of vertebrates the facet or socket of a "ball and socket" joint, e.g. the socket of the *pelvic girdle* which articulates with the head of the *femur.*

acetate a salt of *acetic acid.*

acetic acid the main volatile fatty acid produced as a result of microbial fermentation in the *rumen.* Diets high in long *forages* produce high levels of rumen acetate. As acetate is an important precursor of milk fat, synthesised in the mammary gland, this explains the effect of *forage* diets in maintaining milk fat secretion.

acetonaemia a metabolic disease, affecting lactating cows, in which ketone bodies accumulate in the tissues and are excreted in the milk, urine and on the breath. Common symptoms include loss of appetite and lowered milk produced. It is also referred to as Bovine *ketosis.*

acquired character a modification in the morphology or physiology of an animal or plant which appears during the growth of the individual.

acquired immunity the immunity to subsequent reinfection which is acquired by an animal, when as a result of natural or artificial exposure to a pathogen, (often a foreign protein e.g. bacteria) it develops a specific *antibody.* Contrast *passive immunity.*

acre a unit of area equal to 10 square chains or 4840 square yards. 1 acre = 0.4047 hectare.

actinomycetes micro-organisms, intermediate between bacteria and fungi. Some members are responsible for some crop disease, and others for the spoilage of hay.

actinomycosis See *lumpy jaw.*

acute said of an animal disease which rapidly develops to a crisis.

adaptation the process by which an animal or plant becomes suited to its internal or external environment, or to any changes in that environment.

ADAS see *Agricultural Developmentand Advisory Service.*

adenosine diphosphate (ADP) See *ATP.*

adenosine triphosphate (ATP) See *ATP.*

ADHAC abbreviation for Agricultural Dwelling House Advisory Committee; established under the Rent (Agriculture) Act of 1976. ADHAC's assist local housing authorities, advising them on the degree of urgency with which a farmer may need to repossess a service house from a worker leaving his employment. Committees consist of one worker and one employer representative and an independent member. See also *tied housing.*

adipose tissue a specialised form of connective tissue consisting of vesicular cells filled with fat. Often arranged in lobules and found in certain sites (e.g. subcutaneous, intermuscular and kidney knob and channel) forming large tissue masses. In the live animal adipose tissue has the important physiological roles of energy storage, protection, insulation and lubrication.

adjusted farm area see *adjusted forage area.*

adjusted forage area the forage area of a farm adjusted for the low productivity of *rough grazing.* The area of rough grazing is reduced to a *pasture* equivalent area, based on its stocking capacity relative to that of *in-bye* pasture. Total farm area may be similarly treated to facilitate inter-farm comparisons.

ad libitum a term used in the feeding of farm livestock to indicate that they are given unrestricted access to an unlimited supply of *feed.*

administered prices prices which are determined through various types of policy intervention. These include prices influenced by taxes, subsidies and regulations. In the diagram, the structure of the prices received by EC farmers is described. The basic mechanism raises the price of imports, sold inside the EC, to a *target* level usually by charging a *variable levy* on imports from non-EC countries. Within the EC, the variable levy determines the farmers' price as long as supplies do not exceed internal demand. Once *self-sufficiency* is reached, internal prices may fall to the level at which *intervention buying* occurs. When intervention stocks build up they must be disposed of and this is normally done by selling them on world markets with the aid of an *export refund* or restitution. The effect of these various forms of intervention is to maintain internal prices substantially above the *world market price,* as shown in the diagram. At each level in the diagram alternative terms used in the various different *commodity regimes* of the CAP are listed. The system is administered through intervention Boards in EC Member States.

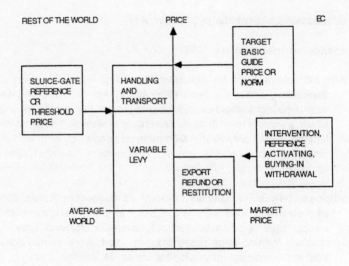

REST OF THE WORLD   PRICE   EC

TARGET
BASIC
GUIDE
PRICE OR
NORM

SLUICE-GATE
REFERENCE
OR
THRESHOLD
PRICE

HANDLING
AND
TRANSPORT

INTERVENTION,
REFERENCE
ACTIVATING,
BUYING-IN
WITHDRAWAL

VARIABLE
LEVY

EXPORT
REFUND OR
RESTITUTION

AVERAGE
WORLD

MARKET
PRICE

adrenal gland an *endocrine* gland which is paired and located near to the kidney. It is composed of two main regions - the medulla which secretes *adrenaline* and the cortex which secretes a number of *corticosteroid* hormones under the control of *acth*.

adrenaline a hormone secreted by the medulla of the *adrenal* gland. It is produced following stimulation of the gland by the *sympathetic* nervous system with which it shares many properties - those of Fight, Flight and Fright. Responses to adrenaline secretion include an increase in heart rate and blood pressure, and a dilation of blood vessels to the heart, muscles and brain.

adventitious roots those which do not derive directly from the primary or tap root but from a stem for example.

aerobic respiration *respiration* occurring in the presence of oxygen.

aetiology the medical or veterinary study of the causation of disease.

afferent a zoological term for 'carrying towards'. Common examples being afferent blood vessels carrying blood to an organ or an afferent sensory nerve carrying nervous impulses to the central nervous system.

afforestation the establishment of forest, usually on agricultural land, by planting trees. In the UK the afforestation since the turn of the century has increased the area of forest from (roughly) 1 to 2m hectares. The tree species most favoured in the hills and uplands, where most planting is done, are conifers.

aflatoxin a poisonous *toxin* produced by the fungus Aspergillus flavus which is found in samples of *groundnut* meal. It leads to a reduction in feed intake, growth rate and feed conversion in animals and there is concern that it may be transmitted through milk and meat to the consuming public where it may be linked with cancer.

afterbirth   the maternal part of the placenta of mammals   which is torn away from the uterus at parturition and   ejected as the third stage of *parturition*.   Given the   opportunity the dams of some species will eat the afterbirth - placentophagia.   Failure to expel the   afterbirth leads to a retained placenta which is associated   with delays in subsequent breeding and with health risks to   the dam.

aftermath   the crops of herbage which become available for   utilisation due to regrowth after an initial cut for silage   or hay in June or July respectively.   These supplies of fresh *herbage,* previously uncontaminated by grazing livestock are valued for good quality, late season *grazing.*

agalactia   failure of the mammary gland to secrete milk.   Found in conjunction with *mastitis* and *metritis* as *MMA.*

aggregation   the binding of individual particles into   larger units or aggregates thus improving the aeration and   *porosity* of the soil.

aggressive behaviour   a type of behaviour including both threats and actual attacks on other animals of the same or   a different species.

agonistic behaviour   a classification of animal behaviour which includes all types of attack, threat, appeasement,   fight and flight.

agribusiness   a large industrial firm which supplies farmers and/or buys their output.   Some farms become   integrated with agribusiness firms through contractual   agreements.

Agricultural Census   a postal census of all occupiers of   agricultural holdings completed on June 4th each year.   There is also a sample census on December 4th.   They   collect data relating to the use of land for crops and   grass, the numbers of livestock and workers. This large   volume of data provides the basis for *MAFF* estimates of the   output of the industry and its aggregate income.   The data   are published in the *MAFF* series *Agricultural Statistics*   where they are broken down to the county level and   tabulated by size and type of farm.   See also Appendix I.

Agricultural Development and Advisory Service (ADAS)   an organisation, funded by *MAFF* providing an advisory service   to farmers, horticultural growers and landowners.   The   resources of the service are shared amongst statutory work,   advice and promotion, and research and development.   See   also *experimental husbandry farms.*   There are four divisions of ADAS: Agriculture, Agricultural Science,   Veterinary, and Land and Water Services; managed through a   regional structure of offices. Agricultural Advisors are   located at the District level and Specialists at regional   headquarters. ADAS operates in England and Wales but in Scotland the advisory service is based on the three colleges of agriculture funded by the Department of Agriculture for Scotland *(DAFS)*. In Northern Ireland a similar system operates through the Department of Agriculture for Northern Ireland *(DANI)*.

Agricultural Holdings Act 1984 effective from 12th July 1984, this Act changed the law on tenancies, in an attempt to reverse the decline of the tenanted sector. Its two main features are changes in the procedures for determining rents, and changes in succession rights. Rents are no longer to be fixed according to an open market valuation. Instead, rents take account of "the production capacity of the holding and its related earning capacity". Existing tenants at the 12th July 1984 keep all their succession rights, usually meaning the retention of the tenancy for up to three generations, established under the 1976 Agricultural Holdings Act. New tenancies, created after 12th July 1984, are to be lifetime only tenancies without succession rights. Short-term letting for up to five years is permitted subject to provisions, including a trial period for an inexperienced tenant. See also *rent review.*

Agricultural Improvement Scheme a farm capital grant scheme, introduced in 1985, whereby farmers are offered an array of grants towards the cost specified capital investments. The rates vary per item of capital and are generally higher for farmers within the *Less Favoured Areas.* Although this scheme introduced rates of grant rather lower than had previously been offered, various environmental improvements were brought within its scope for the first time. See also *structures policy.*

Agricultural Mortgage Corporation (AMC) a lending agency established under the Agricultural Credits Act, 1928. The corporation raises its funds for lending on the money market. It operates from central headquarters in London and uses the main clearing banks as its agents in vetting the credit worthiness of borrowers. The AMC is permitted to lend only on first mortgages on the security of agricultural land. Although the AMC lends for any agricultural purpose, the majority of *loans* are advanced for land purchase.

agricultural policy includes a wide range of Governmental policies administered mainly by the *Ministry of Agriculture, Fisheries and Food (MAFF)* and related departments in the rest of the UK. The Government's main policy objectives were stated in the 1947 Act as: "to promote and maintain a stable and efficient agricultural industry capable of producing such part of the nation's food supply as, in the national interest, it is desirable to produce in the UK and of producing it at minimum prices consistent with proper remuneration and living conditions for farmers and workers in agriculture and with an adequate return on capital invested in the industry. "

These objectives have never been withdrawn, but there has been some re-ordering of priorities as a consequence of joining the *European*

Community on 1st January 1973, and participating in its *Common Agricultural Policy*. See also *Agriculture Improvement Scheme, Annual Review of Agriculture, Marketing Boards.*

agricultural productivity often used to describe total production but, strictly, should refer to output in relation to inputs. Most commonly refers to the level of output per man-equivalent in agriculture. Because the agricultural labour force is declining, output per man has increased fairly rapidly (though at a slower rate in recent years). However, if all inputs are taken into account, the output per unit of all inputs has increased at broadly the same rate as in other industries. See also *yield.*

agricultural statistics data collected through the *Agricultural Census* and other sources. See Appendix I.

Agricultural Training Board established under the Industrial Training Act of 1966, initially to provide training for hired agricultural workers, funded from a levy on employers. The Board now trains both workers and farmers and provides a variety of courses for them at the regional level. It uses the facilities of county colleges of agriculture and the experience of established farmers in its training programme. Its annual budget, now funded through *MAFF,* was £8m in 1985/6.

agricultural unit of account (AUA) The common currency unit used by the *European Community* from 1962 to 1979. Initially the value of an AUA was equal to that of one US dollar. It was replaced by the *European currency unit* (or Ecu) in 1979. See also *green currency.*

Agricultural Wages Boards determine minimum wage rates, weekly hours and working conditions, for hired farm workers. They consist of union representatives of farm workers and employers, together with appointed members including an independent chairman. The wage rates and working conditions determined are legally enforceable. The independent members are usually important in acting as arbitrators between the representatives of workers and employers.

Agriculture Improvement Scheme introduced in 1985, to provide capital grants for a range of activities on farms, replacing the Farm and Horticultural Development Scheme. Eligible farms must be earning less than a stated income before beginning the scheme and less than 120% of the stated income at the end of the scheme. Grants generally range from 5% to 50% of the cost of investing in certain items. New grants are available for environmentally related investment on farms including trees, hedges, bracken control, heather regeneration, waste treatment and energy saving measures. Within the *Less Favoured Areas* most forms of investment receive higher rates of grant and there are special grants available for craft and light industries and tourism.

agrostis see *bent grasses.*

albino an individual animal of any species deficient of pigmentation to the skin, hair, eyes, etc.

albumen a protein-rich, nutritive material which surrounds the yolk in an egg. The 'white' of avian eggs.

albumin one of a group of water soluble proteins which are coagulated by heat. Examples include lactalbumin (from milk), serum albumin (from blood) and egg albumen.

aldrin a contact *insecticide* often used in *wire worm* control.

alfalfa see *lucerne.*

algae poisoning a type of poisoning resulting from the ingestion of *toxins,* produced in decomposing algae, by farm livestock. More common in the USA than the UK.

alimentary system all the organs of an animal, involved in digestion, absorption and nutrition.

alkali disease a chronic disease of domestic animals, characterised by emaciation, stiffness and anaemia, due to an excess of dietary selenium. In its acute form the disease is called 'blind staggers'.

allantois one of the membranes of the developing *foetus* which has respiratory, nutritive and excretory functions.

allele an alternative form of a *gene.*

allelomimetic behaviour social behaviour involving imitation of another animal of the same species. Examples would include grazing behaviour in cattle or sheep, where all the animals tend to display the same behaviour at the same time - they behave as a herd or a flock.

allometric growth a type of growth in plants or animals in which the size of a part is a constant exponential function of the whole or more simply the growth of a part is related to the growth of the whole. Often described by the equation of relative growth $Y=aX^b$ where Y is the measurement of a part of an organism, X that of the whole and b is the relative growth coefficient.

allosome any chromosome other than a typical one, e.g. sex chromosome.

alluvium a soil type derived from river deposits which is usually fertile and able to support good crop growth.

alpha-amylase an *enzyme* which is responsible for the breakdown of starch into simple sugars. Excessive levels of alpha-amylase in a *wheat* sample indicate that it is unsuitable for bread making. See *Hagberg.*

alpha helix a right-hand helical structure of many important biological molecules, notably *DNA.*

alsike clover (Trifolium hybridum) an herbaceous *legume* used for *forage.* Alsike is intermediate in appearance and growth habit between *red clover* and *white clover.* It is a short lived perennial and can be used as a replacement for *red clover* especially in acid and waterlogged conditions, of which it is more tolerant.

alternaria see *leaf spot.*

alternative hosts plants or animals which inadvertantly provide a home for pest or disease organisms, often when the main host is unavailable. This allows the organism to survive an otherwise difficult period. The alternative host may or may not show any adverse signs as a result of the association. An example is *fat hen,* a weed plant which can act as a host to Black Bean *aphid* which spreads *virus yellows* disease of *sugar beet.*

alveolus in higher animals a small cavity of the lungs or the cavity of a gland, e.g. the mammary gland. More generally a small pit or depression on the surface of an animal or a plant.

amaplasmosis a disease, particularly of cattle but sheep or pigs may also be affected, caused by a protozoal infection. The *protozoa* become localised in the red blood corpuscles and transmitted by biting flies, ticks or mosquitoes. The disease is characterised by anaemia, fever and jaundice and is also called Gall-sickness.

ammonia a compound of nitrogen and hydrogen which is a pungent, akaline gas at normal temperatures and pressures. Ammonia is used, in various forms, as a source of nitrogen for plants and animals. See also *anhydrous ammonia, aqueous ammonia, ammonium nitrate, sulphate of ammonia.* Ammonia gas may also be emitted when feedstuffs deteriorate and *proteins* breakdown. The level of ammonia then indicates the extent of degradation. This protein degradation also occurs in the *rumen* where ammonia becomes an important nitrogen source for the rumen bacteria.

ammonium nitrate the most concentrated solid form of inorganic nitrogen *fertiliser. Granules* or *prills* of ammonium nitrate (34% N) are frequently used for *top dressing* crops when a source of *straight* nitrogen is required. Both the ammonium and the nitrate ions are water soluble and therefore readily available for plant growth.

ammonium sulphate see *sulphate of ammonia.*

amnion   one of the membranes of the developing foetus. As well as a nutritive role it serves an important protective role by cushioning the developing *embryo.*

amoeboid of a cell, e.g. a white blood cell; one having no fixed form, which creeps and engulfs food.

amortisation table used to calculate the periodic instalments required to repay an *annuity loan.* The instalments are calculated by multiplying the amount borrowed by an 'amortisation factor' from the table, relating to the appropriate combination of loan life and interest rate.   An amortisation table can also be used to estimate the average annual *depreciation* plus *interest* of an *asset.*

ampulla any of a variety of small membranous vesicles occurring in animals. Examples include a dilated tubule at the end of the mammary gland and the swollen region of the *vas deferens* in the *prostrate* area of the male reproductive   tract.

amylase an enzyme capable of hydrolysing starch.

amylolytic starch-digesting, as in amylolytic bacteria in the *rumen.*

amylose a general term for starch, inulin and related carbohydrates.

anabolism   the chemical changes proceeding in all living organisms involving the formation of complex substances   from simpler ones. Growth is the summation of the anabolism of the various body tissues. Pregnancy anabolism is the phenomenon of increased energy retention by the pregnant female.

anaemia reduction in the levels of red blood corpuscles and thus haemoglobin circulating in the blood e.g. Infectious anaemia, a *septicaemia* of horses due to a viral infection.

anaerobe an organism capable of living in the absence of oxygen. Examples include some species of *rumen* bacteria.

anaerobic respiration respiration which proceeds within a tissue, in the absence of oxygen.

anal atresia the absence of the *anus.* This may occur as a genetic abnormality in pigs and is fatal.

analysis of variance a statistical technique mainly used for biological data which involves the separation of the variance due to one factor, or set of factors, from other factors affecting a set of observations.

anatomy the study of the form and structure of animals and plants.

androgen a male *hormone* produced mainly in the testes but also in other organs e.g. adrenal cortex. It has androgenic effects in stimulating male characteristics. Testosterone and androsterone are two of the more important androgens.

androsterone an androgenic hormone.

anhydrous ammonia ammonia gas liquified under pressure. It is the most concentrated (82% N) type of nitrogen fertiliser available, and is injected into the soil.

animal starch see *glycogen*.

annual charge an estimate of the annual cost of depreciating *assets* such as machinery and buildings. An annual charge is made up of average annual charges for *depreciation, interest* payments and repair costs. Used in *partial budgeting*.

annual percentage rate (APR) the true interest rate after taking into account the frequency with which interest is charged. For example, for a nominal interest rate of 10% per annum, charged monthly, *compounding* would produce an APR of just under 12.6%. See also *flat rate, compounding.*

annual plants those cultivated or weed plants which complete their life cycle from seed to seed in one growing season.

Annual Review of Agriculture introduced in the Agricultural Act (1947), the Review is conducted annually as a series of discussions between officials of the *MAFF* and the *National Farmers Unions*. Prior to 1973 the purpose was to assess the economic status of the industry as a precursor to the Government's determination of agricultural prices. The process ended with publication of its factual conclusions and the Government's price determination in a White Paper. With entry into the EC, the emphasis of the Review shifted: its annual White Paper now consists solely of a detailed factual and statistical statement of the industry's economic situation.

annuity loan a *loan* whereby each periodic instalment of capital repayment plus interest is the same throughout the term of the loan (for a given interest rate). With this kind of loan, the interest component in each instalment is high at first, progressively decreasing, compensated by an increasing capital component.

anoestrus a condition of the non-pregnant female animal when she is not showing recurrent *oestrus cycles.* All species of farm livestock usually exhibit a period of anoestrus after parturition and in pigs this may extend throughout lactation. In sheep and other species which are seasonal breeders there is also a period of seasonal anoestrus. Anoestrus may be overcome by treatment with *exogenous hormones.*

anorexia loss of appetite leading to a marked reduction in food intake.

anthelminthic or anthelmintic a drug administered to animals against intestinal worms.

anther the male organ in a flower which bears the pollen grains.

anthesis the process of flowering which includes the release of pollen and its dispersal to the *stigma.*

anthrax a *notifiable disease* of livestock caused by the anthrax bacillus and transmisable from animals to man.

antibiotic a chemical substance produced by a micro-organism (e.g. fungi or bacteria) which inhibits the growth of rival micro-organisms. Many antibiotics have been isolated and purified and used for animal treatment, for *therapeutic* or *prophylactic* reasons. Legislation restricts the range of antibiotics. A range of antibiotics, also restricted by legislation are used as *feed additives* for growth promotion.

antibody a particular form of *gamma globulin* present in the blood serum of an animal developed in response to invasion by an *antigen.* It confers *immunity* against subsequent reinfection by the same antigen.

antienzymes the antibodies of *enzymes* which neutralise the action of an enzyme; e.g. the autodigestion of the stomach is prevented by the presence of antienzymes in the walls of the stomach.

antigen any foreign substance (e.g. a bacteria or virus), the presence of which in an animal's body results in the production of *antibodies* as protection against infection.

antioxidant a substance which delays the process of oxidation.

antiseptic an agent which destroys or prevents the growth of bacteria.

antitoxin a substance, produced by an animal, which by uniting with a *toxin,* prevents its poisonous action.

anus the posterior opening of the alimentary canal through which undigested residues (*faeces*) are excreted.

anxiety in animal behaviour a secondary drive, established by the development of a conditioned avoidance response. The stimulus then acts as negative reinforcement for other responses or elicits unusual behaviour. It may be seen in intensively housed livestock and is cited by animal welfarists as evidence against such intensive systems.

aorta the principal arterial vessels by which the blood leaves the heart and passes to the body.

apex the tip or main shoot of a plant, the growing point.

aphids insects of the order Hemiptera which are important as crop pests. The aphid family contains many examples such as *greenfly* and *blackfly* all of which cause damage to crops directly by feeding on plant sap, causing *wilting*. However, the main damage is frequently done indirectly by the introduction of *virus* diseases to plants by the mouthparts of feeding aphids. By moving from infected to healthy plants, the aphids act as vectors of the virus disease. Examples of important *viral* diseases which aphids help to spread are *barley yellow dwarf* virus of *cereals*, *virus yellows* of *sugar beet* and *leaf roll* of *potatoes*. Control of aphids and restriction of *virus* diseases is achieved by the use of *systemic insecticides*.

aphototrophic an active negative response of a plant or an animal to a light stimulus.

aphthous fever see *foot-and-mouth disease.*

apical dominance the situation in which the growth of the apical bud (apex) of a plant, more or less strongly inhibits the development of lateral or side shoots below it. The mechanisms of apical dominance appear to involve the production of a plant *hormone* at the *apex* which inhibits lateral shoot development. Removal of the *apex* prevents the inhibition and allows *axillary buds* to develop. In practice, apical dominance is important in restricting the number of *tillers* on *cereal* plants and especially in the management of *seed potato tubers*. If *seed tubers* are allowed to sprout shortly after harvest, then one shoot is produced at the expense of others. These *seed tubers* are said to be apically dominant and will tend to produce plants with relatively few large tubers, early in the season. Such apical dominance can be prevented by cold storing *seed tubers* until shortly before planting when several shoots will develop or it can be destroyed by removal of the *apical bud.*

apical meristem the growing point on the main axis of a plant.

appeasement behaviour a type of behaviour which ends the attack on one animal by another of the same species.

appendix an outgrowth, specifically of the large intestine.

appreciation an increase in the value of an *asset;* the opposite of *depreciation.*

approved products chemicals for agricultural use which have been tested and have received clearance for specific applications through the Agricultural Chemicals Approval Scheme (ACAS).

aquaculture cultivation of the resources of the sea and inland waters.

aqueous consisting largely of water; dissolved in water.

aqueous ammonia a solution of ammonia gas in water. Used as a type of nitrogen fertiliser which is injected into the soil. (21-29% N).

arable pertaining to cultivation. Arable crops are those which are produced by regular cultivation, for example *cereals, pulses, oilseed rape.* Contrast *grasslands.*

Areas of Outstanding Natural Beauty (AONB) areas of land designated by the *Countryside Commission* under the *National Parks* legislation of 1949 and 1968, and confirmed by the Secretary of State for the Environment. There are currently 38 designated AONBs covering nearly 2m ha in England and Wales.

arginine one of the *essential amino acids* which must be supplied in dietary form to animals.

arteriole a small *artery.*

artery a vessel of the vascular system of animals which conveys *blood* from the heart to the body tissues.

arthritis inflammation of a joint of the skeleton.

artificial insemination (AI) involves the implanting, by artificial means, of *semen* containing *spermatozoa* into the reproductive tract of the female. Of the farm species, AI is of most importance in cattle where it has contributed significantly to genetic improvement. Various physiological and managerial factors have limited its use in sheep and pigs.

ascorbic acid see *vitamin C.*

ash the mineral component of a sample of feed. It is the residue left after the thorough burning of the organic matter.

aspergillosis a fungal infection which may cause abortion in cattle or respiratory infection in poultry.

asphyxia deficiency of oxygen in the blood which may occur due to suffocation.

assay quantitative analysis of a substance by chemical or biological means.

assets anything with monetary value that a business owns. Assets are shown on the *balance sheet* categorised according to their *liquidity*. Those which are used within a production cycle or financial year are termed current assets, and include cash in hand, trade *debtors,* produce for sale, stores such as fertiliser and feedingstuffs, and *trading livestock.* Assets which are kept over several production cycles are termed fixed assets. They include machinery and equipment, *breeding livestock* (excluding young stock), buildings and land. Off-farm assets such as stocks and shares, or those held in subsidiary or associated businesses are also distinguished and grouped under investments. *Goodwill,* say between a land agency and clients, has a value and may be included on the *balance sheet* as an *intangible asset.*

assortative mating selection of animals for breeding on the basis of visual characteristics in the *phenotye.*

atavism See *reversion.*

ataxia incoordination of muscles resulting in irregular and uncontrolled movement.

at-foot a dam-young interrelationship. Thus a ewe with lambs at-foot has suckling lambs with her.

atherosclerosis a thickening of the arteries caused by calcareous and fatty deposits. There is considerable interest in the influence of diet, particularly animal fats, on atherosclerosis in humans.

ATP Adenosine triphosphate, a substance which has the vital function of storage, transport and transfer of energy within cells. When ATP is *hydrolised,* it yields inorganic phosphate, ADP (adenosine diphosphate) and energy. The energy released can be used in processes which require it, such as starch synthesis, protein synthesis, movement etc. As the reaction is reversible, the ADP can be made to recombine with phosphate to produce ATP using the energy released during respiration.

atresia process of narrowing or disappearance by degeneration within an animal's body, e.g. follicles within mammalian *ovaries.*

atrophic rhinitis an infectious disease of the pig characterised by inflammation of the nasal mucous membrane and deformity of the snout. Whilst a number of bacterial species are commonly associated with the disease, the causal agent has not been determined.

atrophy degeneration which may be seen as a reduction in size, complexity or function due to disuse.

attenuation the partial or total loss of virulence of parasitic *bacteria, viruses* or *fungi.*

auction market (or mart) a traditional market where livestock are shown in a ring and sold. The bid, or offer price, is raised in steps to a maximum at which level the sale goes to the highest bidder. See also *liveweight marketing,* contrast *Dutch auction.*

Aujesky's Disease a virus disease of cattle and pigs which was made *notifiable* in 1979. It is characterised by intense itching of the hindquarters but other varied symptoms occur e.g. loss of appetite, vomiting, diarrhoea, excessive salivation and convulsions. In 1983 an eradication scheme was started in Great Britain.

Aureomycin an *antibiotic* widely used in the treatment of animals.

auricles 1. A pair of projections in the lower corners of the leaf blades in the *gramineae.* Their size and shape may be used for identification of *species* or *variety.* 2. One of the upper collecting chambers of the *heart* which receive blood from the *veins* before passing it to the *ventricles.*

autogamy self-fertilisation.

autointoxication poisoning of the body by *toxins* produced within it.

automatic cluster removal (ACR) the automatic removal of the *cluster* of the *milking machine* at the end of milking. ACR's operate by sensing the reduction in the flow of milk as milk removal from the gland nears completion.

autonomic nervous system the system of motor nerve fibres which supply the smooth muscles and glands of an animal's body. The system consists of two parts the sympathetic and *parasympathetic.*

autophagous capable of self feeding from the moment of birth.

autosome a typical chromosome: any chromosome other than one of the sex *chromosomes.*

autostoses cartilage bones.

autotrophic bacteria those which are able to utilise carbon dioxide for growth by *photosynthetic* or chemosynthetic means.

auxins growth substances secreted in one part of a plant which have physiological effects in other regions; sometimes called plant *hormones.*

auxocyte any cell in which *meiosis* is started, e.g. the *oocyte* or *spermatocyte.*

available water capacity (AWC) the amount of water held by a soil between *field capacity* and *permanentwilting point.*

avian leucosis a group of fatal diseases affecting the chicken. They are caused by several distinct but related *viruses* and are characterised by abnormalities of the *lymphatic system.*

avitaminosis any deficiency disease caused by a lack of *vitamins.*

awn a slender, bristle-like outgrowth from the *lemma* of a cereal *floret.* The awn may be a prolongation of the tip of the lemma (terminal) e.g. in cultivated *barley,* or it may arise on the back of the lemma (dorsal) e.g. in wild *oats.*

axil the upper angle between a leaf and its stem.

axillary bud the bud which originates in the *axil* of a leaf which can give rise to an axillary branch.

axis 1. The central line of symmetry of an animal, plant or organ. 2. The second cervical vertebra of vertebrate animals which allows for the considerable movement of the neck region. 3. The main trunk of a shoot, root or grass spikelet.

axon the long, impulse carrying process of a typical neurone or nerve cell.

Ayrshire a breed of *dairy* cattle originating in S.W. Scotland. Despite claims of good dairy conformation and longevity the breeds moderate average yield of around 5000kg at 3.9% fat and 3.4% protein has led to its decline in numbers throughout the UK as it has been replaced by *Holstein-Friesians.*

Babcock apparatus a type of test tube centrifuge previously widely used for measuring the butterfat content of milk, but now largely obsolete due to the use of *spectrometry*.

bacillaceae family of rod shaped *bacteria*. Many of the species of which are pathological, e.g. *Clostridium.*

bacillus a rod shaped *bacterium.*

backcross a genetic term for the *progeny* obtained from mating a first generation cross (F1) to one of the original parental types (P1).

backfill permeable materials used to place over *tile* or *plastic drains* to facilitate movement of water into the field *drainage* system. Backfill is normally used to within 25cm of the ground surface. The most commonly used materials are gravels of varying sizes but other permeable materials are also used.

bacon meat, generally from the side and back of a pig, which has been preserved by curing with a salt solution.

bacteria microscopic single cell organisms with rigid cell walls. Three main groups are recognised according to their shape; Cocci are spherical, Bacilli are rod shaped and Spirilla forms are curved or twisted rods. Bacteria are important in the soil, in plants and in animals where they can have both positive and negative effects on production. Examples of positive effects are the fermentation of *silage* by *lactobacilli,* the fixation of atmospheric nitrogen by *Rhizobia* in legumes and the digestion of cellulose in the *rumen* of *ruminant* animals. Examples of negative effects inlcude many plant and animal diseases which are of bacterial nature.

bacteriocide a substance capable of destroying *bacteria.*

bacteriophage a general term for a *virus* which infects *bacteria.*

bacteriostatic describes a substance which is able to inhibit bacterial multiplication.

bag the udder of a cow. Thence: 'bag-up' the term used to describe the enlarging udder of a cow immediately prior to calving as the mammary gland develops and milk secretion begins.

bail milking the milking of cows in a portable shed or bail. This may be in a relatively permanent position or moved from field to field as is common in New Zealand.

balance sheet an account which presents the *capital* position of a business at a point in time, usually the last day of the *accounting period.* It shows where the funds used in the business have come from and where they have gone to, by displaying the business's *liabilities* and *assets.* It is this feature which gives rise to the term Balance Sheet, as the liabilities or the claims on a business, must equal the value of the assets.

balancing charge an adjustment made to *profit* on the disposal of an *asset,* if there is a discrepancy between its depreciated *book value* and the actual price received. See also *depreciation.*

bale a compact parcel of bedding or *forage* material.

ballottement a method of *pregnancy diagnosis* which involves the manual displacement of the *foetus* in the fluid which surrounds it in the *uterus.*

band spraying the process of applying *crop protection* chemicals directionally either between or onto crop rows.

Bang's disease a bovine contagious abortion or *brucellosis.* It is caused by the bacterium Brucella abortus which is sometimes referred to as Bang's bacillus.

bank overdraft short term *credit* granted by a bank. It is generally the cheapest form of borrowing. Interest is charged daily on the balance overdrawn, the limit of which is agreed beforehand. An overdraft is reviewed typically every six months and may be called in at short notice or reduced at any such review. It is intended to finance *working capital* requirements. See also *loans.*

barley (Hordeum sativum) a *cereal* crop grown primarily for grain production in the U.K. although the *straw* may be used as *litter* or as a source of roughage in *ruminant* diets. Although originally grown for human food, barley grain is now used primarily as an animal feed or for *malting.* The grain of barley remains enclosed in the *lemma* and *palea* and all varieties in the U.K. bear *awns.* Both autumn and spring sown types exist. Spring sown types were popular because they were cheap and easy to grow, suffering very little from *fungal* diseases. However, with the wider availability of *fungicides* to control diseases such as *mildew,* the higher yield potential of autumn sown types can be realised and these are now favoured by farmers.

barley yellow dwarf virus (BYDV) a disease of *cereals* transmitted by *aphids.* These introduce the *virus* into early emerging autumn sown crops and the spread may continue throughout mild winters. Patches of stunted, discoloured plants become apparent in spring, when neighbouring plants begin to grow. Early drilled crops are most susceptible. Control can be achieved by an aphicidal spray in late October/early November.

barn a building used mainly for the storage of agricultural products.

barn dried hay made by completing the drying process under forced ventilation conditions in a barn. Because this product is dried in a more controlled environment, it is usually of higher quality than field dried *hay*.

barrow a *castrated* male *pig*. Also referred to as a *hog*.

basal metabolic rate the minimal quantity of heat produced by an animal at rest over a given period of time.

basic slag by-product of old steel making process which contains *phosphate* (approximately 16%). It is valued as a source of *fertiliser* phosphate because the nutrient becomes available gradually and because it has some *liming* properties and contains some *micronutrients.*

basiphil cells 1. A type of white blood cell. 2. Cells of the anterior lobe of the *pituitary* gland.

bastard feathers in birds, the quill feathers (usually three in number) borne on the first digit of the wing.

battery see *cage.*

battery hens laying hens kept indoors in cages often in three-tiered rows. Over 95% of Britain's *eggs* are produced from battery hens as such *intensive* systems achieve a high rate of egg laying per unit cost. Battery systems do however give some concern on animal *welfare* grounds.

baulk see *ridge.*

beans (Vicia faba) annual plants of the family Leguminosae, grown as a cultivated crop for consumption by humans, *(broad beans),* and animals, *(field beans).* Some are sown in autumn, others in spring. Historically, a good *break crop* in a predominantly *cereal rotation;* they fix *nitrogen* and can therefore increase the fertility of the soil. Yields are variable from season to season and the popularity of the crop has declined.

beastings see *colostrum.*

Beaumont period an important factor in the control of *potato blight.* The *fungus* responsible for the disease tends to spread rapidly in warm humid conditions. Thus, when the temperature has been at or above 10°C and the relative humidity above 75%, a Beaumont period is declared, warning farmers of the likely development of potato blight and enabling the application of a protective *fungicidal* spray to prevent disease attack.

bed the name given to the areas of soil within a field in which the main crop cultivation occurs. Plants may be grown in beds to avoid the effects of compaction caused by tractor wheels or to achieve the optimum *plant population* or spatial arrangement.

beef meat from *cattle,* except from young calves which is referred to as *veal.* Beef is often referred to as a *red meat.*

beef carcass classification a marketing service administered by the *Meat and Livestock Commission.* The present system was introduced in 1981 to bring the UK system into line with the EC Beef Carcass Classification Scheme. The aim is to describe carcasses in common terms to provide information to all those involved in beef trading: farmer, wholesaler and butcher. Carcasses are described by sex, weight, fat level and *conformation.* Fat classes run from 1 (leanest) to 5 (fattest) with some classes being subdivided, H or L. Conformation classes run from E (best beef carcass profile), through to U, R and O to P (worst profile). Classes U, O and P are subdivided into upper (+) and lower (-) bands. The most common classification in the UK is R4L.

beef cow a cow or heifer whose primary purpose is to rear calves for beef production. Contrast *dairy cows.*

Beef Regime the policy instruments applied through the CAP to beef production. They include a Variable Premium Scheme for clean (unbred) stock, Intervention Buying for beef of required quality, and a *suckler cow premium scheme.* The Variable Premium Scheme is, in effect, a *deficiency payment* scheme whereby producers' average returns are made up to a predetermined weekly Target Price with a variable premium. Because the premium applies only in the UK it is returnable (through a mechanism described as clawback) on any beef subsequently exported. Intervention Buying prevents the market price from falling below a certain minimum level. The Suckler Cow Premium is payable on all cows used for rearing beef calves. *Hill Livestock Compensatory Allowances* are also paid on beef cows in *Less Favoured Areas.* See also *administered prices.*

beet cyst nematode a potentially serious pest of *sugar beet* which, because it is controlled causes little actual yield loss. 'Beet sickness' is caused by the nematode Heterodera schachtii and can result in crop failure. Control is achieved by *crop rotation,* growing sugar beet after at least two years of non-host crops. This rotation is enforced by the British Sugar Corporation who will only issue contracts to grow beet on land which has had such a break.

behaviour all observable or measurable activities of an animal which come about as a result of its relationships with its environment. In effect this is anything an animal does.

behaviour pattern a set of responses by an animal which are associated in time and are relatively *stereotyped*.

Belgian Blue a *breed* of cattle originating in the Benelux countries, where it is an important *dual purpose breed*. It has recently been used as a beef sire in this country due to its good carcass attributes, in particular its high degree of *double-muscling*. It is however associated with a high level of calving difficulties, particularly in the purebreed.

Belted Galloway a type of *Galloway* cattle characterised by a white belt around the body. It is also called a Beltie.

benefits in kind benefits for which no cash payment is made. These include the consumption of home grown farm produce and the use of goods and services such as housing, the private use of a car or telephone, heating fuel and electricity.

bent grasses herbage grasses of the Agrostis species. Frequently found in pastures though rarely, if ever, sown, these grasses are indicative of low productivity. Agrostis species are tolerant of low soil fertility and are not favoured in the lowlands because they are slow to begin growing in spring and generally lower yielding than grasses such as *perennial rye grass*. Agrostis species are aggressive under poor conditions when, by their creeping habit, they can dominate a pasture. The main types are A. stolonifera (Creeping Bent) and A. tenuis (Brown Top). In the uplands, Bents are of value because they are superior in yield and quality to *Nardus* and *Molinia*.

Berkshire a rusty black coloured breed of pig with white feet, snouts and tails. Of limited commercial importance in the UK.

biceps any muscle with two insertions. Often used specifically for the biceps femoris muscle in the forelimb.

biennial plants those which complete their life cycle in two growing seasons. In the first season, plants store the products of photosynthesis in a storage organ e.g. swollen root, and produce flowers in the second season. Crops may be harvested at the end of the first phase for the storage product e.g. sugar beet, carrots, etc. but will require a second season in order to produce seed.

bifid forked or divided halfway down into two lobes.

big head disease of sheep a swollen head due to either a *clostridial* infection of the head and neck or a form of light sensitisation.

bile a viscous liquid produced by the liver and consisting of water, bile salts, bile pigments, mucin, fats, fatty acids, lecithin and inorganic compounds. It is generally a green or yellow colour, is alkaline and has a bitter taste.

bilharziasis a parasitic disease of man and domestic animals which is caused by blood *flukes* and is endemic in many parts of Africa and the Far East.

bio-assay method of determination of the power of a drug or a biological product (e.g. a hormone) by testing its effect on standard animals.

biocide a substance which destroys plant life.

biological control forms of pest and disease control which do not rely on the application of chemicals. Examples include crop rotation, breeding for disease resistance and use of predatory organisms to control the pest or disease organism.

biological oxygen demand a measure of the polluting value of an effluent. The biological oxygen demand quantifies the organic matter content of the material which may be used as a feed by micro-organisms in water. In feeding and growing, these organisms respire the oxygen in the water reducing it to levels below that needed to support other forms of aquatic life.

biological yield the total dry weight of a crop per unit area, including all root and shoot material. Much of this may not be harvested or have an economic value.

biomass generally the living weight of a plant or animal population. More specifically, the production of micro-organisms under controlled environments.

biometry the application of statistical methods to biological problems.

biopsy veterinary examination of tissue removed from the body of a living animal.

biosynthesis the method of synthesis, or construction, of complex molecules within a living organism.

biotin one of the water soluble *vitamins* of the *vitamin B complex.*

bisexual an animal or plant possessing both male and female sexual organs; an hermaphrodite.

biuret a non-protein nitrogen compound which is formed from *urea* and may be used in *ruminant* diets.

black disease a *toxaemic* disease of sheep caused by *clostridial* infection. Often liver damage is observed.

Blackface see *Scottish Blackface.*

blackgrass (Alopecurus myosuroides) an *annual* grass *weed* of *arable* crops. Blackgrass has become important as a *weed* in areas of intensive and regular *cereal* cultivation. Germinating in autumn, it has a life cycle similar to that of the cultivated *cereals, winter wheat* and *winter barley.* It matures early and can shed seed to cause future problems. Because of the many similarities between the *weed* and the crop plants, control by *herbicides* has been difficult. Although herbicides are now available, they are costly.

blackhead an infectious disease caused by a protozoal infection of the liver and *caecae.* Of domestic birds, turkeys seem particularly prone to the infection.

blackleg 1. A *clostridium* infection of cattle or sheep also known as Blackquarter or quarter ill. It is characterised by fever and swelling of the infected muscles. 2. Bacterial decay of lower parts of stems and *tubers* in the potato crop due to Erwinia carotovora. Mainly borne in *seed tubers,* the disease spreads rapidly under wet field or storage conditions. A few affected plants can be found in most crops but losses in the growing crop are not usually great. 3. Fungal disease of sugar beet causing death of seedlings. Low, uneven populations may result.

blastocyst a structure resulting from the cleavage of the fertilised *ovum.* It consists of an inner cell mass, which will form the *embryo* and associated membranes, and an outer hollow sphere.

blind staggers an acute form of *alkali disease.*

bloat a digestive disorder of *ruminants* characterised by an excessive accumulation of gas in the rumen. It is often associated with the ingestion of lush herbage especially legumes.

Blonde d'Aquitaine a breed of cattle originating from SW France. The breed has built up a reputation in Britain for producing a large calf which grows well and develops into a good *beef* animal.

blood the main fluid which circulates through an animal's body playing a vital transport role. It carries oxygen, nutrients and hormones to the tissues and waste products to the excretory organs. Additionally blood plays an important part in the maintenance of a uniform body temperature. Blood is predominantly (75-80%) water but contains a number of cellular components: red cells, white cells and platelets, in addition to solids and gasses being transported.

blood count a count of the number of red or white cells in blood.

blood flukes trematodes which are parasitic on man and domestic animals via various species of water snails as *intermediate hosts*. Often they attack the liver. In addition to the effect on the living animal they may damage the offal leading to condemnation at slaughter and loss of producer returns.

blood line a loosely used term referring to part of an animal's *pedigree* tracing back to a specific ancestor. A male blood line refers specifically to the males in a pedigree leading back to a certain *sire*. Similarly a female blood line leads back to a certain *dam*.

blood plasma the fluid component of blood.

blood vessel part of the branching network of tube-like structures which transport blood around the animal's body. See *artery, capilliary, vein*.

blowfly myiasis see *strike*.

blowing the process of wind erosion which occurs most frequently on peaty or sandy soils.

Bluefaced Leicester a breed of sheep which are of above average size. Characteristically they have dark, pigmented skin on the top of the head and ears, a Roman nose, upright ears and a tight fleece. The breed is *prolific* and the rams are often used to produce *crossbred* ewes.

Blue-Grey crossbred cattle resulting from mating a white *shorthorn* bull with either a *Galloway* or *Aberdeen Angus* cow.

blueprint term used to define or describe a set of management guidelines for a particular crop aimed at producing high yields.

bobby calf an unwanted calf, usually of a specialist dairy breed, which is not kept for beef production but slaughtered at a few days of age for veal or manufacturing.

BOD See *biological oxygen demand*.

body cavity the space or cavity within an animal's body in which the *viscera* lie.

body wall the skin and muscle layers making up the wall surrounding the body cavity.

bolting the process which takes place when a *biennial* plant atypically produces flowers in the first season. Little storage tissue is produced and crop quality suffers. Frequently used in relation to *sugar beet*.

bolus a ball. More specifically the ball of partly digested food which is regurgitated during *rumination* by *ruminant* livestock.

bomb calorimeter apparatus used in the determination of the energy value of materials including animal feedingstuffs.

bone structural connective tissue the matrix of which is impregnated with salts including calcium phosphate and carbonate. Together the bones of an animals body constitute the skeleton.

bone meal ground bones which may be used as an animal feed or as a *fertiliser*. It is high in *calcium* and *phosphorus*.

borage (borago officinalis) a spring sown crop grown as a source of gamma-linolenic acid. An *oilseed* crop of somewhat limited potential as a *break crop* in a *cereal rotation*.

Border Leicester a hardy, prolific breed of sheep characterised by its long, close wool, white hair on its face and legs, a long bald head with an aquiline nose and ears carried high. It is often used in crossing, e.g. a ram is mated by a *Scottish Blackface* ewe to produce a *Greyface.*

botanical composition the relative proportions of particular species of crops or *weeds* within an area. Values will differ depending upon whether the proportion is measured by weight or by ground cover.

botulism a poisoning caused by ingesting food which has been infected with the clostridial organism Bacillus botulinus.

bovine of, or pertaining to, cattle.

bovine contagious abortion see *brucellosis.*

bovine growth hormone a hormone, produced by the *pituitary gland,* which is involved in many aspects of body *metabolism* including growth and lactation. *Genetic engineering* has allowed bacterially produced bovine growth hormone to become available which when injected into *dairy cows* increases milk production by 20-30%.

bovine hyperkeratosis a disease of cattle which is characterised by emaciation, loss of hair, and thickening of the skin due to poisoning by chlorinated napthalene compounds.

bovine somatotrophin (BST) an alternative name for *bovine growth hormone.*

bowel the hind gut of an animal.

bowel oedema a disease of pigs characterised by nervous symptoms and *oedema* of many tissues especially the *bowel*. It is believed to be caused by either *toxin* production by, or hypersensitivity to, E. Coli.

bracken (Pteridium aquilinum) a *perennial* plant, very common on moors, heaths and on upland soils which are light and acidic. *Rhizomes* spread horizontally, 6-18 inches below the soil surface, producing fronds or ferns at intervals. Bracken reduces the grazing value of land because it is unpalatable. It can produce taints in milk and in extreme cases can poison livestock. The surface *litter* produced by the decaying fronds can also prevent the more desirable grass species from developing. Control of bracken can now be achieved by *herbicides,* but was originally achieved by repeated cutting of fronds as they appeared, in order to reduce the rhizome reserves.

bracken poisoning a disease occurring in cattle and horses due to the ingestion of *bracken.* The main symptoms in cattle are high fever and multiple haemorrhages.

bract a leaf-like structure below a flower or group of flowers.

brain the principal ganglionic mass of the central nervous system which appears as an expanded and specialised region at the anterior end of the spinal cord. It is the centre for the control of many voluntary and involuntary body movements.

bran the husks of ground corn which have been separated from the flower. Used as a fibrous feedingstuff.

brassica a genus of plants, within the family Cruciferae, which contains many groups of agricultural importance. B. oleracea includes plants such as *cabbage, kale,* and *brussel sprouts.* B. napus includes *oilseed rape* and *swedes* and B. rapa, the *turnips.* Plants of the Brassica genus may be annual, biennial or perennial. All have flowers which are a shade of yellow and produce many small rounded seeds.

braxy a *clostridial* infection of the *abomasum* of sheep which causes an acute and fatal *toxaemia.*

break crop a crop which can be used to interrupt a sequence of otherwise similar crops. Its use helps to prevent the transmission of pests and diseases from one crop to the next. For example, the Brassica crop, oilseed rape, can be used to break a run of cereals (Gramineae).

break even budgeting a method of budgeting employed when there is difficulty quantifying an important component of return or cost. It is essentially the same as *partial budgeting,* with the exception that the return or cost item of concern is set at a level such that there is no gain

or loss from the proposed plan. Whether or not this level of return or
cost is achievable must then be judged, and a decision about the project
made on this basis. Also known as sensitivity budgeting.

breast bone the *sternum* of an animal's *skeleton.*

breed 1. A loose term referring to a race, strain, variety or kind of animal
or plant. A breed may result and become stabilised by the continous
inbreeding of an isolated group of animals or plants. 2.   To mate or
reproduce. 3.   To control the reproduction of animals or plants by
selection of certain desirable *characters* for transmission   to their
offspring.

breeding livestock a term used in *valuations* to contrast with *trading
livestock.* Examples of breeding livestock   include dairy cows, suckler
beef cows and ewes.

breeding season in those species of animals which are seasonal breeders,
the period of the year when the females   will show recurrent *oestrous
cycles* during the *oestrus* phase of which they will stand to be mated by
the male. Of the farm livestock, sheep are seasonal breeders with
breeding seasons from August to January, depending on breed. Sheep are
'short-day breeders' - the onset of the breeding season being declining
light:dark ratios, or *photoperiod* effects which are monitored by the
pineal gland which controls the reproductive system via the hormone
melatonin. Other species of animals or birds are long-day breeders.

breed society club established by animal breeders for a specific livestock
breed to look after the general affairs of that breed and to compile and
maintain a herd or flock book of registered animals conforming to the
breed type.

brewers' grains the residue of *barley* after being used for malting in
beer brewing. They may be fed wet or dry, usually to *ruminant*
livestock, as a moderate *protein* and *fibre* source.

brisket the breast or anterior *sternal* region of an animal or a carcass.

British Friesian see *Friesian.*

British White an historic breed of white, polled cattle previously called
Park Cattle and now a rare breed.

British Wool Marketing Board since its establishment, in 1950 this
marketing board has purchased, graded and marketed the wool offered to it
by registered producers.   The Board also provides some technical services
to producers.

broad bean see *bean.*

broadcasting a method of applying either *seeds, fertilisers* or *crop protection granules* to the surface of a soil or crop. Materials which have been broadcast onto the surface of the soil may subsequently be incorporated by *cultivation.* Broadcasting is usually a rapid operation but may be imprecise.

broiler a *chicken* intensively reared for slaughter at approximately 10 weeks of age when it will weigh between 1.5 and 2.0kg.

broken-mouthed a term referring to the loss of a variable number of teeth from the mouth of a *ewe.* It results in a reduced ability to consume and chew the *diet.*

bronchitis inflammation of the *bronchi.* One form in farm livestock may be linked to *husk.*

bronchus one of the two branches of the *trachea* leading to the *lungs.*

brood a set of offspring produced at the same birth or from the same clutch of eggs.

brooder a piece of equipment containing a heat source in which newly hatched chicks are kept under controlled temperature conditions in the immediate post-hatching period.

brown rust a fungal disease of *cereals* caused by Puccinia recondita in the case of *wheat* and Puccinia hordei in the case of *barley.* Scattered brown pustules appear on the leaves of affected plants. This disease develops later than *yellow rust.* Epidemics develop slowly then explode in the warmer weather after *ear emergence.* Control is achieved by growing *resistant varieties* of wheat and by *fungicide* in barley.

brucellosis diseases, especially spontaneous *abortion* in cattle, caused by infection with organisms of the brucella genus of *bacteria.* It is spread mainly via *aborted* calves, *afterbirth* and milk. It causes undulant fever in humans. Brucellosis has now been largely eradicated in the UK due to the successful implementation of the Brucellosis Incentives Scheme introduced in 1970.

Brussels sprouts a crop grown for human consumption. A member of Brassica oleracea, in which the *axillary buds* are formed into tightly packed masses of leaves. Sprouts are available for autumn and early winter use, when harvested fresh but have also become a popular crop for *deep freezing.*

buccal of, or pertaining to, the mouth.

budgetary control comparison of a budgeted plan of cash incomings and outgoings against actual performance, usually on a monthly basis, through one year. Deviations of actual outcome from budget can be questioned, and if possible, remedies found. In this way the performance of a farm is constantly appraised, problems are quickly brought to light and an improved understanding of the farm business can be gained.

bulk density of soil, the extent to which soil particles are packed together. Soils with a high bulk density contain little air and permit only slow water movement.

bulk tank the vat into which the milk from a herd of cows is collected at milking and where it is cooled and held until collected by tanker for delivery to dairies.

bull uncastrated male *bovine.*

bull beef a system of beef production using *entire* bulls in preference to *steers.* The bull has a higher growth rate, superior food conversion and produces a leaner carcass. Bull beef are usually reared intensively (e.g. cereal beef) or semi-intensively (silage systems) indoors rather than at grass where their behaviour would prove unpopular with other countryside users. Bull beef also refers to the meat from such animals.

bulldog calf an inherited form of *achondroplasia* which occurs mainly when *Dexter* cattle are mated together. The condition is due to the inheritance of a pair of semi-*dominant genes* and is usually lethal.

bulling term used to refer to a *cow* or *heifer* showing signs of *heat.*

bulling heifer a maiden *heifer* which has reached the appropriate age and weight for mating.

bullock castrated male cattle.

bunt order see *social hierarchy.*

burdizzo an instrument for castration, similar to pincers, which crushes the *spermatic cord.*

bureau service a farm computer service offered by secretarial and accounting agencies, farm management consultants, the Milk Marketing Board and some other agricultural supply companies. Records from the farm office are sent for processing by a central computer before being returned to the farmer with interpretation and advice. Contrast with *on-farm computing.*

burnt lime see *lime.*

bushel a measure of volume (36.4 litres) now largely of historical interest in the U.K. Formerly used to state the specific weight of a sample of grain.

bush sickness see *pine.*

business growth a positive change in the *net worth* of a business from one point in time to another. See also *profit.*

butter one of the major products manufactured from milk. Butter is one of the agricultural commodities currently in surplus in the EC - Hence the 'butter mountain'.

butterfat the *fat* present in *milk* largely in the form of triglycerides. Butterfat content varies with *breed,* stage of lactation and nutrition but averages 3.85%. Butterfat is one of the milk constituents on which the payment to producers is based and its content is determined by infrared spectrometry which has replaced the previously used *Gerber test.*

butyrate a salt of *butyric acid.*

butyric acid volatile fatty acid which may be formed during the process of *silage* making. Butyric acid is produced by Clostridial organisms which, under adverse conditions, may dominate the silage fermentation process. If so, a secondary fermentation is said to have taken place, and the desirable *lactic acid* is replaced by *butyric acid.* This product is a weaker acid and is foul smelling, rendering the silage less palatable to livestock, less stable and more prone to dry matter losses. Butyric acid is also produced by rumen micro-organisms and is one of the volatile fatty acids which become an energy source for the host *ruminant* animal.

butyric fermentation the fermentation of sugar or starch resulting in the formation of *butyrate.*

byre see *cow shed.*

cabbage member of brassica oleracea grown for both human and animal consumption. A *biennial* harvested after the first year when the tightly interlocked leaves form the bulk of the crop.

cabbage root fly (Delia brassicae) a serious pest of *brassica* crops. *Larvae* feed on the plant roots which may thus be destroyed. Attacked plants are stunted and may collapse or die. Control by use of *insecticides.*

cabbage white butterfly (Pieris species) a pest of all *brassica* crops. Damage is caused by the caterpillars eating leaves and fouling the crops with excrement. Control by use of *insecticides.*

caecum a blind *sac* especially one arising from the large intestine of the alimentary tract. It may be an important site of hind gut fermentation in non-ruminant animals.

Caesarean section delivery of a *foetus* through the incised *abdomen* and *uterus* of the *pregnant* female.

cage an intensive housing system which places restriction on the movement and/or behaviour of an animal, most commonly laying hens or piglets. Over 95% of laying hens are housed in battery cages with the cages arranged in three tiers. Typically there are 3-7 birds per cage, giving space allowances of approximately 500sq cm per bird. There is growing opposition from animal welfare groups against battery cages. In a recently introduced system, *early weaned* piglets are transferred to cages and kept in a warm dark environment until they are transferred to conventional pens at approximately 5 weeks of age.

cake a generic term for processed animal feeding stuffs. Historically the term dates from when flat slabs of residue remained after the compression of *oilseeds* to extract oil e.g. cottonseed cake, palm nut kernel cake. This resultant cake was rich in *protein,* contained residual oil and fibre and was widely used as a feed for cattle. Modern extraction methods mean that the material is now available as a meal which is extensively used by farmers and feed compounders in the preparation of processed animal feedingstuffs by mixing with other ingredients particularly *cereals.*

calcareous soils soils derived from chalk and therefore with a high calcium content.

calciferol see *vitamin D.*

calcium an element essential to life which is an important constituent of bones, teeth and many of the soft tissues of an animal's body. It is present in the various compound forms of *lime* used agriculturally.

calf the offspring of a *cow.* A male is called a bull calf and a female a heifer calf. The term is used until they are one year old.

calf diptheria a bacterial infection of calves which causes ulceration and *necrosis* of the mouth and *pharynx.*

calf scours an important, often fatal, disease which affects both beef and dairy calves. It is caused by a range of bacterial organisms including E.coli. Also called neonatal diarrhoea.

calf tetany a form of *hypomagnesaemia* occurring in calves and caused by a dietary deficiency of magnesium. Also known as milk tetany.

callus a thickening of the skin as a result of irritation or friction.

calorie a unit of heat or energy. It is now largely replaced by the term *joule.* 1 calorie is equivalent to 4.184 joules.

calorimeter the apparatus used to measure thermal quantities e.g. the energy content of a sample of animal feed or faeces.

calving box a small pen where a cow can be housed, away from her herd mates, at the time of calving. The isolation of the cow aids management of parturition and supervision of the cow and calf after calving to ensure early nursing occurs.

calving fever see *milk fever.*

Camborough a *hybrid* breed of pig genetically derived predominantly from the *Landrace* and *Large White* breeds.

Canadian Holstein see *Holstein.*

canine of or pertaining to a dog. In farm animals the canine tooth (where present) is a pointed tooth adapted for tearing: it is located between the *incisors* and *premolars.*

cannibalism a vice or depraved appetite of animals or birds in which the affected individual injures and eats parts of its own body and of other members of the same species. The cause may be any alteration in the animal's environment e.g. climatic, nutritional (mineral or protein deficiency) or social (boredom). It is most common in intensively housed livestock, especially pigs and poultry. Examples include tail biting by pigs, sows eating their own or other sows piglets and feather and flesh pecking by poultry.

cannon bone the bone in the limbs of farm animals formed by the fusion of the two metacarpal (fore limb) or metatarsal (hind limb) bones.

CAP see *Common Agricultural Policy.*

capillary 1.   A tiny, thin walled vessel which together with others, forms a network aiding rapid exchange of substances between the contained fluid and the surrounding tissues. Capillaries may be found in the *lymph* system, *bile* system or the *blood* system where they are between the arterial and venous sides of the circulatory systems.   2.   In soils, very fine continuous pores through which water can pass. Because of the fineness of the pores, water can be drawn up, against gravity, by capillary action thus coming into the rooting zone of the plants. 3. In plants, very fine vessels for the conduct of materials within plants.

capital 1.   A stock of goods which are used in production. Economists distinguish it from the two other factors of production - land and labour. 2.   Accountants by contrast define capital as the financial value of a business belonging to the owner.

capital allowance   the amount that the Inland Revenue specifies may be charged as asset *depreciation* in *income tax* and *corporation tax* assessment.

capital gains tax   levied on the gain in value of an *asset* realised on its disposal. The tax applies to individuals: capital gains accruing to companies are charged to *corporation tax.* There is provision for the deferral of the tax, known as roll-over-relief, if the proceeds from the sale of an asset are used exclusively to purchase a new qualifying asset. The qualifying agricultural assets are land and buildings, fixed plant and machinery. For gains from April 1982, the tax is payable on only that part which exceeds the rise in the Retail Price Index: gains made before then are exempt.

capital transfer tax (CTT)   introduced in 1974, renamed *inheritance tax* in the 1986 budget.

capon   a cockerel which has been *caponised* with the aim of improving carcass quality and reducing the incidence of male secondary sexual activity - crowing and fighting.

caponisation   castration of a cock bird. Normally accomplished by injecting one of the *stilbenes* e.g. hexoestrol or di-ethyl stilboestrol - compounds now banned in the EC.

capping   term applied to soils. Particles at the surface run together when wet and on drying, form a hard crust which it is difficult or impossible for developing seedlings to penetrate.

carbohydrates   a group of compounds which occur widely in plants and animals. They all have the general formula $Cx(H_2O)y$ where x is 6 or a multiple of 6. They are classified into *monosaccharides, disaccharides* or *polysaccharides.* Plants manufacture carbohydrates by *photosynthesis.* These carbohydrates then form the major component of an animals diet with the complex polysaccharides in plants being broken down by animals into sugars by digestion. Following absorption the energy stored in the carbohydrates is released.

carbon the element which is the principal constituent of all *organic* compounds. Carbon circulates between the atmosphere and living organisms via the carbon cycle. Respiration by animals and plants and decay and combustion of organic materials returns *carbon dioxide* to the atmosphere. Carbon dioxide is then available to plants for *photosynthesis.* The *carbohydrates* thus produced are a major energy source for both plants and animals.

carbon dioxide a colourless, odourless and tasteless gas which occurs in the atmosphere. It is used by plants to manufacture *carbohydrates* by the process of *photosynthesis.* It is returned to the atmosphere following animal or plant respiration or by the combustion of organic coumpounds e.g. straw burning.

carcass or carcase a dead body. More specifically in a butchers' terms, the body of a pig after the removal of the *offal,* or the body of a sheep or cattle after the removal of the head, hide, hooves and offal.

carcass classification the categorisation of *carcasses* by common characteristics such as fatness, *conformation,* weight or sex. The aims of carcass classification may be to provide a basis for the payment of producers and/or to assist potential buyers in the selection of carcasses to meet their requirements. See also *beef carcass classification, sheep carcass classification.*

cardiac muscle the contractile tissue forming the mass of the heart. It is involuntary and shows inherent rhythmicity.

cardiac sphincter the *sphincter* surrounding the opening of the *oesophagus* into the *stomach.*

cardiovascular pertaining to the *heart* and *blood vessels.*

carotenes a group of orange-red crystalline hydrocarbon compounds which colour various animal and plant substances e.g. egg yolk, butter and carrots. They are present in the *chloroplasts* of plants and are precursors of *vitamin* A.

carotenoids yellow, orange or red pigments which resemble *carotenes.* Some can act as precursors of *vitamin* A.

carotid arteries in animals the principal *arteries* which carry blood towards the head region.

carpal one of the bones comprising the carpus in the forelimb of an animal. Equivalent to the human wrist.

carpel the structure in which *ovules* are housed.

carrier an individual which carries and transmits certain hereditary factors without any *phenotypic* manifestation. The term is commonly used to refer to an individual which is *heterozygous* for a simple *recessive gene.*

carrot (Daucus carota) a *biennial* plant grown for human consumption. The tap root which is thick and succulent is rich in sugars and contains the red pigment, carotene. Carrots are harvested at the end of the first year of growth before they produce inflorescences.

carrot fly (Psila rosae) a widespread and often serious pest of carrots, also causing damage to parsnip and celery. Larvae feed on the roots of young plants which may be stunted or killed. The tunnelling of larvae in mature roots may make them unmarketable. *Seed dressing* and granular *insecticides* can be used to achieve some control.

cartilage a form of connective tissue in which the cells are embedded in a stiff matrix. Often cartilage is the precursor of bone. In *meat,* cartilage is the gristle.

caryopsis the name given to the seed of cereals and herbage grasses. The *endospermic* true seed is enclosed within the *pericarp* and *testa.* In grasses, the caryopsis may remain enclosed between the *lemma* and the *palea.* The complete unit is regarded as the agricultural "seed".

casein the generic name for the main milk proteins.

cash analysis a method of book-keeping used to record all cash transactions (i.e. *payments* and *receipts)* made during the *accounting period.* Transactions can be itemised under separate headings to include, for example, seed and machinery purchases in the payments section, and wheat and beef cattle in the receipts section. See also *contra.*

cash flow the movement of cash into and out of a business through time.

cassava see *manioc.*

cast ewe an old breeding ewe which is sold from a hill to a lowland farm where in a gentler environment they are kept to produce further crops of lambs.

castrate a young male animal which has been castrated.   Compared with entire males, castrates show reduced secondary sexual behaviour (less fighting, mounting and aggressiveness) making them easier to handle. Castrates also show reduced growth rates poorer food conversion and fatter carcasses than entire males.   Traditionally young males not required for breeding purposes were castrated although there is a growing incidence of using entire male cattle rather than castrates (*steers)* for beef production or boars for pork production rather than castrates (*hogs).* Male lambs are generally castrated and termed wethers.

castration removal of the *testes* of a male animal. The removal may be immediate by cutting the *scrotum* as in pigs or it may be by atrofication following ringing and restriction of the blood supply as in sheep or cattle.

casual labour labour which is neither hired on a full-time basis nor on a regular part-time basis, but   seasonally as required.   Casual workers often perform labour intensive tasks, typically at times of peak work load. Examples include hand picking potatoes, brussel sprouts and other vegetables in East Anglia, hop picking in Kent, corn carting by students at harvest, and helping with lambing.

casualty an animal slaughtered prematurely for meat as a result of an accident.

cation exchange capacity the capacity of a soil to hold ions such as sodium, ammonium and calcium which may subsequently be used for plant growth. Cation exchange capacity is determined by *soil structure* and *soil texture.*

cattle bovine animals which may be categorised in two main groups - European cattle developed from Bos taurus and Zebu cattle developed from Bos indicus. Worldwide there are close to one thousand different breeds of cattle some of which are specialist *beef* or *dairy* breeds whilst others are *dual-purpose.*

celery (Apium graveolens) a *biennial* plant grown for human consumption. The edible parts of the plant are the thick, succulent petioles, which connect the leaves to the short stem, in the first year of growth. Seeds may be sown direct or *transplanted.* Grown on the organic *fen* soils as a field crop. Originally soil was heaped up against the petioles to maintain their white colour but now self-blanching types are available and this process is no longer necessary.

cellulose a *polysaccharide* which is a major constituent of plant cell walls.

cereals plants of the family Gramineae which are grown   specifically for grain production. The most common cereals in the UK are *wheat, barley, oats* and *rye* in decreasing order of importance. Cereals may also be grown for harvesting before they mature when the dry matter can be used for animal feeding. In this context, *rye* is often grown to provide *forage* for grazing early in spring whereas *barley* or *oats* would be more likely to be used to provide a large bulk of material for conservation as *silage.*

cereals regime the EC policies relating the *cereals.* These policies substantially determine the price of cereals, which is both a major crop for human consumption and an important input into several livestock sectors. Main crops covered include wheat (both durum and common), barley, maize, rye, oats and some of their products. Target prices are set in relation to intended price levels at Duisberg (Germany) which is taken to be the main production deficit area. Threshold prices for imports are set below target prices to allow for transport costs between port of entry and Duisberg. Variable levies raise the price of imports to the threshold level. Export refunds are used to allow the disposal of stocks on world markets. During the 1970s a series of intervention price adjustments for individual cereals brought about a two level price structure, with higher prices commanded by common wheat and a lower unified price for the feed grains. Under this regime the EC has become self-sufficient in wheat and barley, but has continued to import maize and milling wheats. Imported substitutes for feed cereals have been regulated by negotiated export restraints (quotas) in countries of origin. A further attempt to regulate the cereal surplus has been through the introduction of *threshold quantities* production above which would reduce price support levels, combined with *co-responsibility levies.* Production *quotas* and *super levies* have also been advocated. See also *administered prices.*

cereal substitutes substitutes used by farmers or feed compounders to replace *cereals* as the major suppliers of energy in an animal's diet. Depending on price and availability, manioc, maize gluten, brewers grains, citrus pulp or sugar beet pulp, as well as other materials, may be used as cereal substitutes.

certified seed seed which has passed specific rigorous tests in relation to *genetic purity,* pest, disease and weed contamination and which has therefore been granted certification for sale. Various different standards of purity are awarded different grades of certification. The purchaser can then be completely aware of the quality of the seed planted.

chaff the remains of the floral structures of plants after the removal of seeds. In *cereals,* this would include the *rachis, glumes, awns* and in *beans, peas* and *oilseed rape,* pod material would be included.

chain harrows items of *cultivation* equipment consisting of interlinked, spiked chains which are used for gentle movement of soil. Chain harrows are used to cover small seeds such as grasses with a shallow layer of soil and to scarify the surface of *pasture* to remove dead plant material and to spread dung patch residues.

challenge feeding see *lead feeding.*

character see *trait.*

charlock (Sinapis arvensis) *weed* plant of the *Cruciferae* family. These plants which produce yellow flowers were formerly problem weeds in *cereals.* Now relatively easily controlled by *herbicides.*

Charolais a breed of beef cattle developed in central France and first imported into this country in the 1960s. They are large, well-muscled cattle which are white or cream in colour. They have grown in popularity, compared with our traditional beef breeds, because of their high growth rates and good carcass characteristics. Double-muscling or *culard* is a common feature of the breed which exhibits a higher incidence of *dystocia* than our native breeds.

Charollais a French breed of sheep recently imported into this country in limited numbers.

chat potatoes *tubers* which are considered too small for human consumption.

Checkmate a service run by the Farm Management Services of the Milk Marketing Board which monitors dairy herd fertility.

Chester White an American breed of pig based upon the Yorkshire and other UK breeds. It is a white breed with some blue freckles and is noted for its leanness and prolificacy.

Cheviot a breed of hardy, white, short-wooled sheep which is clear of wool on its face and legs, has upright ears and an alert appearance. It is medium-sized although the North Country Cheviot (which was developed in Caithness) is larger than the South Country Cheviot, both originated in the Cheviot Hills.

chewing the cud the mastication of food which has previously been swallowed, partly digested in the rumen and then regurgitated. It only occurs in *ruminants.*

Chianina a tall breed of beef cattle originating in Northern Italy where they were originally used for draught purposes. They are white with black hooves, muzzle and horn tips. Although some have been imported into this country they have proved of limited popularity.

chick a young bird at or soon after the time of hatching.

chicken 1. The young of a domestic fowl. 2. The meat of a domestic fowl, irrespective of its age.

chickweeds very common *weeds* in both *arable* and grassland situations. Several types of Chickweed are recognised including Stellaria media, Common Chickweed, and Cerastium holostoides, Mouse-ear Chickweed. They colonise bare ground in *cereals* and in grassland and are often a problem in the *establishment* phase because they cover the ground profusely and can restrict the growth of the crop. They form small white flowers and are rapidly reproduced by seed.

chisel plough *cultivation* implement with strong vertical tines used to break up the soil at depth but not to invert it.

chitting 1. Pre-sprouting of potato seed tubers before planting. Potatoes are kept in trays or boxes at warm temperatures to stimulate bud growth from previously *dormant tubers.* Particularly useful for *early potato* production because the process speeds up the early growth of the crop. 2. Pre-germination of *seed,* of some vegetables is used before planting.

chloromequat a *plant growth regulator* which when applied to cereals tends to shorten the *straw* thus improving the *harvest index* and also increasing *grain yield.*

chlorophyll the green pigment of plants which is concerned with *photosynthesis.*

chloroplast solid inclusion in plant cells containing the green pigment, *chlorophyll.* Chloroplasts give the plants their green colour and are the sites of *photosynthesis.*

chocolate spot a very important fungal disease of *beans.* Botrytis fabae can cause severe damage to winter sowings causing blackening, wilting and almost complete destruction of bean foliage. Control is by application of *fungicide* at the first sign of disease build up.

chorion the outermost membrane surrounding a mammalian *foetus.* The chorion, together with part of the *uterus* forms the placenta.

chromosome located in the nucleus of a cell, the chromosomes carry the *genes* which bear the genetic information specific to that particular plant or animal. The chromosome is composed of DNA and other proteins.

cif abbreviation for cost, insurance, freight; the usual basis on which import prices are quoted as they cross the frontier of the importing country. Cost includes both the purchase price and any import duties, insurance and freight refer to transport costs from the country of origin. Compare FOB.

circulating capital see *working capital.*

clamp an enclosure in which crop products are stored for later use. Often used in relation to *silage*.   A silage clamp is used to make and store *herbage* as silage. The enclosure may be made by building walls of brick, stone or wood or it may be constructed by hollowing out an area from the earth. The stored product is covered to minimise the effects of adverse weather. Clamps are also used to store *potatoes* and other *vegetables.*

claw ill see *foul-in-the-foot.*

clean cattle cattle which have not been used for breeding. Particularly maiden *heifers* but also steers and bulls.

clean grazing a system of grazing where either through following an arable crop or having been cut for conservation or grazed by a different species of livestock, an area of grass is regarded as being 'clean' or free from larvae, of gastro-intestinal parasites. Such a 'clean' or uncontaminated pasture prevents infection of growing animals and therefore gives superior animal performance.

cleaning crop a crop, grown in the *rotation,* which allows effective control of *weeds*. Traditionally, root crops grown in widely spaced rows were cleaning crops because they enabled mechanical weed control by either hand or machine cultivation. The concept of cleaning crops is now less important because of the introduction of *herbicides.*

clean seed specifically seed which is known to be free from any contamination by pest, disease or *weed.* The use of such seed avoids initial contamination of the crop and therefore provides a good start to production. Seed borne pests, diseases and weeds are not introduced into previously 'clean' areas.

cleansing see *afterbirth.*

clear-felling the process of removing all the trees from a plantation within a short space of time. This method of harvesting timber is typically used on commercial plantations. It compares with selective felling, whereby only the mature trees are removed, and thinning, which is practiced earlier in the forest rotation, if at all.

cleg a general term for a troublesome bloodsucking fly, especially of the Haematopota species. They may affect all stock, especially horses - hence the alternative name, the horse fly.

cling a term for diarrhoea in animals, especially sheep.

clip to *shear* or remove the wool from a sheep. The clip is also the wool thus removed from a single sheep or the whole flock.

clod a compacted structural unit of soil which can be produced by inappropriate *cultivation* of soil or compaction by agricultural vehicles. Such clods, once formed, may be difficult to break down into smaller structural units. A poor seedbed will result which may limit germination and can cause problems at harvest time.

clone a group of plants produced by *vegetative propagation* from one original seedling or stock. Because *potato* crops are propagated vegetatively, all plants within one *variety* can be described as clones.

closed herd or flock a herd or flock into which there has been no introduction of new genetic material from outside *blood lines* since its foundation.

clostridium an important genus of *anaerobic* bacteria. Individual species are responsible for various animal diseases e.g. *botulism, tetanus* and *enteritis.* Other species are involved in spoilage and decay especially in *silage* making. If clostridial organisms dominate the *ensilage* process, carbohydrates and lactic acid are converted to butyric acid which is less effective as a preservative and has an unpleasant odour. This activity by clostridia, also known as secondary fermentation, is responsible for the breakdown of proteins in the *herbage* and the release of *ammonia.* Clostridia are introduced into silage by soil contamination.

cloven hoofed a term used to describe animals with a divided hoof such as *cattle* and *sheep.*

clover rot fungal disease of *legumes* especially *red clover* caused by Sclerotinia trifoliorum. Symptoms appear in autumn leaves then die off over winter. The spread of the disease is encouraged by damp, warm weather. The fruiting bodies (Sclerotia) may contaminate seed samples since they can be of a similar appearance to legume seed. Main control is by avoidance of infected fields, removal of excess herbage before winter and use of less susceptible legumes.

clovers *herbaceous legumes* of the Trifolium genus. Several species are of importance as *forage* plants in temperate regions. These include *red clover* (Trifolium pratense), *white clover* (Trifolium repens), *alsike clover* (Trifolium hybridum).

club root a fungal disease of *brassica* crops which places a restriction on *crop rotation.* The causal organism (Plasmodiophora brassicae) can persist in the soil for 3-6 years and will infect susceptible crops, causing *wilting* and yellowing of foliage and weak plants which may die. The roots of affected plants are swollen and deformed. Control is achieved by avoidance of soil acidity through the use of *lime,* long intervals between susceptible crops in the *rotation, resistant varieties* and in the case of high value crops, partial soil sterilisation with *crop protection chemicals.*

Clun Forest a breed of sheep originating from the Midlands. It is characterised by its dark brown face, short upright ears and wool extending over the forehead.

cluster the four teat cups and clawpiece of a *milking machine* which are applied to the udder of a cow.

clutch a batch of eggs laid by a bird. Also, after hatching, the brood of chicks from such eggs.

cobalt a trace element which is generally present in small quantities in soil and herbage. Cobalt acts, often in association with *vitamin B12,* in a number of aspects of an animals metabolism. Cobalt deficiency is often seen as *anaemia* and is referred to as *pine* in sheep.

coccidiosis an intestinal disease of livestock or poultry caused by protozoan parasites. The disease is characterised by diarrhoea and emaciation.

cock generally, a male bird; although more specifically for domestic poultry a male bird over 18 months of age.

cockerel a young male chicken, usually less than 18 months of age after which it is called a *cock.*

Cockle Park mixture a blend of *herbage* seeds popular with farmers because it produces a durable, persistent *pasture* of good yield and quality. The main components are *perennial ryegrass, cocksfoot, timothy* and *white clover.* The name derives from the experimental station in Northumberland where much early work demonstrating the value of these species was undertaken.

cocksfoot (Dactylis glomerata) a type of herbage grass, of high yield potential but relatively low nutritional quality. Occasionally sown in pastures and frequently found in hedgerows. Widely believed to tolerate dry conditions.

coconut cake a *cake* which was previously often included in dairy cow rations although it is decreasingly available.

Colbred a recently produced hybrid breed of sheep based on the East Friesland, Border Leicester, Dorset Horn and Clun Forest breeds. It is a long wool sheep with long legs and a clean white face. It is prolific, milking and largely used with hill ewes to produce crossbred breeding ewes.

coliform bacteria widespread bacteria which are often found in the digestive tract of animals.

coliform mastitis a type of *mastitis* in which the organism E. Coli can be isolated in large numbers from the mammary gland and appears to be a major causative factor.

coli septicaemia a respiratory infection of poultry which often results as a secondary infection to other respiratory diseases and is caused by E.Coli. Young birds are particularly susceptible, particularly in conditions of overcrowding or poor ventilation.

collagen a fibrous constituent of connective tissue which is present in large quantities in skin, tendon, ligament, cartilage and bone.

collateral securities which may be demanded by a lender to cover a loan. Examples include the *title deeds* of land (owner-occupier), guarantees or deposits from business acquaintances or friends, life assurance policies, and stocks and shares.

Colorado beetle (Leptinotarsa decemlineata) a potentially serious pest of potato crops which is not established in Britain. The pest is controlled by strict *notification*regulations aimed at preventing any pest build up. It causes damage by defoliation of the *haulm*.

colostrum the first milk secreted by the mammary gland following parturation. It is high in protein, particularly gamma globulins which are important in the transfer of passive immunity to young, and in fat content. In a few days the colostrum gradually alters in composition to resemble normal milk. Also called *beastings*.

colour marking the ability of a breed of animal to transmit a characteristic colour to its offspring. For example, calves sired by a Hereford bull always have a white face irrespective of the breed of dam: no other breed of bull produces calves with a white face.

combine drill a machine for sowing both *seed* and *fertiliser* at the same time.

combine harvester a machine used to harvest grain crops and some other field crops. The machine separates the seed (grain) from the *straw* and *chaff* which are returned to the field.

combining ability in plant and animal breeding, the ability of a line or strain to produce good crosses independent of the other parent.

Commission of the European Communities a major EC institution, responsible for initiating legislation and policy proposals which are then submitted to the *Council of Ministers* for decision. The Commission is divided into some 20 directorates, responsible for main policy areas such as agriculture, the environment, regional policy, budget and financial control.

commodity agreement an arrangement between exporting countries aimed at maintaining prices or reducing fluctuations in price of a particular commodity. Importers may also be involved in such agreements. There have been agreements from time to time for wheat, sugar and coffee. A common cause of failure of such agreements is their inability to secure the cooperation of all major producers.

commodity cycles fluctuations in prices for particular commodities which arise when production is planned in the expectation that recent prices will be continued into the next production period. When this occurs production and prices tend to fluctuate in opposite directions. The best known example of such effects is the pig cycle which is generally found to be of a four or five year duration. Following a period of high prices producers plan production in the expectation that these prices will prevail: the resulting excess supply drives prices down encouraging producers to abandon the enterprise. The shortfall of supply pushes prices up again and more producers come into production. Contrast *equilibrium price.*

Commodity Intervention Boards see *export refunds.*

commodity mountains a popular term for the *structural surpluses* of agricultural commodities within the EC, e.g. butter mountains, grain mountains.

commodity regime a coherent group of policy measures applied to a particular commodity. See also *administered prices,* and *beef, cereal, milk, sheepmeat* and *sugar regimes.*

Common Agricultural Policy (CAP) of the *European Community* now forms the framework for many of the *agricultural policy* measures currently applying in the UK. Briefly, the objectives of the CAP are to:

- increase agricultural productivity through technical progress and optimum utilisation of factors of production
- ensure a fair standard of living for the agricultural community
- stabilise markets
- provide certainty of supplies
- ensure supplies to consumers at reasonable prices.

The principles embedded in the policy include a single market for farm produce (see *customs union)* the operation of *community preference* with regard to *self-sufficiency* and *financial solidarity* of members in funding the CAP through the *European Agricultural Guidance and Guarantee Fund.* The policy works mainly through *administered prices* which may be made binding on members through EC Regulations (e.g. the Sheepmeat Regulation). Alternatively they may apply through directives, which describe common objectives but allow members some scope to select their own means of implementation (e.g. the *Less Favoured Areas* directives). The common price level established under the CAP has encouraged production, leading to the appearance of *surpluses* of the main commodities (cereals, milk products, beef, wine, sugar, olive oil) which are costly to store or to dispose of. The CAP absorbs some two-thirds of the *EC budget* and is thus criticised by non-farming interests. Proposals for reform have included lowering the common price level, encouraging the transfer of land and workers to other uses or industries, limiting the application of *administered prices* to a defined threshold quantity, production *quotas, co-responsibility levies* and *super-levies* and *set-asides.* The measures applied have not, so far, been sufficient to eliminate the *surpluses.* See also *structures policy, green currencies* and *export refunds.*

common land is an ancient form of land tenure. Land held in common is now registered under the Common Land Registration Act 1965. The rights over the use of a common can be shared by several persons (e.g. grazing rights). Other rights, such as shooting rights, mineral rights and other traditional rights (e.g. turf cutting), can be held by different individuals or in common.

Common Land Register the registration of common land (including town and village greens), its ownership and the rights of commoners under the Common Land Registration Act 1965. The Act followed the report of a Royal Commission in 1958. At the time much common land was imprecisely identified, ownership was unclear, and many commoners and their rights were unknown.

common scab fungal disease of potatoes caused by Streptomyces scabies. Skins of *tubers* become covered in scabs which reduce the market value of the crop. The organism is common in soils, especially in dry conditions. *Irrigation* may help to minimise the effects. Control is by *resistant varieties* and avoidance of affected seed.

community preference the principle that domestic EC demand will be met from internal sources at the expense of imports from third countries. See also CAP.

company a form of business constituted with a separate legal identity from the owners (shareholders) and the persons who have powers in the running of the company (directors). In a farming company, it is common that members of the family are both shareholders and directors. An advantage over other business consitutitions is that the personal liability of shareholders may be limited to the amount of the shares held (i.e. limited liability). A further reason for forming a company under some circumstances is to gain tax advantages. In the UK, about 5% of agricultural holdings are owned and run as private companies.

compensatory growth the phenomenon whereby animals which have been restricted in their feed or energy supply, when realimented, show a greater growth rate than animals of the same age or weight which have not been restricted.   Compensatory growth is often exhibited by two year old beef cattle on a two year system, when following a *store* period in their second winter they show compensatory growth when turned out to grass. It is thought that compensatory growth results in   part from an increased feed intake and in part from a change in the animals hormonal balance.

complement a constituent of blood, the presence of which is necessary for an *antibody* to kill an *antigen*.

complement fixation test a blood test which is used to diagnose specific bacterial diseases e.g. *brucellosis*.

complete diet the supply of feed to ruminant livestock during the winter months in which the *concentrate* and *forage* components are fed as an intimate mix. The complete diet is usually the animals sole source of feed and it is fed to appetite, the energy and protein content of the diet being adjusted to ensure that the animal's intake matches its requirements.

complete diet wagon a large mobile container similar to a *forage wagon* which, by the action of augers, mixes the *concentrate* and *forage* components of a *complete diet* prior to its delivery to the animals.

compound feed a feedstuff produced by a feed compounder which consists of a number of ingredients, including vitamins and minerals, combined in appropriate proportions to meet the requirement of a particular type of livestock. It may be a balanced diet and be fed by itself e.g. to pigs or poultry, or it may be formulated to be fed together with a *forage* to ruminant livestock.

compound fertiliser a manufactured *fertiliser* which contains more than one of the three main plant nutrients, *nitrogen, phosphate* and *potash*. Usually supplied in the *granular* form but may also be liquid or a powder.

compounding 1. See *feed compounding*. 2.   A concept, employed in business management, recognising that money received today can be invested to   earn interest in the future. For illustration, consider £2 invested to earn an *annual percentage rate* of 10%. After one year, 20p interest will have been earned making a total of £2.20. Invested for a further year at the same interest rate, the accumulated total at the end of year two would be £2.20 x 1.10 which gives £2.42.   Reinvested for a third year would give £2.66 and so on.   The general compounding formula is $a(1+x)n$, where a is the initial investment, x is the interest rate expressed as a decimal, and n is the number of time periods considered.

computer see *hardware.*

computer terminal *hardware* used to communicate with a central computer, for example from the farm office to a *bureau service* computer via a telephone link.

concentrates a term used in describing certain animal *feedingstuffs* which have a high feed value relative to their volume. This high feed value may be due to a high content of energy, protein, fat or a combination of these. Concentrates include single feed ingredients which may be a good source of energy (e.g. *cereal grains)* or protein (e.g. oil *cakes* and meals). *Compound feeds* consisting of a balanced mix of ingredients are also concentrates. Concentrates may be manufactured by commercial animal feedingstuff compounders and bought in by the farmer or simpler formulations may be *home-mixed* on the farm.

conditioning the preparation of crops for harvest or storage. 1. *Herbage* crops may be conditioned by mechanical processing to increase their rate of drying by disrupting the surfaces of the plant to increase the rate of water loss. Methods include *crimping* and bruising by laceration. 2. Vegetable crops may be conditioned for long-term storage by manipulation of the storage environment, in the early stages, to destroy *pathogens* and create the correct physiological state within the plant.

condition scoring a subjective scoring of the amount of body reserves (muscle and fat) an animal has at specific reference points - often around the tail-head and loin regions, which is assessed by handling. Condition scoring is mainly used with breeding stock to assess their nutritional status and identify individuals in need of nutritional attention. Scores range (for cattle) from 0-5, with animals of median score showing higher reproductive and lactation performance.

conformation the shape of an animal or carcass. Despite questionable relationships with animal performance, conformation has been an important trait in selection programmes for cattle. The Milk Marketing Board has adopted a linear classification scheme to assess the conformation of the daughters of the sires in its Friesian/Holstein stud. This evaluates a range of characters e.g. height, width and body depth as well as legs, feet, udder, and teats. Assessment of conformation in breeding beef animals centres upon those factors which are judged in assessing carcass conformation. See also *beef carcass classification, sheep carcass classification.*

congenital present at birth, although not necessarily caused by gene action.

conservation 1. Of herbage, the preservation of a crop grown in summer for use during the winter. 2. Of the environment, the maintenance of the environment in a socially acceptable form. See also *wildlife and* *countryside act, environmentally sensitive areas.*

contact with reference to *crop protection chemicals,* contact chemicals are those which immediately affect the target organism on which they fall. They are not taken into the plant and are not retained. Contrast *systemic* and *residual.*

contact animal an animal which has been in contact with a diseased animal and which, if the disease is infectious, may need to be isolated.

contemporary comparison a method of sire evaluation which assesses the mean difference in a performance *trait* (e.g. milk yield) between *heifers* of a particular *sire* and their contemporaries. See also *improved contemporary comparison.*

continuous crossing a *crossbreeding* system in which the females in a population produce their own replacements which will be crossbreeds of a different genetic constitution.

continuous stocking a system of grazing management in which animals have access to a *pasture* for the whole of the grazing season. The *herbage* is therefore being consumed as it is growing. This form of grazing is sometimes called set stocking although this latter term implies that a fixed number of animals graze a fixed area. Contrast *rotational grazing.*

contra a type of entry in a *cash analysis* book, made when a purchase from a supplier has been credited against a sale to the same supplier. This ensures that separate receipt and payments are clearly identified and recorded.

contract a legally binding agreement between two or more parties.

contractor a person who undertakes specific operations on a farm, and usually provides the equipment for carrying out the activity, such as the installation of *drainage* systems, relief milking, or the annual cutting of silage. The contractor is not an employee of the farmer nor has he or she any interest in the farm business.

control area an area declared by the Ministry of Agriculture, Fisheries and Food to be subject to various controls aimed at preventing animal to animal contact and thus containing the spread of a disease. Control areas usually cover a larger area and a larger range of animals than an *infected area.* The movement of animals out of the control area is only allowed at the discretion of the Ministry under a *movement license.*

controlled droplet application (CDA) the application of *crop protection chemical* sprays which consist of droplets within a very narrow size range. This can increase the efficiency of use of the chemical by eliminating the spray drift which often takes place behind conventional sprayers which produce a range of droplet sizes.

controlled environment housing a type of intensive livestock housing where various conditions (e.g. ventilation, temperature, humidity and lighting) are strictly controlled. The aim is to improve animal performance although this has to be balanced against the higher costs incurred.

controlled grazing the regulation of the grazing of pasture by adjusting the balance between livestock numbers and herbage supply. See also *rotational grazing.*

cooperative see *farm cooperative.*

copper a trace element which is important both for metabolic processes of plants and animals. If it is not adequately available then *deficiency diseases* may occur. This is most likely in sheep (see *swayback)* which have a narrow requirement for copper between toxic and deficient levels. Copper is also used as a *growth promoter* in the diets of growing pigs.

coppicing the practice of short rotation timber growing whereby the trees are cut back regularly at short (e.g. ten year) intervals. Whilst bringing the advantage of a short rotation, this method produces timber which is only suitable for a narrow range of uses.

copulation the act of sexual intercourse between a male and a female which leads to *insemination.*

co-responsibility levy a tax, expressed as a percentage of the *target price,* charged initially to producers at an early stage in the marketing process. The proceeds then accrue to the *EC budget.* Such levies have been applied to milk production since 1977 (at 2% since 1980) and for rape-seed more recently. They have also been introduced for cereals at 3% in 1986/7.

corolla the complete set of petals of a flower.

corporation tax charged on company profits.

corpuscle red or white blood cell. Corpuscles circulate in the blood of animals.

correlated response a change in a *character* which is not under direct *selection* in a breeding programme.

correlation the degree of association between two variables. In breeding, see *phenotypic correlation, genetic correlation.*

cosset lamb see *pet lamb.*

cost 1. In accounting, the sum of the *expenses* adjusted for *valuation change* (i.e. expenses plus opening valuation less closing valuation). 2. In economics, the cost, sometimes called the opportunity cost, is the revenue foregone through not pursuing an alternative course of action. For example, the accounting costs of a quantity of homegrown feed is calculated by summing the actual outlay of money needed to produce it, whereas the opportunity cost is the amount of revenue foregone by not selling the feed. The concept of opportunity cost should be employed to appraise the financial consequences of decisions.

Cotswold a long-wool breed of sheep which has declined markedly in numbers.

cotton grasses Eriophorum species, characteristic vegetation of wet boggy moorlands. Plants produce white fluffy inflorescences, hence the name, cotton grass. They are of limited grazing value except in late winter when stems are selected by sheep.

cottonseed cake a *cake,* resulting from the extraction of oil from cottonseed, which is used as a feedingstuff for ruminant livestock. It is only of moderate quality and the presence of gossypol makes it toxic to young pigs and poultry. It is available in *decorticated* or undecorticated forms.

cotyledon 1. Part of the embryo of a seed, the cotyledon is a fleshy lobe connected to the upper part of the rudimentary stem, the *hypocotyl.* Often emerging with the *plumule* after *germination,* the cotyledons are occasionally seen as the first leaves. The number of cotyledons is variable and the flowering plants are divided into two series depending upon whether they have one cotyledon (*monocotyledons*) or two (*dicotyledons*). *Cereals* and *grasses* are monocotyledons, the other main crops are dicotyledons. 2. One of a number of specialised button-like appendages of the *uterus* of the *cow* or *ewe* which serves as the point of attachment of the *placenta.*

couch grass (Agropyron repens) a troublesome *weed* of cultivated crops. A grass which increases by both vegetative and sexual means. Stems produced below the soil surface *(rhizomes)* can produce new plants even when chopped. Control is now achieved by using *translocated herbicides,* which ensure that all parts of the plant are killed. Other common names include Twitch, Wickens.

Council for the Protection of Rural England (CPRE) an environmental pressure group with a broad spectrum of interests, representing the concern of a wide range of people in the *conservation* of the countryside. The CPRE is active in defending the *green belt,* in conserving the *National Parks* and other areas of high amenity value. It participates in public debate on all matters to do with conservation and amenity. The membership of the CPRE is largely urban.

Council of Ministers the EC's main decision-making body. The Council consists of the relevant ministers from member states, e.g. the Agricultural Council includes all ministers of agriculture. Proposals initiated by the *Commission of the European Communities* must be approved by the Council before they can be enforced.

Country Landowners Association, (CLA) an organisation founded in 1908, which represents the interests of owners of agricultural land. The Association lobbies Parliament and negotiates with the *National Farmers Unions* and other interest groups.

Countryside Commission an agency responsible for countryside recreation and conservation. In addition to financing work undertaken by public and private organisations its main activity is the designation of *National Parks* and *Areas of Outstanding Natural Beauty.* The Countryside Commission replaced the National Parks Commission in 1968. Scotland has a separate Countryside Commission.

cover 1. To copulate with or to *serve,* such as when a bull covers a cow. 2. To brood or sit on a *clutch* of eggs.

cover crop 1. In relation to *undersowing,* the crop which is grown more quickly and removed to allow the later development of the slower growing companion crop, which is needed in the longer term. 2. A crop grown specifically to provide shelter and food for *game* birds.

cow a female *bovine* animal. Female cattle are generally termed *heifers* until the time of their second calving.

cow activated concentrate dispensers See *out-of-parlour feeders.*

cow beef beef from the carcasses of cows which have been *culled* for some reason e.g. infertility, mastitis, poor milk yield or old age.

cow families an example of *line breeding* where dairy cows are bred to a common ancestor.

cow genetic index an indication of the genetic merit of a cow relative to a national base. The index takes into account the cows own yields of fat and protein (lactations one to five), the ICC (improved contemporary comparison) of her sire, the cow genetic index of her dam and the herd's genetic level.

cowhouse a dual-purpose building in which cows are both housed and milked. A traditional method of housing in which cows are usually tethered in *stalls* and which is being replaced by systems based on *loose housing* or *cubicles*, which have separate *milking parlours.* Also called a *byre,* shippon or shippen.

crazy chick disease a nutritional disorder in chicks which is associated with Vitamin E deficiency. It is characterised by partial paralysis and a stumbling gait.

credit gaining the use of goods or services before payment is made. There are many kinds of credit - short, medium and long-term - including *trade credit, bank overdraft, hire purchase, loans, leasing* and *mortgages.* The rates of interest charged and the duration or term of the credit may vary.

creditor a supplier of funds, goods or services to whom payment is outstanding.

creep the area of a farm building where young animals can go but which is inaccessible to their mothers. For example, in a *farrowing house* the creep provides the piglets with a source of heat and *creep feeding.* A fence or hurdle through which a young animal but not its mother, can pass is also referred to as a creep.

creep feeding the feeding of a special diet, often of high nutritional quality, to young farm animals in a *creep* which excludes their mothers. Unweaned piglets or in-wintered claves or lambs may be creep fed.

creep grazing a method of pasture management which allows lambs access to specific areas of pasture either before their mothers (forward creep grazing), or from which their mothers are excluded, (sideways creep grazing).

crested dogstail (Cynosurus cristatus) a type of herbage grass which is characteristic of poor quality permanent pastures. Fairly palatable but low yielding, it persists in low fertility conditions. Its wiry inflorescence often remains ungrazed.

crib see *manger.*

crimp 1. To bruise grass with a *crimper.* 2. The waviness of wool, which is measured as the number of crimps per unit length and is an important indicator of quality.

crimper a machine used to bruise and scuff cut herbage in order that it dries more quickly for *silage* or *hay* production.

crisscrossing a type of *rotational crossing* where two 'types' only are used alternately e.g. if A and B are two breeds a crisscross breeding programme might be A x [B x {A x |B x (A x B)|}]. In pig breeding this might involve the same two breeds, Landrace and Large White, being used in alternate generations as sires on home-produced crossbred gilts.

crop area in *agricultural statistics,* the area of the farm utilised to grow crops. Because it may be recorded in either Ordnance Survey or sown hectares (or acres) errors may be introduced into the data. The sown area is less than the Ordnance Survey area due to headland verges, ditches, hedges and waste corners of fields.

crop hygiene the concept of limiting the spread of pests, diseases and *weeds* by maintaining conditions which are unsatisfactory for the proliferation of problem organisms. Such measures include the adequate disposal of contaminated crop residues, the removal of *volunteer plants*, the removal of plants which act as *alternative hosts*, and *crop rotation*.

crop protection chemicals the general name given to those chemicals which are applied to crops to control diseases (usually *fungicides),* pests *(pesticides)* or *weeds (herbicides).* These may be natural or synthetic products.

crossbreeding the mating of animals (or plants) of different breeds in order to combine the best characteristics of the two breeds. In animals the progeny are known as crossbreds and possess *hybrid vigour.*

crossed cheque identified by two parallel lines, a crossed cheque can only be paid into an account (unless made payable to 'self' or 'cash'). Contrast *open cheque.*

cruciferae a family of plants which includes a number of species of importance in crop production. These include the *forage* crops, *turnips, swedes, kales* and *rapes,* and the *vegetables cabbage, cauliflower, brussels sprouts.* Also included is the crop grown for the oil in its seed, *oilseed rape.* Some important *weeds,* for example *charlock,* are members of this family.

crude fibre one of the components of a *proximate analysis* of an animal *feedingstuff.* The crude fibre comprises mainly cellulose, lignin and related compounds.

crude protein an expression of the nitrogen concentration of a material, frequently applied to animal feeds. Crude *protein* content is calculated by multiplying the nitrogen concentration by 6.25 on the misleading assumption that all nitrogen present is in the form of protein.

crush a narrow passage which can restrain an animal both in front and behind to allow close inspection, veterinary treatment, etc.

crushed grain see *rolled grain.*

cryogenic flask a flask used in *artificial insemination* to transport *semen* at very low temperatures.

cryptorchid See *rig.*

cuber a machine used to produce cubes or pellets of animal *meal.* The pellets, which may vary in diameter and length depending on the species they are to be fed to, are produced by forcing the meal together with *molasses* through small circular holes.

cubicles rows of partitioned compartments in a building where cows are housed. Cows are not tethered but may enter and leave a cubicle at will. Each cubicle is intended for a single cow and is covered with some form of bedding (e.g. old dung, sawdust, rubber mat) which is retained by a raised kerb. The rows of cubicles are backed by a dunging passage.

cuckoo lambs late-born lambs e.g. those born after mid-April.

cud the partly digested food which is regurgitated from the *rumen* to be chewed again by ruminants.

culard a French term meaning 'double-muscled'. 'Double muscles' do not occur but certain muscle groups, particularly in the upper hind limb, show relative enlargement. It is a genetically transmitted trait which is particularly common in certain breeds of beef cattle e.g. *Belgian Blue* and *Charolais.* Carcasses from such animals show a higher muscle : bone ratio but there are increased risks of *dystocia* at calving.

cull an animal separated from the breeding herd or flock. Often the animal is old, of poor quality or unsuitable and is removed from the herd and killed for meat production.

culm a term used to describe the stem of a grass or sedge.

cultivar designation for the *variety* or strain of crop plant which is distinguishable as being distinct from other examples of the same crop, but which is uniform and is stable when reproduced.

cultivation the purposeful movement of soil, to create a *structure* suitable for the sowing of *seeds* or to control *weed* plants.

curing in relation to stored crops, the process of wound healing and physiological adjustment after harvesting and before long-term storage. Usually assisted by careful control of environmental conditions e.g. temperature and humidity. For example with *potatoes, tubers* would be stored at $15^{o}C$ and 90% relative humidity for two weeks after harvest before being stored in the longer term at the lower temperature of 7°C.

current account a bank account from which cheques can be drawn. Credit may be provided through this form of account as a *bank overdraft*. Interest is not received on positive balances. Contrast *deposit account*.

customs union an arrangement between countries with regard to trade, whereby they agree to impose a common external tariff on all imports from third countries whilst allowing free trade between members. For example, the EC operates a common market in agricultural and industrial goods between its 12 members, and imposes common external tariffs on imports from third countries. See also *free trade area*.

cutter a general purpose pig slaughtered at 70-80kg liveweight. After slaughter the carcass is cut into different parts which may go to bacon, pork or processing respectively.

cyst a bladder or sac containing fluid. Some pests of crops at certain stages of their life cycle e.g. *potato cyst nematode*. These cysts can be very persistant and remain as potential infections for a considerable time in the soil.

DAFS Department of Agriculture and Fisheries for Scotland.

dagging removal of soiled wool from a sheep's hindquarters in an attempt to prevent fly-*strike*.

dairy a farm building, often adjoining the *milking parlour*, where milk is cooled and temporarily stored prior to transport to a commercial dairy where it may either be used for the liquid milk market or a manufactured milk product (e.g. butter, cheese, cream or yogurt).

dairy cattle *cattle* which are kept primarily for milk production. In the UK, dairy cows number about 3.2M of which *Friesians* are the dominant breed.

dairy farm a farm on which the principal activity is milk production.

dairy followers young stock (*calves* and *heifers*) in a dairy herd which have not yet been in milk but are still growing with the intention of entering the herd as replacements for older, less productive cows.

dairy herd conversion scheme of the EC, introduced in 1977, with the objective of limiting the growth of *intervention stocks* of dairy products. This scheme initially encouraged milk producers to convert to beef production. It also granted premiums (from 1977) to producers, who reduced their milk deliveries, which were designed to compensate them for the resulting loss of revenue. This was not renewed when its Regulation became inoperative in 1983 and was replaced by the *milk non-delivery scheme* when *quotas* were introduced in 1984. See also *dairy regime*.

dairy regime the set of EC policies relating to the production and manufacture of milk and milk products. The policies cover liquid milk, cream, butter, cheese, curds and dried milk products. As with other *administered price* systems, there is a target price for milk and related intervention prices for milk products, which are intended to maintain internal price levels. Threshold prices and variable levies are applied to EC imports of dairy products, and refunds are used to subsidise exports. Support for the dairy sector has become one of the most costly market support regimes. Several responses to rising support costs have been attempted. Milk producers have been encouraged to switch to beef production or to reduce sales under the *dairy herd conversion scheme,* and latterly the *milk non-delivery scheme. Co-responsibility levies* and *quotas* have also been applied to milk production in an attempt to curb *surpluses.* Joint action has been taken by the EC and New Zealand (the main exporter of dairy produce) to reduce the cost of refunds by raising *world market prices* for dairy products.

Dairy Shorthorn a dual-purpose breed of cattle which is of declining popularity. The cattle may be red, white, red and white or roan in colour with characteristic short forward-curling horns.

dam the female parent of a young animal.

DANI Department of Agriculture for Northern Ireland.

Danish piggery a controlled environment *piggery* typically used for fattening pigs and consisting of a range of pens, with dunging passages along the outside walls, either side of a central feeding passage.

Dartmoor a large, long curly-wooled, white faced sheep of common origin to the South Devon and Devon Longwool breeds.

day-old-chick a chick that is dispatched to the buyer within 24 hours of hatching.

deadweight the weight of a *carcass.*

deadweight certification centre a slaughterhouse, which has been approved by the *Meat and Livestock Commission,* where sheep and cattle carcasses are presented for certification as eligible for a sheep variable premium or beef premium payment.

deadweight marketing see *livestock marketing.*

debtor a customer who has received goods or services but has not yet paid for them. Contrast *creditor.*

deciduous the shedding of leaves, often when mature.

deciduous teeth an animal's first teeth which are later shed and replaced by permanent teeth. Also called milk teeth.

decision analysis a way of describing the decision-making process, either to examine and predict the behaviour of decision-makers, or as a planning tool. The approach recognises both the decision-maker's attitude towards risk, and his or her expectation that a particular outcome will occur.

decortication the removal of husks from seeds. *Cakes,* for livestock feeding, which are derived from oilseeds (eg. *cottonseed cake*) may be either decorticated (the husk removed) or undecorticated (the husk left on).

deep freezing the technique now used to store many otherwise perishable foods for human consumption. By maintaining subzero temperatures, the organisms responsible for decay cannot flourish. The development of deep freezing has brought about a change in eating habits because high quality vegetables can be made available at times of the year when they cannot be supplied fresh. It has also influenced growers who can now produce high yields of high quality material specifically for deep freezing.

deep litter a system of bedding cattle, poultry or pigs based upon straw, shavings, sawdust or bracken. In all cases fresh litter is periodically added on top of the mixture of used litter, faeces and urine which is allowed to build up either until the animals are turned out of the building in spring or a crop of birds is removed. At this point the used litter is removed.

deficiency disease a disease of an animal or plant which is due to an inadequacy of a specific essential nutrient e.g. a mineral or a vitamin.

deficiency payments a method of supporting agricultural prices used in the UK for two decades prior to entry into the EC in 1973. The payments bridge the gap between average market prices, freely determined, and a *predetermined guaranteed price level*. Because individual producers sell their output freely, the market price varies from one transaction to another and consequently the individual producer's total return per unit of sale depends on his marketing skill as well as the Guaranteed Price. The deficiency payments system has remained in use under the CAP, for beef and sheep production in the UK. See also *variable premium*.

degradability a term used specifically in protein nutrition to express the proportion of protein or nitrogen which is broken down in the *rumen* of a ruminant animal and is available to the microbial population. The degradable fraction is termed RDP (Rumen Degradable Protein) and that which is not degraded in the rumen is termed UDP (Undegradable Protein).

dehorning the removal of an animal's horns with the intention of preventing damage to stockmen or other animals. This is usually accomplished by removing the horn buds of the young animal by heat or caustic treatment. Horns may also be removed from mature animals under anaesthetic using an electric saw.

demand the amount of a product that consumers are willing to purchase at a given price.

demand schedule the relationship between the price (P) of a commodity and quantity (Q) purchased.It is often represented graphically as shown. Because generally it slopes downwards from left to right, the schedule indicates that demand increases as price falls. See also *elasticities* and *market equilibrium*.

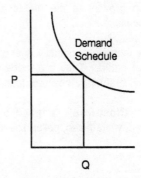

dental formula a formula indicating the number of each kind of teeth in an animal species. The formula shows the teeth numbers for one side of the upper jaw above those of the lower jaw. Thus the dental formula of a pig is:

$$i\,\frac{3}{3}\,,\,c\,\frac{1}{1}\,,\,p\,\frac{4}{4}\,,\,m\,\frac{3}{3}$$

where i = incisors, c = canine, p = premolars and m = molars.

dentition the number and arrangement of an animal's teeth. See also *dental formula.*

deposit account a bank or other account which earns interest on a positive balance, which cannot be overdrawn, and against which cheques cannot be drawn. Contrast *current account.*

depreciation the amount by which an *asset* loses value over a given period, usually one year. It can be considered to be a measure of the consumption of capital through time, and is shown as a cost in a *trading, profit and loss account* and an adjustment to asset valuation on a *balance sheet.* Two main methods are employed to estimate depreciation charges. (a) The Straight Line Method, as the term suggests, assumes that depreciation occurs by an equal amount each year. This is usually assumed for buildings and fixed equipment. The annual depreciation is calculated by first subtracting a *salvage value* from the initial value of the item, and then dividing by the number of years making up its *economic life.* (b) The Reducing or Diminishing Balance Method recognises that there is often rapid depreciation early in the life of an asset, diminishing with age, as is usually the case with farm machinery. Annual depreciation is estimated as a percentage of the opening valuation (i.e. the book value at the beginning of each year). The depreciation rate expressed as a percentage, is chosen to reflect the pattern of the loss in value.

Derbyshire Gritstone a hardy breed of hill sheep, having a mottled black and white face and a good quality fleece, which originates in the Peak District.

dessication drying out. In crop production, the application of a herbicide to stop growth as the plants approach maturity, to assist the harvesting process.

Devon although originally dual-purpose, they are now regarded as a breed of beef cattle. They are moderately small and deep cherry-red in colour. Early maturing, they are found mainly in the S.W. of England.

Devon Closewool a breed of only local importance comprising medium sized, white faced, polled sheep.

Devon Longwool a breed of sheep with a long heavy fleece and wool on its cheeks. It now exists as the Devon and Cornwall Longwool following its amalgamation with the South Devon breed.

dewclaw the rudimentary fifth digit as is found on the heel of cattle or pigs.

dewlap the loose flesh hanging in the throat area of cattle especially Bos indicus types.

Dexter a breed of dwarf *dual-purpose* cattle originating from Ireland. They are usually black, occassionally red, horned and short-legged. Relatively uncommon.

diarrhoea the frequent evacuation of liquid faeces. See also *scours.*

dicotyledon a range of plant types which have two *cotyledons* in the embryo. See *cotyledon.*

diet the intake of food and liquid by an animal.

diffusion the natural process by which gasses move from areas of high concentration to areas of low concentration. Carbon dioxide and oxygen move into and out of plants by this process.

digestibility the proportion of a food eaten by an animal which is not eliminated in the faeces. It gives an indication of the quality of a dietary constituent, most commonly applied to dry matter i.e. digestibility of *dry matter* or *organic matter* or *crude protein.* A specific term often used in advisory work is '*D value*' which expresses the amount of digestible organic matter in the dry matter.

digestible crude protein (DCP) the part of the *crude protein* component of a feed which is digestible and does not appear in the faeces. Until recently DCP has been the chosen method of expressing animal requirements and feed supply for ruminants because of the considerable variation in the content and digestibility of crude protein in feeds for ruminants.

digestible energy the amount of energy in an animal feed after deduction of the faecal energy. Usually expressed as MJ (megajoules) per kg DM (dry matter).

digestion the process by which food ingested by an animal is rendered soluble so that is can be assimilated. A vital part of this process is played by *enzymes* in the digestive juices.

digestive juices juices secreted into the digestive tract of animals, to aid the process of *digestion*, e.g. *saliva, gastric juice, bile, pancreatic* *juice* and *intestinal juice.*

dilapidations a charge made by a *landlord* to a *tenant* leaving a holding, for deterioration in *landlords capital* (such as buildings and fences) occurring during the tenancy. See also *tenant right.*

diminishing balance depreciation see *depreciation.*

diminishing returns see *production function.*

dip either a dipping bath or the proprietary chemical which is diluted and placed in it for *dipping* animals, especially sheep. Dips usually contain organo-phosphorus chemicals.

diploid the number of chromosomes in the nucleus of a cell before cell division (*meiosis*). It is therefore a double number. Contrast *haploid, polyploid.*

dipping the temporary total immersion of an animal in a *dip.* In the UK sheep are the animals most commonly dipped with the intention of killing common *ectoparasites* (e.g. *keds, lice, ticks*), arresting the spread of *sheep scab* or protecting against *blowfly* attack.

direct debit the collection of a payment by a *creditor* directly from a *debtor*'s bank account, where authorisation has been given to the bank in advance. See also *standing order, Giro.*

direct drilling a method of introducing *seed* into a *soil* without any prior cultivation. *herbicides* are used to control *weeds* and seeds are introduced by a direct drill which is adapted to achieve the necessary penetration of an uncultivated soil.

direct income transfers (DIT) also known as income aids, have been proposed by a number of authorities as a method of protecting farmers' incomes without raising commodity prices. The principle of DIT is that farmers would be guaranteed an income independent of their level of production. Those advocating the policy assume that this would meet the income objective of the CAP. It has not yet proved possible to design a workable system of DIT: critics point to its potentially large administrative cost.

direct reseeding with reference to grassland, the replacement of an unproductive pasture by new seeds following *cultivation* to produce a suitable *seedbed.*

disaccharide a sugar composed of two condensed sugar molecules e.g. *sucrose.* One of the classifications of *carbohydrates.*

disc harrows cultivation equipment designed for use after ploughing to reduce the size of soil aggregates. Banks of concave discs are drawn through the soil at a slight angle, achieving the desired effect by both chopping and moving the soil.

discontinuous crossing an animal breeding system in which new crossbreds are produced afresh, from the purebred parents, each generation. The term is usually applied to the production of first crosses and contrasts with *continuous crossing.*

discounted cash flow (DCF) the *cash flow* into and out of a business over time, discounted to a *net present value.*

discounting the converse of *compounding.* It enables the value of money received in the future to be compared with the value of money received today, recognising the 'time value of money'. For example the value of £1 now is less than the present value of £1 received at some future date. For example the *present value* of £1 to be received in one year's time, discounted at 10%, would be £0.909 and in two year's time £0.826. For this calculation the formula is:

$$PV = \frac{a}{(1 + x)^n}$$

where a is the amount to be received at a future date, x is the discount rate expressed as a decimal and n is the number of time periods into the future before a will be received. The concept is employed in the *net present value* and *internal rate of return* criteria for *investment appraisal.*

dished face a face on an animal which exhibits distinct concavity e.g. the *middle white* pig.

Dishley Leicester a breed of improved *Leicester* sheep.

disinfection the thorough cleansing of appropriate buildings, implements, utensils, animals etc. by physical cleaning, the application of approved chemicals, fumigation or steam cleaning. Disinfection may take place routinely, to reduce bacterial contamination, as with the milking plant or it may be carried out to specifically cleanse after an infection has been on a farm.

distillers' grains a by-product of whisky manufacturing which consists of the remains of malted barley and are similar to *brewers' grains.* They are used as an animal feedingstuff and may be fed wet or dry.

ditch an open channel, created to remove water from an area. Many fields are surrounded by ditches, into which *field drainage pipes* may run. Such ditches will form an interlinking network, finally leading to a natural water course such as a stream or river. An alternative name is a dyke.

diversification an increase in the number of farm enterprises, or investment in off-farm activities, thereby spreading the risk of the business.

diversification groups sets of cereal varieties which exhibit resistance to the same race of a particular pathogen. It is suggested that on farms, fields should be sown with varieties from different diversification groups such that if one race of the pathogen attacks, only part of the total area of the crop will be susceptible.

diversification scheme announced in 1987, the scheme provides financial encouragement to farmers seeking *diversification* of their businesses. Eligible farmers must spend at least half their time on the farm and obtain half their income from it. Grants under the scheme cover 25% of the cost of investments of up to £35,000 for expenditure on buildings, equipment and site development connected with processing farm produce, craft manufacture, renovation of farm machinery, farm shops, *pick your own* sites and camping, holiday, catering and sports facilities.

DIY AI do-it-yourself artificial insemination is growing in popularity in dairy herds. It is where cattle are inseminated by the trained farm stockman rather than an inseminator from a central organisation.

dizygous originating from two fertilised ova e.g. dizygotic or non-identical twins. Contrast *monozygous.*

DNA deoxyribonucleic acid, the main constituent of the chromosomes in the nucleus of cells. DNA is the material through which the genetic information relevant to an individual is coded and transmitted to the next generation.

dock the removal of part, or the whole, of an animal's tail. Pigs may be docked to reduce the incidence of tail biting and lowland breeds of sheep are often docked to reduce the accumulation of dirt and faeces on the underside of the tail which would encourage *strike.*

docking disorder a disorder of *sugar beet* caused by free living nematodes (Trichodorus and Longidorus spp.) which damage seedling root systems on light sandy soils. Damage is usualy patchily distributed in affected fields. Control can be achieved by the use of *granular nematicides.*

docks (Rumex species) *perennial weeds* of *arable* crops and grassland. There are several types of dock but R. crispus, Curled dock and R. obtusifolius, Broad leaved Dock are the most common. Thick *tap roots* are produced by plants from seed which, even when broken up, can each give rise to several new plants. Plants also reproduce by seed. Seedlings and young plants may be relatively easily controlled by *herbicides* but mature plants are more difficult to destroy.

dodder (Cuscuta species) a group of weeds which parasitise crop plants. They are devoid of chlorophyll, but twine around host plants, sending suckers into them. The seedling establishes with slender root which dies when the dodder finds a suitable host. Affected host plants are considerably weakened and may be killed. Dodder is recognised as an injurious *weed*.

doe a female deer, hare or rabbit.

dominance hierarchy see *social hierarchy*.

dominant gene in a *gene* pair, the dominant gene is the one which asserts itself over a recessive gene. Thus it is the dominant gene which determines a specific character in the offspring of a plant or animal. (e.g. in cattle the gene controlling horns is dominant over the gene controlling the polled condition: thus most cattle are naturally horned).

dormancy a state of inactivity entered by some plants in response to unfavourable conditions or at certain physiological stages. This usually results in complete absence of visible growth and enhanced powers of survival.

Dorset Down a brown faced breed of sheep which has wool growing over its eyes. It has a good quality fleece and is early maturing producing a good carcass.

Dorset Horn a breed of sheep, derived partly from the Merino, which is noted for its extended breeding season with individual ewes being able to breed at any time of the year. Both sexes have long curly horns and the breed is characterised by its white fleece, white face and pink nostrils and lips. The breed is used with the Finnish Landrace to produce the Finn-Dorset cross - sheep which are both prolific and have an extended breeding season.

Dorset wedge a system of stacking cut herbage in a *clamp* to produce *silage*. Herbage is stacked in a wedge shape using a buckrate or fork lift. The ramp is thus consolidated as it forms, helping to induce anaerobic conditions.

double entry book-keeping an elaborate system of accounting used in larger businesses, where providing information on trade *creditors* and trade *debtors* is important. Contrast *cash analysis* which is the normal method of book-keeping on farms.

double muscling see *culard*.

double suckling a method of beef production where a second calf is introduced and allowed to suckle alongside a beef cow's own newborn calf. Double suckling is only attempted with cows producing sufficient milk for two calves.

down the soft plumage covering young birds or found under the feathers of certain species of birds (e.g. ducks or geese).

Down Breeds - collectively, the Down breeds are hornless, short-wooled sheep with coloured faces and legs which because of their carcass attributes are used as *terminal sires.* They were developed on the hilly, chalk downlands and include the *Suffolk, Oxford Down, Southdown, Dorset Down* and *Hampshire Down.*

down-calver a cow or heifer, which is at or near the point of calving.

downer cow a cow suffering from *milk fever.*

downy mildew 1. A fungal disease of *sugar beet.* The causative organism is Perenospora farinosa. Infected leaves become thickened, puckered and brittle then covered with the downy fungal growth. One effect is to reduce the purity of the root juice and adversely affect extraction of sugar. Control by the use of *fungicides* is possible. 2. A fungal disease of *brassica* crops caused by P. parasitica which is troublesome at the seedling stage.

draff see *brewers' grains.*

draft ewe a ewe sold from a breeding flock whilst it is still young enough to produce lambs. Usually ewes are drafted from a hill flock, after approximately 3 *lamb crops,* to the kinder environment of a lowland farm.

drag harrows cultivation equipment used in the final stages of seedbed preparation or to cover the seed after sowing. Several rows of short vertical tines are drawn horizontally through the soil.

drain a channel or passage down which excess water may flow. In agriculture drains may be installed in fields in which natural water movement is inherently slow leading to waterlogging of soils and poor crop production. Drains are normally laid such that excess water is transported along pipes to the lowest point of the field or to a natural water course. The depth, frequency and pattern of drains will vary with soil type. See also *mole drainage, plastic* and *tile drains.*

drainage the complete system of, or the process of installing, field drains. Although occasionally carried out by farmers, it is more often carried out by specialised drainage *contractors.*

drake a male duck.

draw to select: as in 'to draw lambs for market' or 'to draw ewes for mating groups'.

dredge corn traditionally the growing of two *cereal* crops as a mixture in one field. *Oats* and *barley* are the main components but *peas* and *beans* may also be added.

dried grass grass which following cutting, has been artificially dried to a low moisture content. It is used as an animal feedingstuff either in the form of a cob or wafer for ruminants or milled into a meal for use in pigs and poultry *diets*.

drill 1. See *ridge*. 2. A machine for introducing seed into the soil.

drilling with reference to field crops, the process of introducing *seed* into the soil by machine. Such machines may be simple, involving only one crop row or drill, or more complex, sowing several parallel rows or drills at one pass. The machines are usually adjustable in respect of sowing depth, *seeding rate* and possibly width, between rows. See also *combine drill, precision drill.*

drilling to a stand sowing the correct number of seeds per hectare to achieve the desired *plant population* without the need for further thinning.

dry cow a cow between lactations and not producing milk. Often, although not always, she is pregnant.

dry feeding a feeding system, often used for pigs and poultry, in which the *meal* is fed to the animals in a dry state without the addition of water.

dry matter the organic and inorganic components of a feedingstuff. The *proximate analysis* of a fresh sample yields six components; water and the five components of the dry matter (ash, crude protein, crude fibre, ether extract and nitrogen free extract).

dry off the reduction or cessation in milk yielded by a female towards the end of *lactation*. The term is particularly used for the dairy cow but may be applied to other species. The cow may dry-off naturally or the cowman may hasten the drying off process by a reduction in the frequency or thoroughness of the milking process.

dry period a term, most commonly applied to dairy cows, to describe the period between *lactations* when the animal is not producing milk. It is usually of about 60 days duration.

dry rot a soil borne fungal disease of potatoes causing rotting of *tubers* in storage. The disease is caused by Fusarium species. The symptoms are wrinkled skin and internal cavities with an indistinct margin between healthy and diseased tissue. Control by avoiding diseased seed and excessive mechanical handling.

dry sow a sow not producing milk. Often, although not always, she is pregnant.

dual-purpose breed a classification which may be applied to any of the farm species. Thus: poultry breeds considered good for both egg laying and meat production or cattle considered useful for both milk and beef production etc. Generally the performance of a dual-purpose cattle breed would be inferior to a specialist beef breed for beef production or to a specialist dairy breed for milk production.

dung the *faeces,* or undigested food, of an animal which is passed out of the *anus.*

dunging passage the passage in a livestock building into which animals kept in *cubicles, pens* or *stalls* void their dung.

Durham historically, a breed of large cattle with short horns which was developed in the Tees Valley area of County Durham. It gave rise to the main *shorthorn* breeds of cattle.

Duroc a breed of pig imported from North America. It is red coloured and used in *cross-breeding* programmes.

dusts formulations of *crop protection chemicals* which are applied as fine solid particles. Dusts may be applied in such a way that they adhere to foliage or that they reach the soil.

Dutch auction a method of *auction* not traditionally used in the UK. The offer price is successively lowered, and the first, and therefore highest, bidder is the purchaser. It is a suitable procedure for computerised marketing.

Dutch barn a general purpose storage building which is primarily used for straw or hay but may also be used for implements, livestock, animal feedingstuff etc.

D value the *digestibility* of the *organic* matter in the dry matter of plants. D value is one of the main indicators used by advisors to describe the quality of a food for animal production.

dyke See *ditch.*

early bite *forage* which is available for grazing particularly early in the growing season before the onset of main grass growth. Crops used to provide such forage include *rye* and *Italian ryegrass*. Early bite may also be produced by the early use of *nitrogen fertiliser*.

early potatoes immature *tubers* from potato crops harvested in June and July for immediate consumption. These have a high value because of their pleasant taste and texture and limited availability. Certain varieties are grown for early production because of their suitable growth characteristics in spring. Large quantities are imported, mainly from Mediterranean countries.

early weaning a system of livestock husbandry in which the young are removed from the dam earlier than would be considered usual. There has been a trend towards early weaning of piglets at about 3 weeks of age and calves from dairy cows are often removed from the dam at a few days of age and reared on early weaning systems.

ear marking the marking of an animal's ear for identification purposes. This may be by means of a tag, tattoo or distinctive cut of notches.

East Friesland a breed of dairy sheep originating from Holland. It is a large, long, slim breed which is prolific and has a high yield of milk with a high butterfat content.

easy feed a system of feeding in which livestock are allowed easy access to feed usually along a feed passage or from a bulk hopper.

EC budget the funds raised from EC member states which finance various EC activities. The funds consist of up to 1.4% of each member state's *Value Added Tax* plus the revenue from sugar and other agricultural levies and customs duties on industrial imports. The cost of the CAP amounted to some two-thirds of the EC budget in 1987. See also *European Community* and *financial solidarity*.

E Coli Escherichia Coli is a bacterium commonly found in the digestive tract of most animals. Specific strains cause *diarrhoea* or specific diseases e.g. coli septicaemia.

Economic Development Committee for Agriculture also known as EDC for Agriculture and the Agricultural 'Little Neddy'. The role of the Committee is to advise the National Economic Development Council on matters relating to the development of the industry. The Committee was established in 1966, consisting of representatives of employers, land owners, farm workers and the Government, together with independent members. The Committee was reconstituted as the Agriculture Ad Hoc Section Group of the National Economic Development Office in 1988.

economic life the life of a fixed *asset* assumed for the purpose of budgeting or *investment appraisal,* which may differ from its physical life. With an uncertain future,   it is the time span within which it is deemed necessary for a project to be viable. See also *depreciation.*

economic rent see *rent.*

economic yield 1. Of capital, see *rate of return.* 2. That part of the crop which is the main reason for its cultivation and when sold, provides the revenue, e.g. in potatoes, saleable tubers constitute the economic yield.

ectoparasite a *parasite* living on the outside of its host e.g. a tick or a louse. Contrast *endoparasite.*

Ecu See *European currency unit.*

eelworm see *potato cyst nematode.*

efferent a zoological term for 'carrying away'. Common examples being blood vessels carrying blood away from an organ or a motor nerve carrying nervous impulses away from   the central nervous system. Contrast *afferent.*

effluent waste material which may be in a gaseous, liquid or solid form. Common forms of agriculturally important effluent are slurry or silage effluent.

egg an ovum, or the female *gamete,* of any species. More specifically the oval shaped body laid by female birds consisting of *albumen* and *yolk* (containing the gamete) surrounded by a calcareous shell. If fertilised, the yolk develops to produce a young *chick* which hatches from the shell.

egg classes current EC marketing regulations possess three quality classes. Class A (fresh eggs), Class B (second quality or preserved eggs) and Class C (non-graded eggs intended for the manufacture of foodstuffs for human consumption).

Eggs Authority operated between 1971 and 1986 with a remit to improve the marketing of eggs. The Authority activities were in promotion, market intelligence and research. It was financed by a levy, collected by hatcheries, on day-old chicks for laying.

egg tooth a horny structure on the bill of a chick which it uses to crack the egg shell from within when hatching. The egg tooth is discarded soon after hatching.

egg weight grades under EC regulations, eggs in *egg classes* A and B are weighed and allocated to one of seven weight grades (Grade 1, 70g and over, Grade 7 under 45g).

eild not yielding milk or *barren.*

elasticities summarise the characteristics of *demand* for, or *supply* of, a commodity. They indicate the effect of specified variables, for example price or income, on quantity demanded or supplied. Developed countries, especially for staples such as bread and potatoes, have income elasticities of demand which are near to zero or even negative. Income elasticities for luxury foods may be higher. The income elasticity of demand for food is generally low indicating that as people become wealthier they spend a smaller proportion of their total income on food. Similarly, the price elasticity of supply may be very low for an agricultural commodity, in the short run, indicating that the amount offered for sale will not be responsive to substantial changes in price. See also *demand schedule, supply schedule* and *market equilibrium.*

electric dog a mechanism consisting of a movable electric wire which can be drawn up behind cows in a collecting yard to encourage them to enter the *milking parlour.*

electric fence a system of readily mobile fencing which is used to facilitate *controlled grazing* of grass, kale or roots by livestock. The thin wire, or wires, supported by easily movable insulated posts, carry pulses of electric current which may be either battery generated or from the mains.

embryo a young animal or plant in the early stages of development post-fertilisation. The animal embryo is located in the uterus of its dam and will develop into a foetus. The embryo of a plant seed is located in an inner, protected location.

embryo transfer the transfer of an *embryo,* in the early stages of its development, from the oviduct of its mother (the donor) to the uterus of another female (the recipient). The embryo then develops inside the recipient which has no genetic influence on it. See also *MOET.*

Employment Protection (Consolidation) Act 1978 legislation covering the *contract* between employer and employee, providing employees with a degree of security of employment. Disputes can be referred to the Advisory, Conciliation and Arbitration Service (ACAS).

endemic a term used to describe plants or animals which are indigenous to, or occur naturally in, a given area.

endemic disease a disease which is generally found in an area even though it may not be in evidence at a particular time.

endoparasite a *parasite* living on the inside of its host e.g. *tapeworm* or *gut roundworms.*

endosperm the food storing tissue formed outside the *embryo* of a *seed* after *fertilisation.*

endowment loan a loan in the borrowed capital is not repaid until the end of the term, but *interest* is charged throughout the term on the total amount of capital borrowed. Repayment of the loan is secured by taking out an endowment life assurance policy which matures at the end of the term. See also *credit* and *loan.*

English Leicester a breed of sheep often referred to as the *Leicester.*

ensilage a process in which fresh *forage* e.g. grass or maize undergoes controlled fermentation under anaerobic conditions to produce a product which will store for future use. Sugars in the fresh product are converted to organic acids e.g. lactic and acetic, by bacteria which then become inhibited as the pH falls to approximately 4.   The stable product is called *silage.* The stores in which silage is made and kept are called *silos.* Silage has become progressively more popular in the UK since 1960 and is now the main method of conserving forage for winter use.

enterprise a sector of a farm business for which there are identifiable *returns*, e.g. a dairy herd, 18 month beef herd, or wheat.

entire a male animal which has not been castrated.

environment most generally, the physical conditions in which an activity takes place. The term is used in several contexts, for example:- 1. Agriculture and the environment denotes the problems and conflicts between the private activity, farming, and the public enjoyment of rural amenities of all kinds. 2. Environmental pollution is a subset of the problem arising mainly when farmers allow noxious substances (smoke, fertiliser, effluents) to reach the wider public: farmers also suffer the pollution of their environment. 3. In farm management, the external economic conditions which influence decisions (e.g. prices and costs). 4. In animal breeding, the determinant of an animal's *phenotype* which is not due to its *genotype* but to environmental influences such as nutrition, climate and disease. 5. In crop production, the environment is the combined expression of the effects of climate, soil and man on conditions for crop growth. This may be expressed at a macro level, where large scale differences in soil or weather would be recognised, or at the micro level, where smaller more subtle differences in aspects of climate would be acknowledged.

environmentally sensitive areas (ESAs) areas of high scenic and wildlife interest, designated under EC Regulation 797/85 (see *structures policy);* there may be special national incentives applied within them to encourage production compatible with environmental objectives. At the time of writing the UK Government has chosen the first seventeen areas to be so designated, covering 0.75M ha. Within these areas farmers undertaking to farm consistently with prescribed guidelines for five years receive annual payments per hectare of land affected.

enzootic abortion a contagious form of abortion in sheep caused by a virus which affects the placenta causing abortion about two weeks prior to lambing. It is called enzootic because it is more prevalent in certain districts - NE England and the Scottish Borders.

enzootic bovine leucosis a slow blood cancer, or leukaemia, of cattle. Causes or predisposing factors are not well understood. It may remain completely benign for all of an animal's life but if it becomes malignant it is usually at around 5-6 years and is fatal.

enzootic disease an animal disease which is prevalent in certain areas or districts e.g. *enzootic abortion*. Contrast *enzootic disease.*

enzyme a catalyst produced by a living plant or animal cell. It is a protein which promotes a specific chemical reaction whilst remaining unchanged itself.

epidemic an outbreak of an *epizootic disease* which affects a large number of animals in one area at one time and is easily transmitted from place to place.

epidermis the outer layer of cells of plants or animals. In animals, the integument or skin.

epigeal with reference to *germination,* the situation in which the *cotyledons* of the germinating seedling appear above the soil as seed leaves.

epistasis interaction between *genes* at different *loci.*

epizootic disease a disease which spreads rapidly and affects animals in large numbers over large areas e.g. foot-and-mouth disease.

equine of or pertaining to a horse or horses.

eradication scheme a programme designed to eradicate a particular disease e.g. *brucellosis.* The scheme operates in an eradication area and involves the testing of animals followed by the slaughter of individuals or herds found to have the disease in question.

ergot a disease of *cereals* and *grasses* caused by the fungus Claviceps purpurea. The disease is most apparent when the ears of the crop ripen, when large black *sclerotia* replace the grains. These may fall to the ground or be harvested. In either case, they form the basis for future infection. Ergots in food crops are poisonous and dangerous to both humans and animals.

erosion a process of wearing away. Applied to soil, it describes the process of loss of soil due to the action of wind or water. Wind erosion or *blowing* occurs on light sandy or peaty soils under dry conditions. In strong winds, soil particles are either rolled along the surface or swept up in the airstream and deposited later in hedgerows etc. This can cause loss directly, by loss of the soil, and indirectly by damaging or removing the seedlings which may be growing in the soil. Erosion by water may occur near rivers in flood conditions or on steep hillsides where gulleys of run off water may form, carrying soil down the slope. Erosion may also occur by oxidation of *peat* when land is *drained* for agricultural use e.g. Fenland.

eructation the belching of gases from the stomach through the mouth. The eructation of methane from the *rumen* of ruminant livestock is particularly common.

erysipelas an infectious disease, caused by a streptococcal bacterium, which is characterised by a high fever and hot, reddish inflammations of the skin. Of the farm species, pigs are most affected and severe cases may result in infertility, abortion, lameness or respiratory problems.

essential amino-acid one of the *amino-acids* which an organism can not synthesise and must therefore be obtained from its environment. In animal nutrition, *lysine* and *methionine* are amongst the essential amino-acids likely to be limiting.

Essex Saddleback a dual-purpose breed of pig which has been amalgamated with the Wessex Saddleback to form the British Saddleback. It is a black pig except for a white saddle covering the front legs and extending over the shoulder. Also, the hind feet and tail are white. The breed has traditionally been used in the production of *cross-bred* sows particularly for outdoor sow keeping systems.

establishment of crops. The achievement of a satisfactory population of crop plants from *seed.*

ether extract the fraction of an animal *feedingstuff,* determined by *proximate analysis,* which contains the *fats* or *oils* and the fat soluble vitamins.

European Agricultural Guidance and Guarantee Fund EAGGF (also known by its French acronym of FEOGA), refers to the funds, allocated from the *EC budget,* from which the CAP is financed. The Guidance Section of the fund which finances *structural policy* amounted to some 4% of FEOGA expenditure in 1988 and the remainer was devoted to Guarantees.

See *Common Agricultural Policy*. The relative importance of individual *commodity regimes* is indicated in the table.

EAGGF Guarantee Expenditure, 1988

Percentage Distribution by Commodities

Cereals	20.4	Milk Products	22.5
Sugar	6.8	Beef & Veal	10.9
Olive Oil	5.0	Sheepmeat & Goatmeat	3.2
Oils & Fats	8.8	Pigmeat	0.7
Wine	5.1	Eggs and Poultrymeat	0.6
Tobacco	3.2	Other (including MCAs)	12.8
			100.0

European Community (EC) the *customs union* of 12 countries, established by the Treaty of Rome in 1957. The UK has been a member since January 1973. See also *Commission of the European Communities* and *Common Agricultural Policy.*

European currency unit (Ecu) the currency in which common *administered prices* of the CAP are declared. Introduced, with the European Monetary System in 1979, its day to day value is calculated as the weighted average of member states exchange rates, against the US dollar. The proportions of each currency in the weighted average may be varied from time to time. See also *green currencies.*

European size unit (ESU) a measure of farm size, used in the *farm classification* system of the EC. It is based on enterprise *standard gross margins,* with one ESU equal to 1000 *European currency units* of *standard gross margin.*

eviscerated having had the *viscera* removed. Thus: an eviscerated *carcass.*

ewe an adult female sheep.

ewe hog a female sheep between weaning and its first shearing.

ewe lamb a female sheep either unweaned or less than six months of age.

Exmoor Horn a breed of hill-sheep with a white face, curled horns and a soft fleece. It is largely found in the Exmoor area and has been crossed with the *Devon Longwool* to create the *Devon Closewool.*

exogenous hormone a hormone which is injected or implanted into an animal to alter its physiology.   Exogenous hormones may be used to manipulate reproduction   e.g. progesterone, or to act as *growth promoters* e.g. oestradiol. Many synthetic exogenous hormones have been outlawed by the EC e.g. hexoestrol and diethyl stilboestrol.

exotic a plant or animal which does not naturally occur in a specific location but has been introduced from outside (or abroad). Contrast *endemic.*

expenses in accountancy, *payments* adjusted for trade *creditors* at the beginning and end of the accounting period, that is payments plus opening creditors less closing creditors.

experimental husbandry farms   part of the research and development function of *ADAS* is executed through these farms which were established with the aim of demonstrating the commercial farming application of technical innovations.   The farms are distributed throughout the UK, most of them specialise in particular aspects of husbandry as indicated by their location.

export refunds (also called export restitutions)   subsidies to exports under the CAP, to allow the disposal of commodities most of which have previously been bought into *intervention*.   When *world market prices* are lower than the *intervention prices* at which surplus commodities are purchased, their sale on export markets is subsidised with export refunds. Their rates of refund are determined by *commodity intervention boards* on a regular basis and are in some cases negotiated on individual transactions. See also *intervention board for agricultural produce, administered prices* and *Common Agricultural Policy.*

extensification scheme   introduced under *structures directive 1790/87*, in 1987, this scheme provides incentives for farmers to reduce their cereal hectarage or the size of their beef enterprises. The required reductions are at least 20% of either cereal area of number of beef units, without a concomitant increase in the production of other surplus products. The scheme is effectively a *set-aside* policy applying to a limited range of products as a whole, (wine is also included). Its success will depend on the extent to which its constraints on expansion of alternative enterprises succeed, and whether it is attractive to a sufficient number of farmers.

externality an economic term including all actions which affect others but which cannot be priced through a market.   For example, pollution of water courses with *silage effluent* constitutes an externality, if there is no way the farmer can be induced to compensate those he is harming. Externalities can also be beneficial as, for example, when a farmer or landowner maintains his land in a way such that other people derive enjoyment from it for which they do not pay.

eyespot a very important fungal disease of cereals which can effect young plants in autumn and early spring. Elliptical *lesions* are formed on the leaf surface, hence, eyespots. Often the stem kinks at the infected region and the crop *lodges,* grains fail to fill out and low yields result. The disease organism Pseudocercosporella herpotrichoides, survives onformer crop residues so some control can be achieved by the use of *break crops.* *Fungicides* may also be used to prevent infection. A similar disease, *sharp eyespot*, is caused by the fungus Corticum solani. As the name suggests the disease lesions have a more clearly defined margin.

F_1 the first filial generation: the first generation offspring from a given mating.

F_1 **hybrid** the first generation offspring from a cross mating between two dissimilar parents. F_1 hybrids are now used to produce certain commercial crops e.g. *brussels sprouts, kale, maize.* The seed is usually expensive because it has to be produced annually from the crossing of two *pure breeding* parents of the F_1. They may also be difficult to maintain. The F_1 plants may well show *hybrid vigour* and are often extremely uniform and therefore easy to manage.

F_2 the second filial generation produced by breeding the F_1 *inter se.*

factors of production generally anything which promotes production: specifically an economic term applying originally to land, labour and capital, but later extended to include managerial enterprise. The factors of production earn incomes which together aggregate to the value of the *net output* of an industry, such as agriculture.

factory farming emotive phrase for systems of intensive livestock production.

faeces the undigested food of an animal which is passed out of the *anus*. Also called *dung.*

fallow the situation in which a field is allowed to remain uncropped. It may still be cultivated to achieve *weed* control.

false seedbed soil cultivated prior to *seed drilling* and left to allow *weeds* to *germinate.* The *weeds* are then removed by further cultivation or *herbicide* use immediately before drilling.

false staggers a condition of sheep caused by maggots of the *sheep nostril fly.* The maggots subsist on the mucous membranes of the sinuses of the sheeps head thus causing inflammation which affects the brain and gives the sheep a dazed appearance. Also called false gid.

family selection the *selection* of individuals on the performance of their relatives (*sibs, halfsibs* or *progeny*). This results in selection between families rather than between individuals.

farm animal welfare council an advisory body set up in 1979 to keep under review the welfare of farm livestock not just on agricultural land but also in transit, at markets and at *abattoirs.*

farm business survey (FBS) established in 1936, a survey commissioned by the MAFF, now carried out from eight regional centres in England and one regional centre in Wales. The objectives are to review the economic conditions of farming, to monitor year to year changes, and provide information for policy, research and farm advisory purposes. MAFF publishes annual reports based on the survey entitled *Farm Incomes in England* and *Farm Incomes in Wales*. Annual regional publications are also produced by the respective centres.

farm classification the grouping of farms by precise criteria, which define farm types. The definition of a group depends on the purpose of classification and the distinctive features of farms in a region. Criteria include enterprise output, *standard man-days*, and *standard gross margins*. For example, in the northern region *farm business survey,* lowland dairy farms are defined as those on which "... 50% or more of the standard labour requirement is attributable to the dairy herd...". See also Appendix, Table 3.

farm co-operative a form of business organisation owned and democratically controlled by its members. Co-operatives may be formed for the marketing of produce, the purchase of inputs or the ownership and operation of equipment. Some combine more than one of these functions. There are also *farmers groups* which undertake similar functions and may have a co-operative business structure.

farmers groups include *farm co-operatives* and other forms of organisation (e.g. public and private *companies*) which buy output from, and sell inputs and services to, farm businesses. They seek to exert market power on behalf of farmers and members. The groups may belong to the UK Agricultural Supply Trade Association (UKASTA) which represents the agricultural supply industries at national level.

farmers' list see *merchants' list.*

farm fresh eggs a descriptive term which, under the EC marketing arrangements, can only be applied to eggs in Class A. See also *egg classes.*

farm income problem an expression covering unfavourable aspects of farm incomes. It may mean the relative level of farm incomes compared with non-farm incomes, the instability of farm incomes, the wide range in size of income between farms and the long-term tendency for farm incomes to fall. An important aim of *agricultural policies* is to ameliorate the farm income problem. See also *elasticities, direct income transfers.*

Farming (Forestry) and Wildlife Advisory Groups (F(F)WAGs) established during the 1970s, these Groups provide a forum for discussion of *conservation* issues relating to agriculture. They differ from other environmental groups in that the MAFF also participates. Other participants include representatives of agencies such as the

Forestry Commission, Countryside Commission, the NFU, the CLA, the farmworkers unions and various conservation groups. F(F)WAGs are autonomous at the county level (with financial support from the Countryside Commission) and offer advice to farmers on environmental matters.

farm size may be measured in either physical or economic units. Measures of physical size include farm area, cropping area (on arable farms), the number of dairy cows (on specialist dairy farms), the number of ewes (on upland and hill farms). Measures of economic size include total farm output, standard man-day requirements, total standard gross margin, European size unit, net worth and turnover.

farmworkers' unions in England and Wales the agricultural section of the Transport and General Workers' Union and, in Scotland, the Farm Servants' Union. Formerly there was an independent National Union of Agricultural and Allied Workers in England and Wales which represented the interests of all hired workers in agriculture. This amalgamated with the Transport and General Workers Union in 1983. The unions are concerned with the pay and conditions of hired farmworkers. They negotiate wages through the Agricultural Wages Board and represent the interests of their members with the employers. Current membership of farmworkers unions is in the region of 60,000.

farmyard manure (FYM) organic fertiliser consisting of animal dung and urine mixed with bedding material such as cereal straw. It has beneficial effects on soil structure as well as its nutrient content.

farrow the act of parturition in pigs when a sow gives birth to a litter of pigs.

farrowing crate a crate, usually constructed of metal, in which a sow is housed in the period immediately prior to, at, and for a few days after farrowing. The crate restrains the sow and thus reduces piglet deaths due to overlying or savaging by the sow. At the same time however the piglets are allowed access to the mammary glands of the sow to suckle.

farrowing house a pig building designed specifically to house sows at and immediately after farrowing. Often the house contains a number of farrowing crates arranged in rows.

fat fat lambs or fat cattle are sheep or cattle which having been reared for meat production are deemed to have acquired the desired level of finish or sub-cutaneous fatness to meet the market requirement.

fat class both the beef carcass classification service and the sheep carcass classification scheme classify carcasses on the basis of two main variables: conformation and fat. The fat class is a subjective visual appraisal of the degree of *sub-cutaneous* fat on the carcass, ranging from 1 (very lean) to 5 (very fat).

fat hen (Chenopodium album) a *weed* of *arable* crops. It is an *annual weed.* The leaves of the seedling have a distinctive white powdery appearance and the mature plant has a strong upright stem bearing many seeds. It is easily controlled in the seedling stage by *herbicides.*

fats a group of organic substances consisting of the glycerides of higher *fatty acids.* The fatty acids present in a fat determine its nature e.g. fats are often found in the form of a liquid or *oil* in plants whereas they are in a solid form in animals. Most plant materials are low in fats, the exception being specialised storage seeds e.g. castor oil seeds. In animals, *adipose tissue* is a specialised form of connective tissue consisting of fats which are deposited largely as an energy store.

fatstock livestock which have been reared, or fattened, for meat production.

Fatstock Marketing Corporation (FMC) a wholesale meat company reputed to be the largest meat group in Europe, and centrally involved in the procurement of livestock, slaughtering and distribution of meat and meat products.

fatty acids organic acids which occur in *fats.* The lower members of the series, the *volatile fatty acids,* are liquids, whilst the higher members are solids insoluble in water but soluble in ether. Fatty acids may be chemically saturated or unsaturated depending on whether further atoms can be added to their chemical structures. Many animal fats are saturated, whilst plant fats contain a higher proportion of unsaturated fatty acids. In human nutrition, the anti-fat lobby regards unsaturated fatty acids in a more favourable light than saturated fatty acids.

fauna the collective term for the animals occurring in a particular region or period.

feather an outgrowth from the skin of a bird. Together, the feathers form the plumage.

fecundin a *pom* which is a solution of steroid protein immunogen which when injected into female sheep immunises then against their own reproductive hormones and increases *ovulation rate* and *lambing percentage.*

feed the range of food or *feedingstuffs* available to an animal.

feed additive a substance added to an animal's diet often as a *growth promoter.*

feed block a manufactured block containing a number of *feedingstuffs.*

They usually contain an energy source, often molasses, as well as protein, vitamins and minerals. Their use is most common on poor pastures, particularly in hill areas, for sheep.

feed compounding the production of *compound feeds* for livestock which is usually done on a large scale in an industrial feed mill.

feed conversion ratio (FCR) the ratio between feed consumed and liveweight gain. It gives a measure of the efficiency of an animal at converting feed into body tissue with a low ratio indicating high efficiency.

feeder a structure from which livestock receive their feed. They vary in complexity from simple troughs to systems which dispense feed either mechanically or electronically.

feedingstuff one of the range of potential feeds available to farm livestock. Amongst these would be fresh forages, conserved forages (e.g. hay or silage), *concentrates* and succulent feeds.

feedlot an area of land on which animals are kept at very high density but which does not supply any food. All the animals' feed requirements therefore have to be met by feed brought into the feedlot. Feedlot systems may be used for beef cattle and are more common in the USA than the UK.

feed ring a large circular container in which forages may be placed and livestock allowed to feed from.

fell a term, particularly common in N England, to include hill and upland pastures and moorland.

femur the proximal bone of an animal's hind limb.

fens areas of peaty soil which is extremely high in organic matter. Found around the Wash, these soils, when artificially *drained,* are extremely fertile, light and easy working. They are frequently used to produce high value vegetable crops. The fens are low lying, often at or below sea level, and were formed when vegetation failed to decompose due to the excessively moist conditions which prevailed. In some areas, considerable depths of peat have accumulated but following *drainage, oxidation* is taking place and the depth of peat is declining continuously. At the edges of the peaty fens are areas of silty fen, formed by the silty deposits from the original flood waters. Successful farming on the fens depends upon the continued effectiveness of the *drainage system* which usually requires pumps to lift the water into the main *drains* or *levels.*

FEOGA see *European Agricultural Guidance and Guarantee Fund.*

fermentation the breakdown of organic substances, induced by *micro-*

organisms or enzymes, which often involves the evolution of heat and gas. Examples of fermentation in agricultural systems include the process of *silage* making where anaerobic bacteria convert the sugars in grass to lactic acid or the activities of the rumen micro-organisms.

fertilisation   the union of male and female *gametes* to produce a *zygote.* In plants this occurs following pollination and in animals following either natural or *artificial insemination* when the *semen* of the male comes into contact with the *ovum* of the female.

fertiliser   general name for materials applied to soil in order to increase the supply of one or more plant nutrients. Inorganic fertilisers are either 'straight' supplying only one major nutrient, or 'compounds' supplying a combination of nutrients. Organic materials may also be used as fertilisers. See *farmyard manure* and *slurry.*

fever   a rise in the temperature of an animal's body above that which would be considered normal.

fibre   the constituent of animal feedingstuffs which includes *cellulose, hemi-cellulose* and *lignin.* Feeds with a high fibre content generally have a low nutritive value as much of their energy is unavailable to the animal. However *fermentation* within the *rumen* of ruminant animals makes some of this energy available and the inclusion of fibre in ruminant diets is therefore important for rumen function. There is growing evidence that some dietary fibre may aid digestion in all species.

field bean   see *bean.*

field book   used to record details of field operations carried out through the crop year. The date, operation, and physical quantities of any materials used are entered together with any observations on *weed,* pest, disease, crop or soil condition. One page is reserved for each field on the farm, allowing reference between years. From this information potential husbandry problems may be identified.

field capacity   with reference to soil water, field capacity is the point at which the capacity of a soil to retain water is completely met. Any further additions of water would lead to excess water draining away by gravity, or if that were not possible, to the onset of *waterlogging* in which air spaces become filled.

financial ratios   relationships between components of the *balance sheet,* and relationships between the capital employed in a business and profitability. The reason for constructing ratios is to examine *liquidity, solvency* and the efficiency with which capital has been used to generate *profit.* In farm management the more important ratios include: the current ratio (current assets to current liabilities), as a measure of liquidity; the liquidity ratio (current assets less stocks to current liabilities) as a measure of immediate liquidity; the net capital ratio (total assets to total external liabilities) as a measure of long-term *solvency* (see also *gearing)*; return on capital (profit to capital, including returns on total *assets, net worth,* and *tenant's capital*) expressed as a percentage. See also *rate of return.*

financial solidarity the important principle operative within the *European community* whereby members agree to finance the budget in common. See also *EC budget.*

finish an animal is referred to as finished or as having acquired a degree of finish when it has reached a suitable weight and/or condition to be marketed for meat. Finish is subjectively assessed mainly by the degree of *sub-cutaneous* fat deposition. The term is more commonly used when referring to cattle or sheep than with pigs.

first-calf heifer a *heifer* in its first lactation i.e. a cow which has borne its first but not a second calf.

fishmeal an animal *feedingstuff* of high feed value due especially to its high protein content; often 66%. It consists of dried and ground fish or fish filleting residues which may have been caught specifically for conversion to fishmeal or may be surplus to requirements for human food.

fixed costs costs which exist independently of the level of production in the short term and do not vary directly with the area of a particular crop or the number of livestock. They must be paid out of the farm *gross margin* before an income or *profit* is made. Examples include the costs of *rent,* administration, building repairs, machinery *depreciation* and the wages of regular workers. Contrast *variable costs.*

flaked maize an animal *feedingstuff* derived from *maize* which has been steam treated, rolled and dried. It is rich in highly digestible *starch* and is often included in pig diets.

flare a layer of fat surrounding the kidneys.

flat deck piggery a *piggery* used for rearing weaned piglets between the ages of 2 and 8 weeks of age. Typically they are housed on floors of mesh or perforated metal through which *faeces* can pass for collection in a *slurry* channel. The pigs have *ad libitum* access to feed from self-feed hoppers. Typically the heating and ventilation systems are linked to give good environmental control.

flatpoll a type of *cabbage* used for cattle feed. Substantial yields of low dry matter feed of high *metabolisable energy* content can be grown.

flat rate the rate of *interest* quoted as a percentage of the initial amount borrowed. The flat rate varies with the length of the repayment period and the frequency of payments, making it an unsuitable measure for the comparison of loans or hire purchase agreements. For this purpose, the *annual percentage rate* which is almost double the flat rate, may be found in published tables.

flat rate feeding a system of *concentrate* allocation to dairy cows in which animals are fed a fixed quantity of concentrates per day from calving to *turn-out* irrespective of yield or stage of lactation. Variations on the system may involve one or two steps in the feeding rate or the subdivision of the herd into groups on the basis of yield potential.

flax crop plant grown for its stem fibres from which linen is manufactured. Not now a popular crop, this type of Linum usitatissimum has been selected to exploit the production of vascular tissue which includes, long slender fibres which are not strongly lignified. The extracted fibres are soft, flexible and extremely strong. The plant is an *annual* and other selections are grown for the oil content of the seeds, i.e. *linseed.*

flea beetle (Phyllotreta species) insect pest of *brassica* crops. The beetles cause serious damage to newly emerged seedlings, making holes in the leaves and checking plant growth. *Seed dressings* and post emergence *insecticides* can be used to give control.

fleece the coat of wool of a sheep.

flies generally, winged insects. More specifically, the Diptera: two winged insects which have mouth parts modified for piercing and sucking of either blood or plant cell sap. A number of species of fly are of importance in agriculture as they cause damage both directly and indirectly through the transmission of disease to plants and animals. Some are parasitic (e.g. *gadfly)* whilst the larvae of others affect livestock (e.g. *warble fly)* and crops (e.g. *frit fly).*

flocculation in clay soils the process of formation of loose *aggregates* of several clay particles. Flocculated clays retain *soil structure* on wetting and allow reasonable passage of water. Deflocculated clays on the other hand will tend to slump on wetting and become relatively impermeable to water.

flock the collective term applied to sheep, goats and birds.

flock book the *pedigree* records of a particular breed of sheep which are maintained by the *breed society.*

flock master the owner, or shepherd, of a flock of sheep.

flock mating a *mating system* used with both sheep and poultry, where several males are allowed to mate at will with the females of the flock.

Contrast *handmating.*

flora the plant population of any area under consideration.

floret in the Gramineae, the term used to describe the true flower with its associated *bracts,* the *lemma* and *palea.* Each floret is a potential site of *seed* production.

fluke parasitic flatworms found in the liver, blood vessels, guts and lungs of animals. In farm animals *liver fluke* may be a serious problem especially in sheep and cattle.

flush a rapid growth of herbage. The term is most commonly applied to grass when a flush of growth occurs in favourable conditions e.g. in spring or following a drought.

flying flock a flock of sheep brought onto the farm, usually for less than a year, and then sold out. The type of sheep involved may vary from *store lambs* for fattening, *ewe lambs* to be reared and sold for breeding or *draft ewes.*

flying herd a herd of cattle brought onto the farm for one lactation and then sold out. Typically no breeding of the animals takes place and all *replacements* are brought in.

fob abbreviation for free on board, the usual basis on which export prices are quoted. They include the cost of transporting goods to port of exit and loading on to the ship together with the sale price. Additional costs have to be borne by the importer. Compare *CIF.*

fodder beet a form of beet (Beta vulgaris) used for feeding to livestock from autumn onwards. These *biennial* plants produce a swollen tap root in the first year of growth. It is this, together with the leaves which can be fed to animals. These are different selections of the same plants as *sugar beet.*

fodder crops those grown for animal feed, examples include *grass, kale, swedes.*

foetus a young animal developing within the *uterus* of its mother.

foggage a term used to describe the material grown on a pasture during late summer, not grazed, but allowed to remain in situ for use by grazing animals over autumn and winter.

folding restricting animals (particularly sheep) into a small area by temporary (sometimes electrified) fencing as a means of controlling their grazing.

follicle stimulating hormone (FSH) a gonadotrophic hormone produced by the pituitary gland which stimulates growth of the Graafian follicles in the *ovary* of the female and *spermatogenesis* in the *testes* of the male.

followers 1. Animals which are not yet mature but which are intended to replace their mothers in the herd or flock. The term is often used of dairy calves and heifers which are not yet in milk. 2. Animals given access to pasture after a preferentially treated group. See *leader-follower* system.

Food From Britain an organisation founded in 1983 with the aim of promoting increased exports of British food. It was set up with an initial grant from Government of £14M which was to run for five years. It has since obtained some private support for its continued existence.

foot-and-mouth disease an acute contagious disease of cloven-hooved animals (e.g. cattle, sheep and pigs), caused by a virus. The disease is characterised by blistering of the mucous membrane and skin particularly in the clefts of the feet (causing lameness) and the mouth (leading to excessive salivation). Infection leads to reduced animal performance, but death is unusual. The disease is *endemic* in many parts of the world. Although the UK is free of the disease, occasional *epidemics* may occur. The disease is *notifiable* and both diseased animals and contacts are slaughtered. Foot-and-mouth disease is highly infectious and may spread by the wind, birds or infected animal tissues (e.g. offal or bones).

foot bath a shallow bath or trough which may contain water or various chemicals (e.g. copper sulphate, formalin or disinfectant). Cattle or sheep may be periodically driven through a foot bath with the intention of washing or hardening the hooves or acting to prevent or cure disease of the hoof (e.g. *foot rot).*

foot rot an infection of both the horny and adjacent soft parts of sheep's feet which results in lameness and reduced animal performance. It is caused by Fusiformis species of bacteria and is highly infectious.

forage food for livestock. Usually forages are recognised as the bulky component of the diet where energy is provided in a fairly dilute form. *Hay* and *silage* are both forms of forage.

forage box a large mobile container which is used to transport and dispense *forage* to animals. It may be used to transport grass to zero-grazed animals but is more usually used to move *silage* from a *silo* to a trough or feed-race where it is unloaded in steady flow by means of a moving floor or belt.

forage harvesters machines used to harvest *forage* crops such as grass and maize. They vary from simple tractor-drawn machines which cut and convey the forage from the field into a trailer, to more complex self propelled machines which may chop and condition the forage in the process. Examples include double-chop and precision chop machines.

foreman an employee with the responsibility for day to day management of an individual enterprise or operation, or for the organisation of other workers.

fore-milk the first milk removed from the cows udder at milking. It is often expressed by hand into a *strip cup* and examined for abnormal appearance e.g. mastitic clots.

Forestry Commission a public agency with the dual role of forest enterprise and forest authority. In the former role it purchases land for afforestation and manages the public forests. In the latter role it administers planting grants which encourage the establishment and management of private forest. The total area of forest in the UK amounts to 2M ha, of which more than half is privately owned.

formic acid an organic acid widely used in agriculture as a *silage additive.* Applied at a rate of 2-5 litres per tonne of *herbage,* it helps to reduce silage pH quickly and to inhibit undesirable micro-organisms.

forward a slightly vague term used in both crop and animal production to indicate crops or animals that are more advanced in their development than might be considered usual. Thus cattle which are referred to as forward stores are well developed for their age or with reference to that particular time of the year.

forward contract a *contract* in which a price is agreed for a quantity to be delivered on a specified future date. See also *futures contract.*

foul-in-the-foot an infection of the feet which causes swelling and lameness in cattle. The infective organism, Sphaerophorus necrophorus, acts at the site of a wound particularly in the interdigital region of the hooves of the hind feet.

four-tooth sheep a term used to classify sheep on the basis of their permanent teeth. Typically an animal which is 18-21 months of age.

fowl cholera an acute and usually fatal septicaemia of domestic poultry caused by the bacterium Pasteurella ariseptica. The disease is characterised by dejection, loss of appetite, fever and profuse green coloured diarrhoea.

fowl paralysis see *Marek's disease.*

fowl pest a term used to embrace fowl plague and *Newcastle disease* which are both diseases of poultry.

free trade area an area defined by a group of countries agreeing to trade between themselves without quota or tariff restrictions. It differs from a *customs union* in that it does not impose a common external tariff on imports.

Friesian the Friesian or Friesian/*Holstein* breed accounts for about 90% of the *dairy cows* in England and Wales. It is the top producing breed averaging around 5600kg at 3.8% fat and 3.3% protein, with pure *Holsteins* averaging a little higher in yield. They are black and white cattle originating in Holland from where they have been exported throughout the world. In the UK the British Friesian was developed as an excellent *dairy breed* capable of producing a good *beef carcass,* whilst in America the *Holstein* breed was developed purely for its milking potential. In recent years a large amount of Holstein blood has been re-introduced to the UK to increase size and yields.

frit fly (Oscinella frit) an insect pest of many crops, especially *cereals, maize* and *grassland.* The damage to crops is caused by the larvae damaging and sometimes killing out the central shoots of plants, leading to shrivelled grains. Complete death of plants may occur as crops establish, however, even in established *pastures,* considerable, though not visually obvious, damage can occur. The pest can be controlled by the use of *insecticides.*

full-mouthed a term used for livestock (especially sheep and cattle) which have a full set of permanent teeth. Thus a ewe is said to be full-mouthed between ceasing to be a *six-tooth sheep* and becoming *broken-mouthed.*

full-time farmer either the occupier of a full-time holding, or a farmer who obtains his whole livelihood from agriculture. Contrast *part-time farmer.*

full-time holding a holding which provides enough work to employ at least one person for a full working year. Holdings are classified as full-time if they generate a minimum number (usually 250) of *standard man-days.* They may also be defined on the basis of other measures of business size such as *standard gross margins.* Contrast *part-time holding, farm size.*

full-time workers all hired and family workers who work at least 40 hours per week. Full-time hired workers are entitled to at least the basic minimum agricultural wage.   Family workers may be paid less then the basic minimum. Contrast *part-time worker.*

funds flow statement shows the source and application of funds, that is the movement of *assets, liabilities* and *capital,* during a year. Contrast *balance sheet* which shows the capital position at a point in time.

fungicide a chemical which kills or restricts the development of fungal organisms. Fungal diseases may attack stored seeds and growing crops. Fungicides are applied, either as *sprays* or *dusts* to growing crops and as seed dressings in an attempt to restrict damage and yield loss.

fungus an organism which has a filamentous structure. These filaments form a mass of strands called the mycelium. Fungi do not photosynthesise but absorb nutrients through their walls. Fungi are responsible for many plant and some animal diseases.

furrow the line of overturned soil created by one *mouldboard* of the *mouldboard plough.* Also used to describe the depression in the soil caused by taking out a slice. Hence the undulations produced in the "*ridge* and furrow" system of drainage in old *pastures.*

futures contract a legally binding agreement to buy or sell a specified quantity of a commodity on a given date in the future at the prevailing price in the *futures market.* See also *hedge, forward contract.*

futures market a commodities market in which *futures contracts* are traded for speculative gain or in order to reduce the risk associated with adverse price fluctuations in the spot markets. In the UK there are futures markets for potatoes, wheat and barley, pigmeat and beef. See also *spot price, hedge* (2).

FYM See *farmyard manure.*

gadfly a large bloodsucking fly of the Tabanus species whose biting may cause distress to livestock during the summer months.

Galloway a breed of *beef* cattle originating in SW Scotland which has a thick, usually black coat. It is slow to mature but is hardy and able to do well on poor upland grazing.

game wild animals defined under the Game Act 1851 and subsequent legislation. The birds include pheasant, red grouse, black grouse, partridge and ptarmigan. Various acts have limited the times of year when game may be shot (i.e. to shooting seasons), and have further regulated shooting through game licences. Certain species of wild bird and animal may also be killed or taken during specified open seasons, regulated under the *Wildlife and Countryside Act 1981.*

gamete a reproductive cell of a plant or animal. A *haploid* male gamete unites with a haploid female gamete to produce a *diploid zygote.* Thus in animals an *ovum* is fertilised by a *sperm,* and in plants an ovule by a pollen grain, to produce a zygote.

gamma globulins simple proteins which are found in blood and milk, particularly *colostrum,* where they have an important role in conferring immunity against disease to the young animal.

gangrene of potatoes is a disease which causes rotting of *tubers* during storage. The organism responsible is Phoma exigua which infects tubers which are damaged at lifting or grading. *Tubers* show sunken areas of irregular shape and internal cavities with a distinct margin between healthy and diseased tissue. Control is by careful handling of *tubers* and allowing a *curing* period after handling to assist wound healing.

gang work day chart a method of comparing labour availability with labour requirements, usually for the period of peak work load, providing a more detailed analysis than *labour profiles.* A gang work day chart takes into account that each farm operation needs one or more workers.

gapes an infection of the respiratory system of poultry which is caused by the presence of small worms, the nematode Syngamus trachea, which causes the bird to gasp for air, or 'gape'.

garget see *mastitis.*

gastric juices a mixture of digestive juices secreted into the *stomach* of an animal to aid digestion. They include hydrochloric acid and enzymes (e.g. pepsin and rennin).

gathering the collection of sheep from the hill, often with the use of sheepdogs. Sheep may be gathered for shearing, dipping, weaning etc.

gearing   in financial management, the proportion of long-term *capital* provided from external sources, rather than by the owner's capital (*net worth*).   It can be expressed for comparative purposes as a ratio, of long-term loans to owner's capital.   When a high proportion of the total capital employed is borrowed, the business is said to be highly geared.   There is the possibility of a high return to the owner's capital, but the business may risk bankruptcy as interest payable on long-term loans must be met. A business which has a low gearing ratio stands less risk of going bankrupt, but might bring a lower return on the owner's capital.

Gelbvieh   a breed of cattle originating in lower central Germany and which was improved by crossing with *Simmental* and Brown Swiss in the seventeenth century.   The coat colour varies from cream to reddish-yellow.   Although essentially a *beef breed,* the milk production of the Gelbvieh is good.

geld   to *castrate.*

gelt   1.   An alternative form of the *geld.*   2.   A regional form of *gilt.*

gene   the basic unit of inheritance which maintains identity of a particular characteristic (e.g. sex, colour, size, milk yield) from one generation to the next.   Genes are arranged in pairs on homologous *chromosomes* with each parent contributing one to the pair.   Some genes act in an additive manner.   Alternatively one gene in a pair may be dominant over the other which is recessive.

gene frequency   the proportion that a given *gene* constitutes of the total genes at that *locus* in a population.

generation interval   the average age of a group of animals at the birth of their first progeny.

genetic correlation   that part of the *phenotypic correlation* between two *characters* due to genetic causes.

genetic drift   changes in *gene frequency* due to chance.

genetic engineering   a rapidly developing technique whereby *DNA* alteration and manipulation of the *genes* on the *chromosomes* is used to alter the quality of the offspring.   In this way it is hoped to produce superior crops and animals with desirable traits (e.g. disease resistance, greater size, improved feed conversion ratio etc.).   A specific example of genetic engineering is the insertion of the gene for *bovine somatotropin* into a bacterial chromosome which is then allowed to multiply normally: the bovine somatotrophin thus produced is then collected and purified and may be used to treat animals where it has been shown to increase milk yield in dairy cows.

genetic variation variation due to differences in the inherited characteristics of an animal or plant rather than due to *environmental* causes.

genotype the genetic constitution of an individual.

genotype-environment interaction the situation in which the magnitude of genetic differences and the ranking of genotypes depends on the environment in which they are measured. Thus the level of nutrition (environment) might influence the ranking of different breeds of cattle (genotype) for growth rate.

genotypic selection a selection technique based on *progeny testing* with a very large number of progeny so that the *breeding value* of the parent is more precisely known.

genus a taxonomic group in the classification of living organisms which is further subdivided into *species.*

Gerber test a test involving sulphuric acid and amyl alcohol which may be used to measure the fat content of milk. Its use by the MMB has been superceded by infrared spectroscopy.

germination the first stage of growth of a seed into a young plant or *seedling.* This process is usually associated with the uptake of water. The other main requirements are the presence of oxygen and a warm temperature.

gestation the period of *pregnancy.* Gestation is the act of retaining and nourishing the young in the uterus and the gestation period is thus the interval between conception and birth. Typical gestation lengths are - cattle 284 days, sheep 148 days, pigs 115 days.

gibberellins a group of plant *hormones* which are complex organic compounds. Applications of gibberellins to growing plants are likely to promote rapid extension growth with an elongation of *internodes.* Although this changes the appearance of plants, the total weight or yield is seldom affected.

gilt a young female pig. The term is usually applied until the production of the first *litter* although it may be used until the first *litter* is *weaned.*

gimmer a female sheep between its first and second shearing.

gizzard the highly muscular stomach of a bird in which food is ground up - this process being assisted by the swallowing of grit and small stones.

gley   a soil type formed by the process known as gleying where, in occasionally waterlogged soils, some ions are reduced and redistributed in the *profile* leading to colour changes. Gley soils are greyish in colour where ferrous iron predominates, but in aerated areas such as root channels, the brown ferric iron is formed, leading to a   mottled appearance. The existence of these symptoms therefore indicates periodic waterlogging.

Gloucester a breed of cattle which is now quite rare. Dark brown in colour with a distinctive white strip running down the back, tail and between the hind legs to the udder and belly, Gloucester cattle were once common in the west country where their milk was used in the manufacture of Double Gloucester cheese.

Gloucester Old Spot a rare breed of pig originating from the Severn Valley of the west of England. It is lop-eared and characterised by black spots on a predominantly white coat. It is reputed to be a hardy breed able to survive on waste materials and to forage effectively.

glucose   also called dextrose or grape-sugar, glucose is a monosaccharide sugar and is thus a *carbohydrate.* It is the primary product of plant *photosynthesis* although it may subsequently be converted to more complex carbohydrates.   Glucose is the immediate energy source of both plants and animals, who are able to break down *starch* or *glycogen* to provide glucose.

glume the outer bracts or scale leaf of a *spikelet* in the flowers of plants in the *gramineae.*

gluten a protein storage product in *wheat grain*. The nature of gluten is responsible for the coherent dough which can be produced from *wheat* flour and gives its valuable baking qualities. The quantity and quality of the gluten in a sample of *grain* will partially determine its bread making qualities.

glycogen a soluble *polysaccharide* form of *carbohydrate* which consists of a number of *glucose* molecules. Glycogen is a major energy storage compound of animals and is found in many tissues, especially the liver and muscles. It is broken down to yield glucose when energy is required.

goat (capra hircus) is a *ruminant* animal of minor agricultural importance in the UK. Recently, however, there has been a doubling of goat numbers between 1974 and 1984 to 48,000 (as assessed by the *agricultural census),* but as many goats are kept on unregistered small holdings the true number is likely to be nearer 100,000. In the UK goats are mainly kept for milk production and the main breeds are of Swiss derivation e.g. Saanen, Toggenberg.   Goats milk, and milk products have a ready market in health stores as it is readily digested and does not provoke an allergic reaction (e.g. eczema or asthma) in consumers allergic to cows milk. There is also a growing market for the goat meat amongst ethnic minorities as well as increasing interest in the production of goat fibre (e.g. cashemere and mohair). In many other countries of the world goats are of much more importance than in the UK and their ability to browse on vegetation of poor nutritive value is widely exploited.

gonad the organ of an animal which produces *gametes*. The *ovary* of female and the *testis* of the male are thus both gonads.

gonadotrophin a hormone (e.g. *follicle stimulating hormone* or *luteinising hormone*) produced by the *pituitary* which acts on the *gonads* to bring about the development of *gametes*.

goose a large bird of the duck family. Domestic geese (which are descended from the wild Greylag goose) are largely kept to provide table birds for Christmas. The majority of geese in the UK are in small *free-range* flocks although some large scale commercial units exist.

grading the categorisation of produce according to quality standards. Examples include *carcass classification schemes* and the grading of many fruits and vegetables.

grading-up the continued crossing with *purebred* animals of an improved breed with a view to the replacement of the original population. Many Dairy *Shorthorn* cattle herds were graded-up by continued crossing with *Friesian* bulls. The proportion of Friesian blood (initially 0%) increases (50%, 75%, 87%, 93% etc.) with the mating of each generation by a pedigree Friesian bull until pedigree Friesian status is attained.

grain the *seed* for which *cereal* crops are grown. Grain may be used for human or animal consumption because of the high energy value of the reserves stored in the *endosperm* of the seed.

grain drier a device for reducing the moisture content of *grain* prior to, or during storage. Grain can be stored for extended periods of time without deterioration, only if it has a moisture content of less than 14%. Various forms of drier exist from those which dry small batches of grain, through to those which dry a continuous flow of grain to *storage driers* in which the final drying takes place in store.

grains see *brewers' grains.*

grain weevil an insect pest of stored grain. Weevils bore into stored grain in autumn to lay eggs. The resulting larva feeding produces hollow grains. Grain can be treated with *insecticide* as it goes into store.

Gramineae family of plants which includes many agriculturally important species. These include the *herbage* grasses and the *cereals,* grown for both human and animal consumption. All produce a grain (caryopsis) and have similar general growth *habit.*

gram negative a classification of bacteria which do not stain when treated with a basic dye.

gram positive a classification of bacteria which stain when treated with a basic dye.

granules the physical form of many *fertiliser* and *crop protection chemicals.* Granules are solid sources of the chemical in question, aggregated into particles of reasonable size for distribution through farm spreaders. They are less messy to handle than powders and are generally manufactured to tolerance levels which enable effective, accurate dispersal.

grasslands areas of land primarily used for livestock feeding where the main species are likely to be *grasses.* In the UK these areas would include those fields where grasses have recently been sown as part of a *crop rotation,* the fields in which grasses have been established for many years and some areas of rough grazing may also be involved. On rough grazings, grasses may be present as minor components, or may not be present at all. Other species such as *heathers* may dominate.

grass let (grass park or keep) see *grazing agreement.*

grass staggers See *hypomagnesaemia.*

grass tetany see *hypomagnesaemia.*

grazier a person who keeps cattle on any form of grazing land e.g. pasture, meadows.

grazing the process by which animals feed from a growing crop often *grass.* Different forms of grazing management are practiced; these include systems where animals are allowed to graze part of the total crop for short periods of time (*rotational grazing*) and those where animals are allowed to graze over the whole growing season (*continuous* or *set stocking*).

grazing agreement a licence or let to permit grazing or mowing only, granted for a given period of less than one year, commonly 364 days. As long as livestock are removed by the end of the period, the agreement cannot become a protected tenancy. See also *Agricultural Holdings Act 1984.* See *grass park.*

grazing livestock units (GLUs) factors based on the relative *metabolisable energy* requirements of different classes of livestock. The following factors are commonly applied:

Cattle		Sheep	
Bulls	0.8	Rams	0.2
Dairy cows	1.0	Lowland ewes	
Beef cows (exc. calf)	0.8	and ewe hoggs	0.2
Cattle > 2 years	0.8	Hill ewes and	
Cattle 1-2 years	0.6	ewe hoggs	0.1
Cattle < 1 year	0.4	Other sheep	0.1

In farm managment, GLUs provide an approximate way of allocating the *forage* area and associated *variable costs* between livestock enterprises.

grazing pressure the relationship between the number of grazing livestock and the amount of available herbage. It may be considered a more useful term than *stocking rate* which relates the number of grazing livestock to the area of land irrespective of its herbage yield.

grazing system the method of organising the *grassland* available on a farm to feed the groups of *livestock* present. Various recognised alternatives exist from simple systems involving no rationing (*set stocking*) to more complex systems involving subdivisions of the total area (*strip grazing, paddock grazing*).

Green Belts land designated in local structure plans under the Town and Country Planning Act (1947) on which it is presumed unlikely that permission to develop (i.e. to build, or change use) will be granted by planning authorities. Green Belts surround most of the major conurbations in the UK. The Belts vary in shape and size and covered 2M ha in 1983. An impact of such designation is that it prevents owners of agricultural land selling at an enhanced price for urban development: where the rules are relaxed landowners may realise capital gains.

green bottle fly see *sheep maggot fly*.

green crop see *fodder crop*.

green currencies (Green £, Green Franc, etc.) the level of farm *administered prices* determined by the EC for member states are expressed in *European currency units* (ECUs). These prices are then translated into national currencies using green exchange rates which are determined by the *council of ministers*. Because actual currency exchange rates (determined through financial markets) may differ from green rates, distortions in trade between EC member states can result. In order to prevent this, a system of trade taxes and subsidies, *Monetary*

Compensatory Amounts (MCAs) have been introduced. These add to, or reduce, the prices of imports into, and exports from, member states so that the common price level of the CAP is maintained. For example, in August 1986 the actual sterling exchange rate was 1 ECU = £0.75 whereas the Green Rate was 1 ECU = £0.65.

green manure generally, any plant material *cultivated* into the soil to increase its organic matter content. More specifically, green manure crops can be grown with the sole intention of using the crop to provide such organic matter. The most effective crops are *legumes* which apart from adding organic matter, also supply *nitrogen*.

Green Pound see *green currencies*.

Greyface a *crossbred* sheep which results from using a *Border Leicester* ram on a *Scottish Blackface* ewe. Greyfaces are most common in N England and Scotland where the ewes are typically crossed with a terminal sire breed (e.g. *Suffolk*) to produce good quality lambs.

grice a small pig.

grit small fragments of inorganic materials which are fed to poultry. They may be insoluble e.g. flint, and assist the functioning of the *gizzard,* or they may be soluble e.g. limestone or oyster shell and serve as a source of calcium required by laying poultry for egg shell production.

grits coarsely ground grain.

gross energy the energy value of a material (e.g. a feedstuff). It is the energy that would be liberated if the material was fully combusted in the presence of oxygen. Not all the gross energy in a feedstuff is available to an animal - some is not digestible and is voided in the faeces - what is digested is referred to as the *digestible energy*.

gross margin *output* less *variable costs,* a measure of performance, enabling comparative assessment of individual enterprises. The concept was developed as an aid to planning the combination of enterprises on a farm, and continues in common use. See also *linear programming, standard gross margin*.

groundnut the groundnut or peanut is the source of *cake* or *meal* which may be either decorticated or undecorticated forms. It is imported from the tropics and used for livestock feeding - particularly to ruminants.

grower in poultry production, a young bird between 8 and 20 weeks of age.

growth curves graphical expressions of the relationship between the size of part or the whole of a plant or animal against some other variable (e.g.

time).   The most commonly used growth curve is the sigmoidal relationship of weight against time. See also *allometric growth.*

growth promoter a substance which when administered to an animal leads to either an improved growth rate and/or an improved food conversion efficiency. Growth promoters may be in the form of implants (e.g. steriod hormones) or as *feed additives* (e.g. copper, antibiotics).

guarantee threshold a policy instrument applied under the CAP whereby price guarantees are reduced automatically once a particular (threshold) level of production is reached.   They have been applied to cereals, cotton, milk, rape, processed tomatoes and sugar. The present arrangements for cereals introduce a price reduction in the year following that in which the threshold is exceeded; it has been proposed that the reduction should be brought forward to the year in which the surplus occurs.

Guernsey a breed of *dairy cattle* which originated from the Channel Island of the same name. It is characteristically golden-red coloured and somewhat bigger than the *Jersey.* It accounts for 1.7% of the dairy cows in England and Wales. It gives slightly more milk than the Jersey, but the quality is lower at around 4.6% fat and 3.6% protein.

gut a non-specific term used to refer to either the *stomach* or all the *alimentary system.*

habit the general appearance of a plant often considered in relation to its recognition.

haemoglobin a protein compound, containing iron, which combines readily with oxygen to form oxyhaemoglobin. The haemoglobin gives the erythrocytes or red blood cells their red colouration. It is responsible for the transportation of oxygen around an animals body as part of *respiration.*

Hagberg falling number test. A laboratory test carried out on samples of *wheat* to determine their suitability for bread making. The test indirectly determines the amount of *alpha amylase* in the grain. A low, falling number indicates that the sample contains *alpha amylase* which has begun to break down the starch in the *grain,* rendering it less effective for bread making.

half-bred or half-breed an animal of mixed breed. The term is most commonly used of sheep where specific crosses result in the Welsh half-bred (Border Leicester ram x Welsh ewe) and the Scotch half-bred (Border Leicester x Cheviot).

half sibs half-brothers and half-sisters. Usually the offspring of a single sire, out of different dams, occasionally *vice-versa.*

hammer mill a piece of machinery used for grinding *cereals* into *meal* to be used as animal *feedingstuffs.* It operates by a series of rapidly rotating hammers smashing the grain until the particle size is reduced to allow it to pass through holes in a perforated screen. Alterations in screen mesh sizes allow variation in the fineness of the grinding of the grain. Contrast *roller mill.*

Hampshire an American breed of pig which is black with a white saddle resembling the *British Saddleback* from which it is thought to be descended.

Hampshire Down a breed of *polled* sheep which originated from *Southdown,* Berkshire Knot and Wiltshire Horn breeds. The breed is characterised by dark brown faces and legs and close wool over the forehead. Often used as a *terminal sire* for fat lamb production.

hand mating an animal mating system in which the mating of a specific female to a specific male is supervised by the stockman. Often the two animals are temporarily isolated from their herd or flock mates.

hang the carcass of an animal or bird may be allowed to hang, often on hooks at room temperature or in a chiller, in order to allow the condition of the meat to improve.

haploid the term used of cells having a reduced, single set of *chromosomes,* such that their total chromosome number is equal to half that of *diploid* somatic cells. *Gametes* (e.g. *ova* and *spermatozoa*) are haploid cells.

harden off the gradual exposure of plants which may have been grown in a protected environment (greenhouse) to cooler conditions in order that they may adapt to the changed conditions and not be adversely affected by an abrupt transition.

hardware the electronic and mechanical components which make up a computer. They consist of the central processing unit (CPU) which controls processing and communicates with various peripheral devices, namely, a keyboard for entering data or computer programs, an external device for long-term storage (e.g. disc drives), a visual display unit (VDU) - similar to a television screen - to display information temporarily, and a printer for permanent records (hard copy). Contrast *software.*

hardy a term applied to either animals or plants which are capable of surviving unfavourable winter weather.

Harper Adams Piggery a low linear building (often a lean-to) which is used for fattening pigs. It consists of an indoor *pen* and a partly covered outdoor run.

harrow an implement for the *cultivation* of soil. Arrangements of spikes or tines, either rigid or flexible, are drawn through the soil to break it into smaller *aggregates.* Harrows are often used to cover *seed* with soil after sowing. See also *disc harrow, chain harrow.*

harvest the process of gathering the product from a crop.

harvest index the *economic yield* (2) of a crop expressed as a fraction of recoverable *biological yield.* Thus in *cereals*, grain weight divided by the combined weight of *straw, chaff* and grain.

hatch a hatch is a *brood* of chicks. The terms is also used to denote the act of a young bird breaking out of its egg. Eggs may be hatched naturally by a hen sitting on them or an artificial incubator may be used in a *hatchery.*

hatchery a place where eggs are artificially incubated e.g. for the production of day-old-chicks.

haulm the foliage of the *potato, pea* and *bean* crops.

hay dried herbage material which can be stored for consumption by animals at a future date. Hay is made by allowing cut herbage to dry in the field in the sun and wind to a dry matter content of approximately 85%, at whichlevel, micro-organisms which might cause decay are inhibited. The drying process is long and weather dependent, hence the quality of the final product is variable. Hay can be made from herbage grasses or *legumes* such as *red clover* and *lucerne.* Once dry, the hay is usually compressed into *bales* for removal from the field and subsequent storage. Hay was, until recently, the main form of stored herbage in the UK. Now *silage* has become more popular because it is less weather dependent, its production is easier to mechanise and it can be more effectively handled in bulk. See also *barn dried hay.*

hay additives materials added during the making or storing of *hay* to improve the storage properties and/or the nutritional value of the product. Examples include *propionic acid* and *ammonia.*

haylage a form of stored herbage which, as the name suggests, is intermediate between *silage* and *hay.* Very dry herbage (more than 50% Dry matter) is chopped finely and *ensiled,* usually in a *tower silo.* A very restricted fermentation takes place before a stable product is reached. Regarded as a high quality, but high cost, form of *forage* storage.

hay rack an open frame, constructed of wood or metal, into which hay is put and from which *cattle* and *sheep* are allowed to eat.

headland the area at each end of a field used for turning *tractors, cultivation* and *harvesting* equipment. Because of the additional compaction caused by these activities, the yield of crops on the headlands may be less than on the rest of the field.

Health and Safety Acts a series of statutes, laying down regulations aimed at protecting employers, employees and members of the public from health and safety hazards, including those on a farm. Enforcement is under the direction of the Health and Safety Commission and its inspectors.

heart 1. A hollow muscular organ which acts as a pump to propel blood around an animal's body. 2. Soil is said to be in 'good heart' if it is fertile and capable of producing good crops. Conversely, infertile soil is said to be in 'poor heart'.

heat a female animal is said to be 'on heat' at the time of *oestrus* when she will stand to be mated by the male.

heather (Calluna vulgaris) the most common form of heather is a shrub often found in upland areas used for rough grazing. Heathers are found on strongly acid soils, often associated with other plants such as *nardus* and *molinia.* The young immature shoots of heather have some nutritional.value to sheep but the more mature shoots become woody and unacceptable to grazing livestock. Other forms of heather include Erica species. Mature shoots of heather may be burned to allow new vegetative shoots to regenerate from the base of the plant.

heavy hog a general purpose pig killed at heavy weights the carcass of which is used for a variety of purposes including *bacon* and manufacturing.

hedge 1. A field boundary consisting of growing wood plants. 2. A form of trading on the *futures market*. The purchase and sale of a *futures contract*, in conjunction with a sale of the commodity on the spot market (see *spot price*), can guarantee the trader the price of the initial futures contract.

heft a group of hill or mountain sheep which have become acclimatised to a particular area. Although free to roam, due to the absence of fences, they graze the same areas as their dams and where they were born.

heifer a young female *bovine*. A heifer calf is less than 1 year of age, after which it is referred to as a heifer until the birth of its second calf. Further classifications include: maiden heifer - one which has not yet been mated for the first time, in-calf heifer - one pregnant for the first time and the heifer lactation - the first lactation.

herb a plant which is herbaceous has no tall woody persistent stem but produces shorter stems as temporary structures for one year only. All *annuals* and *biennials* are herbaceous, and there are many herbaceous perennials. They do not produce woody stems. Contrast *shrub.*

herbaceous a term applied to plants which do not become woody.

herbage plant material available for use by livestock which derives from *herbaceous* plants.

herbicide a chemical which is used to destroy vegetation, especially *weeds.* Many herbicides show selective action and can be used to remove weeds from a growing crop.

herbivore an animal which eats *herbage,* especially grass. Amongst the farm livestock the ruminants (cattle, sheep and goats) are herbivores, whilst pigs are *omnivores.*

herd a collective term for a group of animals (e.g. cattle or pigs).

herd basis the permitted exclusion of changes in *breeding livestock* valuation from taxable income by treating mature breeding animals as fixed *assets.* An increase in valuation due to inflation is not counted as *profit* for tax purposes and no *capital gains, income* or *corporation tax* is paid on the sale proceeds from herd disposal. It was introduced to provide a way of reducing the effect of inflation on tax liability.

herd book a register of animals of a particular breed of cattle or pigs compiled by a *breed society*. The herd book of an established breed is said to be 'closed' - only *progeny* of registered animals may be registered. The herd book of a recently established breed society is 'open' while the animals comprising the parent stock of the breed are being registered.

herdsman a person in charge of a herd of animals, particularly cattle.

Herdwick a hardy breed of mountain sheep which is of local importance in the Lake District of England. Although the lambs have considerable black colouration older animals are predominantly white with a coarse fleece.

heredity passed on, or capable of being passed on, from one generation to the next.

Hereford the Hereford is the most popular breed of *beef cattle* in England and Wales and accounts for almost half of the beef *inseminations* carried out by the MMB. It has been known in Herefordshire for many centuries and its characteristically white face colour marks both pure-bred and cross-bred progeny. It is used extensively for crossing on to dairy cows to produce an easy calving and a low incidence of *dystocia*.

heritability the ratio of genetic variance to *phenotypic* variance. It is the proportion of the observed superiority, or inferiority, of selected animals which reappears in their progeny.

heterosis the extent to which the *progeny* of a cross differ (in either direction) from the average of the parental types in a given *character*. Positive or desirable heterosis is called *hybrid vigour*. Heterosis is higher in traits of low *heritability* such as reproductive traits.

heterozygote a *zygote,* or individual, derived from the union of different *genes*. Hence the condition heterozygous.

Hexham Leicester see *Blue-Faced Leicester*.

Highland a hardy breed of cattle which is uncommon outside its native regions of the Highlands and Islands of Western Scotland . The breed is characterised by long horns and thick shaggy hair which varies in colour (red, fawn and brown are most common). It is not a breed of high production potential being slow maturing, but it is able to survive on poor mountain pasture.

hill farms a broad categorisation of farm type located in hill and upland regions, depending on livestock rearing for the majority of its income. For the distinction between hill farms and upland farms, see *less favoured areas, upland farms*.

Hill Livestock Compensatory Allowances (HLCAs) an annual payment per head of livestock (headage payment), paid under the provisions of EC directive 75/268 (and successors), to compensate for farming in disadvantaged conditions found in designated *Less Favoured Areas.* For the UK in 1988, the allowances were £54.50 per suckler cow, £6.75 per ewe of an approved breed and £4.50 per ewe of other breeds. The level of payments was restricted to a maxima of £60 per hectare or 6 ewes per hectare. In marginal land areas given Less Favoured Areas status for the first time in February 1985, the HLCAs were paid at half the rates for approved breeds subject to overall maxima of £45 per hectare and 9 ewes per hectare.

hill sheep sheep of a hardy breed (e.g. Cheviot, Blackface, Welsh, Swaledale) kept on *hill farms* with access to poor quality hill or mountain grazing at low stocking rates.

hilt see *gilt.*

hind a female deer.

hire purchase (HP) a form of medium term *credit* granted by a finance company. The purchaser pays a deposit followed by regular installments of the outstanding price plus interest through the hire period. At the end of this period, ownership passes from the finance company to the purchaser. *Interest* charges are commonly quoted on a *flat rate* basis. Contrast *leasing.*

hirsel a *heft* of sheep or the area over which such a group of sheep are grazing.

hock the joint, often projecting in an 'elbow-like' manner on an animal's hind leg.

hoe a device with a blade for chopping out *weeds.* The simplest forms are hand held, whereas more complex machines covering several crop rows may be used. *Tractor* mounted steerage hoes can be used to remove weeds from between several adjacent crop rows.

hog a castrated male pig.

hogg or hogget a sheep (either male or female) between the time of weaning and its first shearing. Thus sheep in their first year of life being *finished* on *roots* during winter are hoggs.

Holstein also called the Holstein-Friesian or Canadian Holstein. A subpopulation of the *Friesian* cattle which originated in Holland. It was imported into N America in the 1880s where intense selection for dairy *traits* has led to a high producing breed which has been re-introduced into the UK and is often used as a sire on Friesian dams.

homefarm the main farm on an estate or group of farms owned by one *landlord.* Homefarms are now often farmed by their owner.

Home Grown Cereals Authority (HGCA) established under the Cereals Marketing Act of 1965 with the aim of improving the marketing of UK cereal production. In 1972 the HGCA was assigned the task of acting as agent of the *Intervention Board for Agricultural Produce* established under the CAP. It also reports price information to the European Commission in Brussels, on behalf of MAFF. THE HGCA is financed by a levy on domestic production, which is collected at the first point of sale, currently amounting to 1p per tonne; the Exchequer may also contribute. See also *Agricultural Marketing Boards.*

home mix an animal feed produced on the farm by mixing cereals and bought in *straights* or concentrates. Contrast ready mixed *compound feeds* bought in from *feed compounders.*

homozygote a *zygote* or individual derived from the union of identical *genes.* Hence the condition *homozygous.*

hoof the structure covering the distal ends of the digits of the limbs of the farm livestock. It is composed of closely packed epidermal cells which have become cornified, and serves a protective function.

hoose see *husk.*

Hops Marketing Board Limited a *co-operative* organisation for hop growers, established in 1982. It took over some of the functions of the original Hops Marketing Board, whose monopoly powers had been challenged by the European Commission.

hormone an internal secretion produced by an animal or a plant and having a stimulatory effect of a specific physiological action. Animal hormones are produced by endocrine glands (e.g. the pituitary) and are carried to other organs in the blood. Important hormones include insulin, growth hormone, corticosteriods, testosterone, oestrogen, adrenaline etc. Plant hormones include *auxins.*

host an animal or plant infected by a *parasite.*

humus part of the organic matter in soils. It is the amorphous brown to black material in the soil organic matter which bears no trace of the anatomical structure of the material from which it was derived. Humus is not a single substance so does not have a constant composition. Humus can assist in the process of soil *aggregation* improving *soil structure* and water retention. Two extreme types of humus are recognised *mull* and *mor humus.* Mull humus is produced when the surface organic litter is mixed with the mineral soil beneath whereas mor humus remains on the surface and is separate. Mulls are usually less acid than mors.

husk 1. A disease of cattle and sheep due to infestation of the *bronchi* by nematode worms. The symptoms of the disease are a husky cough and difficulty in breathing. 2. The outer covering of *cereal grains* which may be removed during *threshing.*

hybrid an animal or plant which is the offspring of parents of different *breed, variety* or *species.*

hybridisation the process of cross fertilising two dissimilar individuals to produce a *hybrid.*

hybrid vigour the superiority in a given character, or the desirability (especially in terms of thrift or fitness) of a cross over the mid-parent.

hydrolysis the process of decomposition of a compound by reaction with water in which the water is also decomposed.

hydroponics the practice of growing plants without soil or compost. The nutrient requirements of the plants are met from a carefully balanced solution of mineral elements which is continuously replenished.

hyperkeratosis excessive growth of the outer horny layer of the skin.

hyperplasia an increase in the number of cells present in a plant or an animal.

hypertrophy an increase in the size of a plant or animal tissue without any increase in cell number. Contrast *hyperplasia.*

hypocalcaemia See *milk fever.*

hypogeal with reference to *germination,* the situation in which the *cotyledons* of the germinating *seed* remain below the ground.

hypomagnesaemia a condition resulting from low levels of blood magnesium in animals and which is characterised by shivering and staggering. It is most commonly seen in cattle following their *turn-out* onto spring *pasture* having been wintered indoors. Death of animals with hypomagnesaemia is rapid and therefore prevention by trying to ensure an adequate intake of magnesium (via the *concentrate* feed, water supply, pasture dusting or placement of a magnesium bullet in the *rumen*) is recommended. Also called Grass Staggers or Grass Tetany.

hypothalamus a region of an animal's brain, the many functions of which include the production of *hormones* which affect the *pituitary* gland and a role in the control of behaviour, hunger and thirst.

identical twins twins of the same genetic constitution arising from the same fertilised *ovum*. See also *monozygous*. Contrast *dizygous*.

Ile de France a french breed of sheep thought to be derived from the *Merino* and *Leicester* breeds. Although not widespread in the UK it is most commonly used as a *terminal sire* to produce crossbred lambs for meat production. The rams are characterised by pink noses and by wool covering the top of their heads.

ileum the posterior part of the small intestine of an animal's digestive tract.

ilium the major bone of the pelvic girdle.

immunisation the process of making a plant or animal *immune* against an *antigen*. This foreign substance is usually a disease-causing organism but may be a form of the animal's own hormones in order to manipulate reproduction (e.g. *fecundin*). Immunisation against disease is usually achieved by injecting a *vaccine* or an *antitoxin*.

immunity the state of being immune: the ability of a plant or animal to resist the effects of an infective agent e.g. disease.

implant a substance placed into an animal (e.g. under the skin) to modify its *metabolism*. Until their recent ban by the EC anabolic steroids were often administered to growing cattle in the form of an implant.

improved contemporary comparison (ICC) a form of *contemporary comparison* used by the *milk marketing board* in assessing the relative worth of dairy bulls. It is 'improved' as it corrects for variation among the contemporaries in factors which might affect lactation performance for example age at, or month of, calving. ICC values are then presented for an individual bull for a number of traits. For example for an individual Friesian bull to be in the top 1% of the breed it would need the following ICCs for any trait: milk yield (kg) +531, fat yield (kg) +19.4, protein yield (kg) +14.0, fat % +0.23, protein % +0.10.

improvement grants See *Agricultural Improvement Scheme*.

inbred line a family or group of animals or plants which is obtained by continued close *inbreeding* and consist of individuals presumed to be more or less *homozygous* for the same *genes*.

inbreeding the mating of individuals which are more closely related than the average of the population to which they belong. Contrast *outbreeding*.

inbreeding coefficient a measure of the amount of loss of *heterozygosity* due to *inbreeding*. More precisely it is the chance of the two *gametes* uniting to form an individual being derived from a common ancestor.

inbreeding depression a decline in vigour and associated *characters* due to *inbreeding*.

in-bye land a term used on upland and hill farms to describe the most productive land surrounding the farmstead. Usually situated in valley bottoms it is fenced against rough grazing. The in-bye is usually fertilised and has often been improved by *liming* and/or reseeding. It is the area of a farm which provides *hay* or *silage* for winter feed and the highest quality *grazing*.

in-calf a descriptive term for a pregnant cow.

incisors an animal's front teeth specially adapted for cutting.

income aids see *direct income transfers*.

income tax a progressive tax levied directly on the income of individuals, employees and those trading as sole traders or in partnership. It is not levied on *company* profits (*corporation tax*). See also *pay-as-you-earn*.

incomplete penetrance the degree or extent to which a trait is shown by some individuals having the *genotype* which normally produces the *character*.

incubate the process of causing eggs to *hatch* either naturally by a hen sitting on them or artificially in an *incubator*.

incubation period 1. The period intervening between the infection of a host plant or animal by a parasite organism (e.g. *bacteria, virus*) and the appearance of the first symptoms. 2. The period required to *incubate* an egg from the time it is laid until the chick hatches out.

incubator apparatus used in the artificial *incubation* of eggs. Temperature and humidity are precisely controlled and often eggs are automatically turned.

indigenous See *endemic*.

individual selection selection on the basis of records of individuals as opposed to the records of relatives (*family selection*).

infected area an area, designated by a statutory body (e.g. MAFF or a local authority), within which animals have to be kept isolated. The area, which may be a farm or a number of adjoining farms, is defined in a notice which is served when an animal is known or suspected of having a *notifiable disease*. The period of isolation allows tests to be conducted to establish the presence or absence of the disease, to make arrangements to deal with infected animals and to prevent the spread of disease outside the area by animal to animal contact.

infectious anaemia a *septicaemia* caused by a *virus* which causes an *anaemia*. Horses are particularly susceptible.

infectious bovine rhinotracheitis (IBR) An acute *virus* infection of the upper respiratory tract of cattle. It is characterised by nasal discharge, runny eyes, increased salivation, high temperature and reduced appetite.

infectious bulbar paralysis See *Aujesky's disease.*

infectious diseases diseases of plants or animals which may be transmitted from individuals which have the disease to previously disease-free individuals.

infectious ophthalmia See *New Forest disease.*

infertile 1. An animal or plant which is not capable of producing *gametes* normal for their sex and which are capable of *fertilisation* and formation of a new individual. The infertile state may be temporary or permanent. 2. A soil which is deficient in plant nutrients.

infiltration rate see *permeability.*

inflorescence a group of flowers on a common axis or stem. Two forms of grass inflorescence are illustrated above.

inheritance tax introduced in the 1986 Finance Act to replace *capital transfer tax,* it is levied when wealth passes out of an individual's estate on death or, at a reduced rate, during the previous seven years. It is of particular relevance to owner-occupier farmers and landowners holding wealth in the form of land. The tax is levied at a single rate of 40% above a threshold value of £110,000. Relief is given for agricultural property, including buildings, at 50% of the value transferred for land with *vacant possession,* and 30% for tenanted land.

in-lamb a descriptive term for a pregnant *ewe.*

in-milk a descriptive term for a lactating cow producing milk.

inoculation of seed is the process of introducing micro-organisms into the soil together with the seed as in the case of *lucerne seed* inoculated with Rhizobium meliloti, to encourage the process of nitrogen fixation.

in-pig a descriptive term for a pregnant sow.

inputs the purchased goods and services which, when applied to agricultural *factors of production* yield the *gross output* of the industry.   Inputs include feed, fertiliser, fuel, veterinary services and many other items which contribute to the *yield* produced.

insecticides *crop protection chemicals* used to control insect pests. They may be natural or synthetic.

insemination the procedure of bringing the male and female *gametes* into close proximity to allow *fertilisation* to occur. In animals under natural conditions the female becomes inseminated with the male gametes present in *semen* during *copulation.*   In farm animals especially cattle, this may be replaced by *artificial insemination.*

insulin a *hormone,* produced by the pancreas of an animal, which plays an important role in the maintenance of blood sugar levels by converting glucose to its storage compounds e.g. glycogen.

insurance a *contract* in which a premium is paid to an insurer in return for full compensation in the event of fire, theft and accident.   Crops and livestock may be insured against certain disease and weather risks.

intake   a commonly used abbreviated term for an animal's voluntary feed intake.

intensive a term used to describe systems of agricultural production which use high levels of inputs to achieve high output. Thus intensive cereals are those produced using high *seeding rates,* heavy dressings of *fertilisers* and large amounts of *crop protection chemicals* in attempts to achieve high yields. Similarly,   *intensive livestock* systems aim to maintain high levels of individual animal performance at high *stocking rates.* These systems may also be described as high input - high output systems.

intensive livestock production *intensive* systems of livestock production which are characterised by high inputs in the hope of achieving high outputs. Animals are kept indoors at high *stocking rates* on high cost diets which it is hoped will give maximal animal performance and both high biological efficiency and high economic efficiency (by reducing per capita costs). Intensive livestock production systems such as sow stalls, veal crates and hen battery cages are coming under increasing public pressure on animal *welfare* grounds.

interaction in animal breeding interaction can occur at three levels. 1. Between the genotype and its environment. See *genotypic-environment interaction.* 2. Between *loci.* See *epistasis.* 3. Between *alleles.* See *dominance.*

intercropping the practice of planting two or more dissimilar crops in separate but adjacent rows in order to make optimum use of the *environment.* Examples would include the use of trees in *pastures* to provide shade and timber without greatly influencing *herbage* production.

interest periodic charges paid by customers on *bank overdrafts* and *loans* and to customers on their *deposit accounts.* They are usually expressed as a percentage or proportion of the appropriate capital sum. See also *real rate of interest, annual percentage rate.*

intermediate host the secondary or alternative *host* in which part of the life-cycle of a *parasite* is spent when it is not in the host animal. The *liver fluke* has the snail as an intermediate host.

internal parasite a *parasite* which lives inside the *host* animal e.g. stomach or intestinal worms. Also called Endoparasite: contrast External Parasite or Exoparasite.

internal rate of return (IRR) a measure used to appraise an investment (see also *investment appraisal*). It is the *discount rate* which yields a *net present value* of zero. Investment in a project would be suggested if its IRR was higher than the IRRs of alternative investments and higher than the cost of borrowing funds. See also *discounting.*

internal respiration the metabolic process which occur within cells of plants or animals which use oxygen and result in the release of energy in a form in which it can be used e.g. the breaking down of complex organic compounds into simpler compounds. Also called Tissue Respiration.

internal transfers the movement of crop produce or livestock between *enterprises* on a farm. Examples include the transfer of young stock to the mature breeding herd, and the use of homegrown grain for on-farm feed or as seed for next year's crop. Attention must be paid to the recording and valuation of these transfers if accurate enterprise *gross margins* are to be calculated.

internode the part of a stem between two adjacent *nodes.*

Intervention Board for Agricultural Produce the agency responsible for administration of the EC intervention system in the UK. It delegates responsibility for cereals to the *home grown cereals authority* and for red meat to the *Meat and Livestock Commission.* The main activities are the payment of *export refunds* and positive *monetary compensatory amounts* (MCAs). The analogous *variable levies, duties* and negative MCAs are handled by the Customs and Excise Department. The Board also handles production aids for particular activities. It reports both to Parliament and to the *European Commission.* It handles some 800,000 transactions annually.

intervention buying the purchase of specific commodities, by the appropriate EC agency, at a predetermined price. Minimum quality standards must be achieved for commodities bought into intervention. See *administered prices, intervention board for agricultural produce.*

intervention price see *administered prices.*

intervention stocks the amount of a commodity, held in intervention stores, under the *Common Agriucltural Policy* at a point in time. The stocks may be related to a year's consumption or production, in order to illustrate their significance. For example EC intervention stocks of grain at the end of 1987/88 amounted to 9% of the year's total consumption and 10% of the year's production.

intestinal juice a digestive juice secreted by the walls of the *intestine* and which contains a number of enzymes which breakdown the constituents of feed prior to their absorption.

intestine the part of an animal's *alimentary system* which leads from the *stomach* to the *anus* and is an important site of *digestion* and absorption.

intrascope an optical probe used to measure backfat thickness at specific points on a pig carcass.

investment appraisal assessment of the financial reward from using capital in new projects. Appraisal techniques include *payback period, rate of return, net present value, internal rate of return.*

invoice a document which forms the legal basis of a transaction and details the supplier, customer, goods, price and *value added tax.* It is issued by the supplier to the customer as a formal demand for payment.

in-wintered animals which are housed during the winter as opposed to being kept outside. Contrast *out-wintered.*

iodophor a liquid containing iodine which is used as a *teatdip* as part of a programme aimed at preventing *mastitis.*

irrigation a system of applying water to land. A necessary part of crop production in dry countries or dry areas. Water may be applied through a system of sprinklers or rain guns or, especially in other countries, by periodically flooding the land from a system of irrigation channels. Water used for irrigation may come from nearby streams or rivers and can be extracted only if the farmer obtains a licence. Alternatively the farm may draw water from a suitable borehole. Theoretically irrigation water should be applied to return the soil to *field capacity* but the availability of water and equipment may limit the extent to which this is possible.

Italian ryegrass (Lolium multiflorum)   a highly productive   but relatively short-lived cultivated grass of Mediterranean origin. This grass is easy to establish from its large seed and grows quickly. It is well adapted to forms of management based on infrequent cutting. It is also popular with farmers because it begins to grow at temperatures below those to which other grasses respond and   therefore produces more herbage for early *grazing*. It is commonly used in *leys* of two of three years duration.

Jacob a primitive multi-horned breed of sheep. The wool from its multicoloured fleece is used for spinning.

Jersey a breed of *dairy* cattle which originated from the Channel Island of the same name and which is one of our smallest and earliest maturing breeds. It now only accounts for 1.6% of the dairy cows in England and Wales. It is a breed noted for its high milk quality, producing an average yield of just under 4000kg at 5.2% fat and 3.8% protein.

Jersian a F_1 *hybrid* produced by crossing a *Friesian* cow with a *Jersey* bull.

Johne's disease a chronic disease of sheep, goats and particularly cattle caused by the bacterium, Mycobacterium paratuberculosis. It is characterised by enteritis which causes severe inflammation of the *intestine, caecum* and *colon*. The main symptoms are *diarrhoea* and emaciation.

joint-ill See *navel-ill.*

joule unit of energy.

June return the popular name for the *agricultural census,* for which most of the forms are returned in June.

juncus see *rushes.*

kale family Brassica oleracea a crop grown in the UK for *fodder*. Plants are grown for the edible leaf and stem tissue which is fed to animals during the autumn and winter. Several types of Kale are grown ranging from *thousand head kale* which is much branched, leafy and quite hardy, to *marrow stem kale* which produces a stout, thickened stem and relatively fewer but larger leaves. The stem is used as a reserve food store by the plant and is eaten by livestock. Because of the woody vascular tissue, some of the stem is of limited *digestibility*. Kales are of low dry matter but relatively high in protein. They may be fed in the field by *folding* or *strip grazing* or they may be cut and fed to livestock indoors.

ked small brown hairy, wingless bloodsucking fly (Melophagus ovinus). Keds are ectoparasites of sheep and the constant irritation they cause leads to a reduced animal performance.

keep *grass* or any other *fodder crop* on which livestock are fed either at grazing or as winter keep.

kemp the coarse, brittle fibres of a sheep's *fleece* which are shed as the fleece grows. Unlike the true wool fibres, kemps are difficult to dye.

Kerry a breed of black dairy cattle found mainly in SW Ireland and suited to harsh conditions. It is not of major economic importance as it is low yielding.

Kerry Hill a breed of sheep originating in the Welsh Borders. The ewes, which have a black and white speckled face, are prolific and often used for crossing by rams of *down breeds* as *terminal sires.*

ketosis the excessive formation of Ketone, or acetone bodies in an animal's body resulting from the incomplete oxidation of body fats. Ketosis is likely to occur when an animal is deficient in dietary energy and is mobilising excessive amounts of body fat e.g. the dairy cow in early lactation or the ewe in late pregnancy where ketosis is referred to as *pregnancy toxaemia.*

key money a lump sum of money paid by an incoming tenant over and above the rental, in order to secure a tenancy from a landlord.

kibbled broken into fairly coarse fragments e.g. kibbled maize.

kid a goat less than 1 year of age.

killing out percentage the weight of a *carcass* as a percentage of the *liveweight* of the *animal*. Typically killing out percentages are 55% for cattle and 52% for sheep and give an indication of the meat yield of a carcass after the removal of gut-fill, offal, blood, hide, feet and head. The killing out percentage of pigs is higher as the carcass includes the head, feet and skin. Age at slaughter, breed, degree of fatness and production system all affect the killing out percentage.

knacker an animal slaughterer. More specifically one who deals with casualty animals (either dead or alive) whose carcasses are not destined for human consumption.

k value the efficiency with which *metabolisable energy* is used by the animal for *maintenance* or productive purposes (e.g. growth, reproduction, lactation).

labour profile sometimes constructed in farm planning to show the pattern of seasonal labour requirements. The time scale may be monthly within the production cycle, or for a period of peak work load, when there is likely to be a labour shortage. The profile is generally built up using *standard man day* data for each farm operation considered. See also *gang work day chart.*

lactate a salt of *lactic acid.*

lactation the production of milk by the *mammary glands* of a female. The period of lactation is initiated by *endocrine* changes following the end of *pregnancy* and *parturition.* Lactation length in the *dairy cow* is optimally 305 days and is often managerially determined at shorter lengths in other farm species: beef cattle (6 months), sheep (3 months), pigs (5 weeks). Milk production is affected by the frequency and intensity of milk removal by either the young or the milking machine. The yield and composition of milk produced during a lactation is affected by many factors both *genotypic* and *environmental.* See also *milk yield, lactation curve.*

lactation curve the relationship between *milk yield* and *time.* For all species the lactation curve rises to a peak quite rapidly and then slowly declines over the remainder of *lactation.* For dairy cattle peak yield may be 30kg at seven weeks after calving followed by a rate of decline of 2.5% per week.

lactic acid an organic acid which is important in several contexts. In *ensilage,* the production of lactic acid as the desirable end product of fermentation by *lactobacilli,* results in a stable and good quality *silage.* Lactic acid may also be produced in the *rumen* as a result of microbial fermentation in situations of low pH.

lactobacilli group of micro-organisms which ferment soluble sugars to produce *lactic acid.* Members include L. plantarum, Streptococcus faecalis.

lactose a disaccharide sugar consisting of glucose and galactose and found only in *milk.*

laid crop the description of a crop which has been damaged by the weather and is no longer upright. See *lodge.*

lairage a pen where animals are temporarily housed e.g. at *abattoirs, markets* or docks when awaiting slaughter, sale of export.

lamb 1. A sheep less than 6 months of age. 2. The meat from the carcasses of young sheep. 3. The act of *parturition* when the *ewe* gives birth to lambs.

lamb crop See *lambing percentage.*

lamina 1. Part of a leaf, specifically the flat part, or blade. 2. The sensitive layer immediately inside the horny wall of the *hoof.*

lambing percentage the number of live lambs born to 100 ewes presented to the ram for mating. Higher values will be obtained if all lambs rather than live lambs are considered or if ewes lambing rather than ewes mated are considered.

laminitis inflammation of the *lamina* of an animal's *hoof.* It is most common in cattle and horses. The causes are not known although the incidence is higher when large amounts of concentrates high in *cereals* are fed due to the end products of *digestion* which these produce.

land classification a system of ranking land on the basis of its physical characteristics. The MAFF uses an Agricultural Land Classification with 5 main grades. In England and Wales there is very little grade 1 land (the best) and only 15% of grade 2. Grade 3 accounts for virtually half of the agricultural land area and is subdivided into three subgroups. The remainder is in grades 4 and 5. In Scotland nearly three-quarters of the agricultural area is classified as grade 5 and less than 3% in grades 1 and 2.

land conversion the process of removing land from agricultural production and transferring it to other uses. In the UK the two main alternative uses are urban development and forestry.

landlord the owner of land or property who lets it to a *tenant* for a negotiated *rent.*

landlord's capital is traditionally owned by the landlord rather than the tenant. It is the long-term *capital,* comprising land, roads, *drains,* buildings and any 'improvements' made by the landlord.

Landrace a breed of white pigs originating in Scandinavia. It is lop-eared and has been extensively used in the UK together with the Large White both in *crossbreeding* programmes and in the formulation of the various *hybrid* pigs available from the *pig breeding companies.*

land reclamation the restoration of land to agricultural or amenity use following a period of decay or dereliction. The term may apply to areas affected by the waste products of industries such as mining. It is also used to describe the process of *pasture* improvement in the *uplands* where areas, previously uncultivated and of negligible output, are brought into production by the introduction of improved *herbage* species and better management.

land use the distribution of land between different uses. In the UK the substantial majority (78%) of the land surface is used for agriculture. Some 8% is used for forestry and woodland, 8% is urban and the remaining 6% is classified to other uses. See also Appendix Table 1.

lanolin a grease derived from the *fleece* of a sheep.

Large Black a breed of black pigs which are now rare.

Large White the major breed of pig. Animals are white in colour and characterised by forward pointing ears and a long snout. Although *pure-bred* herds exist, the main role of the Large White is in *cross-breeding* programmes with the *Landrace* as a major *genetic* inclusion in the various *hybrid* pigs available from the *pig breeding companies*.

larva a stage in the life cycle of an insect from the time of leaving the egg until the development of the *pupa*. This form is often a voracious feeder and may cause damage to plants on which the larvae feed.

latent mosaic see *mild mosaic.*

lateral with reference to *drainage,* the pipes which collect surplus water and transport it to the main drain.   A *drainage system* will thus consist of several main drains and numerous laterals.

lateral roots those emanating from the main or *tap root. Sugar beet* plants have two rows of lateral roots running down the length of a *tap root* whereas *carrots* have four.

layer a bird in a production cycle of egg laying.

laying period the period during which poultry continue to lay eggs. For most egg-producing strains of hen this will extend from the commencement of egg-laying at 22 weeks of age for 50 weeks at which point they are usually slaughtered.

lea alternative form of *ley.*

leaching the downward movement of plant nutrients through the soil profile due to the influence of excess water. Leaching can lead to the loss of bases such as calcium and a consequent increase in soil acidity and contribute to the pollution of water supplies.

leader-follower a system of *grazing* in which a group of animals (leaders) are given preferential access to grazing with the remaining animals (followers) grazing the same area after the leaders have been moved on to new grazing. Examples of leader-follower systems would be high yielding cows followed by low yielding cows or first year heifers followed by second year heifers.

lead feeding a system of dairy cow feeding in which *concentrates* are offered to the cow at a level in excess of her requirements as calculated from standard recommendations. Lead feeding is said to reduce the mobilisation of body tissue and encourage high peak *milk yields.* Also called *challenge feeding.*

leaf area index a term used in crop physiology to quantify the area of leaf of a crop in relation to the area of land on which it grows. For each crop, it gives an indication of the likely interception of solar radiation by the leaf surface.

leaf blotch see *rhynchosporium.*

leaf drop streak see *severe mosaic.*

leafless peas a type of *pea* plant in which the compound *leaf* is genetically modified to produce small *stipules* and *tendrils* in place of leaflets. The plant appears to be leafless. Developed initially for *vining* in the expectation that leafless varieties would remain more erect and easy to harvest, yields have been somewhat lower than desirable. Several varieties of semi-leafless type, with large stipules but no leaflets, now offer a more acceptable commercial compromise.

leaf roll a widespread viral disease of *potato* crops which is transmitted by *aphids.* Infected plants may suffer a 50% loss of yield. In the first year of infection in the field, the symptoms are few, with a slight rolling of the upper leaves of infected plants. However, if plants are grown from infected *tubers,* the rolling of leaves is extensive and it is at this stage that the yield penalty is incurred. Control is achieved by a combination of using *resistant varieties, certified seed* which is known to be free from the *virus* and by the use of *systemic insecticides* to control the *aphid vector.*

leaf spot a severe fungal disease of *oilseed rape* and other *brassica* seed crops being sown for seed. The causative organism Alternaria brassicicola is seed borne but may also be carried in the air. The symptoms are circular brown/black spots on leaves and later on pods resulting in premature ripening and loss of seed. The disease can be controlled by *seed dressing,* and by spraying established plants with *fungicide.*

leaseback the process whereby *freehold* land or property is sold by its occupier and then leased back from the new owner. It is a way of raising *capital* for farm business expansion, usually the purchase of more land.

leasehold a system of land tenure based on *contracts,* or leases, which have several years duration and which specify the rights and obligations of *landlord* and tenant.

leasing a form of medium term *credit*. The owner of machinery or other equipment agrees to grant its use to a business, through a specified period, at a rent. At the end of the lease, commonly three years, continued use is usually permitted in return for regular nominal payments. At no stage does ownership pass to the user. Contrast *hire purchase*.

leatherjacket (Tiputa paludosa) a pest of crops especially *cereals* and *grass*. Larvae of the Cranefly hatch after eggs are laid on grassland or weedy stubble. They feed on the young crop in the following spring. The crop appears patchy, the below ground parts of the plants having been eaten. Control is achieved by ploughing grassland before eggs are laid and by *insecticide* use.

legumes plants belonging to the Leguminosae family. The subfamily Papilionaceae contains the temperate species of agricultural importance; *clovers, lucerne, peas, beans*. All have a branching tap root which is invaded by *rhizobial* organisms which produce *nodules* on the roots. These organisms are capable of utilising free nitrogen in the air. A state of *symbiosis* is then established in which the plant benefits from fixed nitrogen while the bacterium has access to a supply of carbohydrate. Legumes are thus independent of mineral *nitrogen* supplies from the soil and require no additional inputs of *fertiliser* nitrogen. Residues of nitrogen are made available to the crops which follow the legumes in the *rotation*. Legumes were therefore of considerable importance historically as one of the main methods of restoring soil *fertility* before inorganic *fertilisers* were so widely available.

Leicester a large, white-faced, hornless breed of sheep which has a curly fleece. It is also called the Leicester Longwool or English Leicester.

lemma the outer bract in the *floret* of a grass *inflorescence*.

leptospirosis a disease of animals caused by infection by an organism of the genus Leptospira. In cattle, L.hardjo causes *abortion,* severe *mastitis* and reduced milk yield. L.australis can cause infertility in pigs.

lesion an area of damaged tissue, different in appearance from the unaffected tissue around it.

Less Favoured Areas (LFAs) areas within the EC where it is recognised that agricultural conditions are particularly difficult and that special policies will apply. LFAs may be defined as mountain areas, small areas subject to specific handicaps, or areas where 'the maintenance of a minimum population or the conservation of the countryside are not assured". The LFAs in the UK are defined under the last of these three conditions. The boundary of the UK LFAs is similar to, but somewhat wider than, that applying under the Hill Farming and Livestock Rearing Acts of 1946: most of it follows the 250M contour. It was extended from 7.5M ha to 8.7M ha in 1985 and two types of area are now recognised: Severely Disadvantaged (essentially the pre-1985 area and Disadvantaged

Areas (the 1985 addition). The whole LFA now includes 46% of the UK agricultural area. *Hill Livestock Compensatory Allowances* are paid to farmers within the LFAs and specific high rates of grant under the *Agricultural Improvement Scheme* apply. Farmers in the LFAs may also participate in the normal *commodity regimes* e.g. for beef and sheepmeat. Payments under the LFA directive receive a 25% contribution from the *EC budget,* the remainder is funded from national exchequers. See also *Agricultural Improvement Scheme.*

let down the release of milk from the *mammary gland* as a result of the milk ejection reflex. The reflex is neuroendocrine, with the afferent arc being neutral following nerve stimulation in the teat either by the suckling young or the washing and handling of the udder before machine milking. The efferent arc is *endocrine* and involves *oxytocin* which causes cells in the mammary gland to contract and eject the milk through the teat to the waiting young or the milking machine. In dairy cows the process of let down can become a conditional response.

lethal gene a *gene* which causes the early death of an organism.

levels the name given to the main *drainage* channels in the *fens.*

ley a field of grassland sown for a particular purpose and often for a prescribed number of years. It usually refers to the shorter-term grasslands which frequently contain a large proportion of sown species. Hence these are often the most productive grasslands.

liabilities claims on a business accruing to those who have provided the funds used to acquire *assets.* There are three broad categories of liability: (a) claims due to the owner(s) of the business (see also *net worth);* (b) current liabilities, which may have to be met at short notice, usually within one year, e.g. trade *creditors, bank overdraft* and outstanding tax due; (c) longer-term liabilities, which are payable usually after one year, e.g. long term *loans* and *mortgages.*

lice See *louse.*

lignin the fibrous material found in certain plant structures, notably *stems,* which confers structural strength. Plants which contain large amounts of lignin, e.g. mature grasses and cereal *straws,* are less digestible to livestock. This is because the lignin itself is not digestible and because the cellulose with which it is associated is also of reduced availability. Lignified fibres may have economic importance e.g. *flax* and timber.

ligule projecting flap of non-vascular tissue at the junction of the *leaf blade* and the leaf *sheath* in the Gramineae. Its size and shape may be used to identify species and *varieties* of plant.

lime the general name given to materials which are added to the soil to counteract soil acidity. This may be calcium oxide, also called *burnt lime* or *quicklime,* calcium hydroxide which is also called *slaked lime,* or more commonly, finely ground calcium carbonate or limestone rock. Materials differ little in their effectiveness, provided they are applied at the same neutralising rates. Liming of acid soils will cause an increase in soil pH and in the calcium ion concentration in the soil solution. Calcium ions displace aluminium ions from clay particles. In some instances over liming of soils may cause or induce deficiencies of other ions e.g. manganese.

liming see *lime.*

Limousin a breed of *beef cattle* originating in the Limoges area of west-central France. It is known for its high growth rates and for producing a very good *carcass.* It has increased markedly in popularity with dairy farmers as it produces a good *cross-bred* calf.

Lincoln Longwool one of the largest of the UK sheep. It is polled with a white face which is often partly obscured by wool growing over its forehead and eyes. Its fleece is long and shiny.

Lincoln Red a breed of red, horned cattle related to the *shorthorn* but developed in Lincolnshire. Although formerly a dual-purpose breed they are now less popular and used largely as crossing sires on dairy cows to produce beef calves.

line a group of animals which are distinct in *pedigree* over several generations.

linear assessment a method of evaluating conformation characteristics of animals including stature, legs, udder, teats. The MMB uses a method of linear assessment to assess the *conformation* of the daughters of the sires in the *Friesian Holstein* stud.

linear programming a mathematical technique, generally computerised, whose main agricultural applications are in farm planning and the formulation of least cost feed rations for livestock. An objective function (e.g. *gross margin*) is either maximised or minimised subject to various constraints. The aim may be to produce a farm plan which maximises total farm *gross margin* within the availability of land, labour and rotational constraints, or to formulate a feed ration which satisfies specified nutrient requirements at least cost. The latter application has found universal acceptance amongst *feed compounders,* as well as some farmers. Linear programming has not proved to be a popular method of practical farm planning, due to the considerable expertise needed to construct a linear programming matrix and to interpret the results.

line breeding *inbreeding* to a single, common ancestor.

liner the tube (often rubber) which lines the *teat cup* of a milking machine.

linkage in genetics, the association of two or more *genes* which are usually near each other on a particular chromosome so that they tend to be inherited together. See also *sex linked.*

linseed (linum usitatissimum) an annual plant grown for the oil contained in its seeds. Linseed oil is used in paints, varnishes etc. and in foods. The crop has a feathery leaf structure and produces flowers ranging from bright blue to white in colour. Different types of this plant are grown for the fibres in the stem. See *flax.*

liquid fertilisers formulations of plant nutrients which are applied to crops as liquids. These include solutions of nutrients such as urea, suspensions and in some cases materials such as *ammonia* which is a gas at normal temperature and pressure but may be applied by injecting the liquid form under pressure. See *anhydrous ammonia.*

liquidity the ease with which an *asset* can be converted into cash: an expression of the ability of a business to meet its financial commitments as they arise.

litter 1. Loose organic material which has absorbent properties and can be used for the bedding of livestock. Examples include *straw* sawdust, wood shavings, bracken. 2. All the young born to a female at one time at a particular parturition. A ewe might have a litter of 2 but the term is most commonly applied to sows which might have a litter of more than 10 piglets.

liver a large glandular organ in animals which is associated with the digestive system and secretes *bile.* It plays an important part in excretion and other aspects of the general body *metabolism.*

liver fluke a parasitic flatworm (Fasciola hepatica) which infests the liver of animals (especially sheep and cattle). They cause inflammation, diarrhoea, loss of body condition and reduced milk yield. The eggs of the flukes pass out in the animal's *faeces* and subsequently hatch to produce larvae which infect their *intermediate host,* the snail. After developing, the larvae leave the snails and form cysts on grass and subsequently are re-ingested by sheep and cattle which thus become infected. Also called Liver Rot.

livestock a general term applied to domesticated livestock e.g. cattle, sheep. pigs, poultry, horses.

livestock units the different classes and ages of *ruminants* may be related by the term livestock unit which is based on their different *metabolisable energy* requirements. The term is most commonly used with grazing animals as *grazing livestock units*.

liveweight the weight of a live animal, often including a contribution from gut-fill unless the animal has been fasted. Contrast *deadweight.*

liveweight marketing the marketing of live animals, usually at an *auction market.* This method of marketing is commonly known as "on the hoof". An advantage, over the alternative of selling *deadweight* directly to an abattoir, is that stock can be withdrawn by the seller if prices are not favourable. The opportunity to socialise and discuss farming matters with neighbours is a further attraction of auction markets.

loam the texture of a soil which consists of approximately similar proportions of sand, silt and clay sized particles. This distribution of particle size, together with the presence of organic matter, confers upon this *soil texture,* characteristics of good drainage, waterholding capacity and nutrient supply. Loam soils are therefore considered good for most types of crop production.

loans *credit,* granted by a bank or other institution, usually for a defined period. Long-term loans are used to finance permanent improvements such as the erection of new buildings or the purchase of extra farm land. Repayment can be either by the method of *reducing balance, annnuity* or *endowment.* Contrast *bank overdraft.*

locus the point that a *gene* occupies on a *chromosome.*

locust bean fruit of the carob tree which is used in animal feeds. It is sweet and tends to be palatable when fed as part of a coarse mix to cattle.

lodge in crop production, the term used to describe the collapse of upright crops. Lodging may be induced by wet and windy weather when the crop is in a vulnerable state, at a particular stage of maturity or perhaps affected by disease (e.g. *eyespot*). In some crops e.g. herbage seeds, lodging is inevitable and not too disadvantageous but in others e.g. *cereals* it is highly undesirable.

Lome Convention an agreement whereby EC member states attempt to assist some countries of Africa, the Caribbean and the Pacific (ACP). The countries who have signed this agreement are allowed some access to EC markets without paying import levies on named commodities. The most widely known commodity covered by the convention is sugar. See *sugar regime.*

Longhorn an historic breed of hardy cattle characterised by long, forward and downward curving horns. Coat colour is highly variable. Although once important as a beef breed, it is now rare.

long-wooled sheep there are a number of long-wooled sheep breeds including the *Border Leicester, Devon Longwool, Dartmoor, Leicester, Lincoln Longwool, Romney, Teeswater* and *Wensleydale.*

Lonk a mountain breed of sheep found in the North Pennines and related to the *Swaledale* breed which it resembles.

loose housing a system of housing in which animals are group-housed, unrestrained on litter (often straw). Loose housing systems may be used for cattle or pigs and contrast with *cubicles* or more intensive *sow stalls* or *tethers.*

loose smut a fungal disease of *cereals* caused by Ustilago nuda. Infected plants appear normal until *ear* emergence when ears emerge with masses of loose black spores in place of grains. These spores infect healthy ears, invading the developing embryo but remaining invisible until plants are grown from the infected seed. Control is through legislation to limit the sale of infected seed but can also be treated with *systemic fungicide.*

lop-eared said of an animal whose ears hang loosely and partly cover the eyes e.g. *Landrace* pig.

louping ill a paralytic disease principally affecting sheep, cattle and grouse which is caused by a virus transmitted by *ticks* (Ixodes ricinus). It is characterised by acute fever and nervous symptoms. The disease is most common in sheep grazing hill pastures in N England and Scotland.

louse a wingless parasitic insect. Most are blood-sucking and are found on the skins of livestock e.g. *ked.*

lowland farms a broad categorisation of farm type. Located in regions of the country where the land surface is close to sea level and where soil, climate and topography do not inhibit production. Contrast *upland farms* and *hill farms.*

lucerne (Medicago sativa) a *legume* crop cultivated for *forage.* A very important crop internationally, grown in the USA where it is called *alfalfa,* but used only in certain areas of the UK. A long tap root enables the crop to resist moisture stress and produce good yields in hot dry climates. In the UK it grows best in the south east of the country, producing high yields without any *fertiliser nitrogen,* but it can be grown in most situations if the soil is not too acidic or waterlogged. Because of its growth habit, lucerne is better suited to cutting than to *grazing* so it tends to be grown for *hay* or *silage.*

Luing a hardy, early-maturing breed of beef cattle developed from the *beef shorthorn* and *highland* breeds in NW Scotland.

lumpy jaw a disease of animals caused by the fungus (Actinomyces boris).

The name derives from the swelling of the jaw bone which results from penetration of the fungus into small mouth wounds which may have been caused by barley *awns,* loose teeth, damage due to foreign bodies etc. Also called Actinomycosis.

lungs the respiratory organs of animals. They consist of two vascular sacs filled with constantly renewed air. They have a well-developed blood supply to which oxygen passes in exchange for carbon dioxide.

lupin (Lupinus angustifolius, L luteus, L albus) a crop of minor importance in the UK which can be grown for *forage* or for the protein in the *seeds.* Sometimes seem as an alternative land user to *cereals* which are surplus to requirement in the EC, lupins are unlikely to become a major crop.

luteinising hormone (LH) a hormone secreted by the anterior *pituitary* which causes *ovulation* and growth of the *corpus luteum* in the female. LH is one of the active constituents of Pregnant Mare's Serum Gonadotrophin, the exogenous hormone used to increase prolificacy in sheep and superovulation of cattle. In the male LH stimulates the *testes* to produce *androgens.*

lymph a colourless circulating fluid which arises at the capillary beds of the circulatory system of animals. It is collected in the lymphatic vessels and closely resembles blood plasma in composition.

lymphatic system a system of vessels through which *lymph* circulates and which communicates with the venous system. Lymph glands are found on its course.

lysine one of the *amino-acids* essential for animal growth. In non-ruminant diets based on *cereals* lysine is often one of the first limiting amino-acids and therefore an animal's lysine requirement is often specified in diet formulation.

Maedi-Visna a slowly progressive virus disease of sheep and goats. Typically the disease takes about four years to develop following infection. At first the symptoms are slight but the animal's breathing then becomes faster, shallower and more laboured until it dies 2-9 months after the first appearance of symptoms. No treatment is available. The disease was first reported in Iceland but is now widespread in the UK. It is thought that infection occurs from the ewe to the lamb via the placenta and milk. The disease is also readily spread by close contact between animals. A Maedi-Visna accredited flock scheme was introduced in 1982, with registration requiring regular inspections and three consecutive clear blood tests.

maggot a legless *larva* of certain flies of the Diptera order. Maggots of many flies are pests of livestock (e.g. *blow fly, warble fly)* and crops (e.g. *crane fly, frit fly).*

maiden a virgin female. A maiden *heifer* is a young cow which has not yet been mated.

maincrop potatoes potato *tubers* harvested in the mature state at the end of the growing season (September-October). Because the skins have formed on the tubers, these crops are suitable for storage, to be consumed later in the winter. Maincrop potatoes may be used for *ware,* for processing or livestock feed. (Contrast *early potatoes).*

Maine-Anjou a large breed of roan and red and white beef cattle imported to the UK from France.

maintenance an animal has a requirement for *energy* and *protein* for maintenance. This is to maintain body temperature, repair cells, turnover cell proteins etc. An animal's requirement for maintenance must be met before any surplus nutrients are used for production e.g. growth, lactation, reproduction.

maize zea mays, an annual plant, grown widely in hotter parts of the world for *grain* production but used in the UK only for *forage.* This is because suitable warm and sunny conditions for grain production occur too rarely in the UK to enable regular use of the crop for that purpose. Even when grown for forage, maize is restricted to the south coast of England or the localised areas of favourable climate. When harvested for forage, it is usually made into *silage* which is valued for its high energy content.

maize gluten a *by-product* resulting from the processing of grain *maize* for milling and other manufacturing. Maize gluten is generally high in *protein* but can be variable, depending on the manufacturing process. It is used as an animal *feedingstuff,* especially for dairy cows.

malt culms a *by-product* of the malting process which are used as an animal *feedingstuff* especially for dairy cows.   Also called malt coombs.

malting   the process of germinating *barley* grains to bring about *enzyme* reactions which break down the starch in the grain to produce sugars. Once this process has begun, it is stopped by drying the grain to produce 'malt' which is   used in brewing and distilling.   Certain *varieties* are particularly well-suited to malting.

maltose a disaccharide sugar which is formed from the breakdown of starch during seed germination or digestion.

mammary gland   skin glands which secrete milk to feed the   young. Possession of mammary glands is the characterisric feature of female animals. The cow has 4 mammary glands comprising the *udder,* the ewe has 2 glands and the sow has 12-16 glands. The secretion of milk by the mammary glands is controlled by the balance of *hormones.* See also *lactation.*

management agreements   contractual arrangements between central or local government agencies and farmers, under which farmers agree, in return for compensation, to refrain from improving their land. The main statute under which such agreements are negiotiated are the *Wildlife and Countryside Acts* (1981 and 1985).   Such agreements are normally used in areas of high *conservation* (2) or   recreational value.   They are particularly important in   *National Parks*, *AONBs* and *Sights of Special Scientific Interest.* In *Environmentally Sensitive Areas* a management package defines the obligations of all participanting farmers.

management and investment income   a measure of the reward, to management and the return on *tenant's capital* invested in a farm. It is defined as *net farm income* less   a notional value for the unpaid manual labour of farmer and spouse.

mange a skin disease of animals caused by *mites,* which results in hair either dropping out from certain areas or being rubbed away by the animal due to persistent itching.

mangels a crop grown for *fodder.* A member of the family Chenopodiaceae, this *biennial plant* produces a swollen root   during its first year of growth.   These swollen roots are   harvested and stored for feeding to livestock in late   winter. The crop is of decreasing importance because of its considerable bulk and difficulties of mechanisation. A low dry matter but high energy crop grown in the southern part of the country. Also called mangolds.

manger   a trough often located indoors, in which food for livestock, particularly cattle and horses, is placed.

mangolds see *mangels.*

manioc a tropical plant, the tuber of which yields cassava or tapioca. It is imported into the UK and used as an animal *feedingstuff.* It is high in starch content but very low in protein.

Mansholt Plan a radical plan for the reorganisation of the CAP, published in 1968. Its author, Sicco Mansholt, was the Commissioner for Agriculture and he proposed that the agricultural area of the then EC should be reduced by 5M ha (some 7% of the agricultural area of the EC of Six) between 1970 and 1980, to reduce the pressure of *surpluses* on the *EC budget.* The plan was not adopted but is still recognised as a serious attempt to reform the CAP.

manure general name for substances added to soil to increase the level of fertility. It most frequently refers to organic materials of plant and/or animal origin which may supply nutrients in both organic and inorganic forms. See also *farmyard manure, green manure.*

Marchigiana a breed of all white beef cattle from Italy which have been used to a limited extent as crossing sires on dairy cows in the UK to improve the beef potential of calves.

Marek's disease a contagious viral disease of chickens affecting the peripheral nerves and usually characterised by paralysis of the legs and wings.

marginality see *production function.*

margin over concentrates an economic measure of the performance of dairy cows, defined as milk *output* less concentrate *costs* and expressed either on a per animal or per hectare basis. Contrast *margin over feed and fertiliser.*

margin over feed and fertiliser an economic measure of the performance of livestock enterprises; defined as *output* less the *costs* of feed and fertiliser applied to forage crops, expressed on a per animal, per hectare or per enterprise basis. See also *margin over concentrate.*

market equilibrium occurs when the market price (Pe) is just sufficient for the quantity offered for sale to exactly equal the quantity consumers are willing to buy. This is the point at which *demand* (D) and *supply* (S) *schedules* intersect (Qe). The equilibrium price (Pe) is sometimes called the market clearing price.

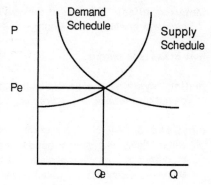

marketing boards were introduced in the UK under the Agricultural Marketing Acts of 1931 and 1933, following a period of acute agricultural depression and the exposure of the agricultural industry to foreign competition. The intention was to give farmers control over prices at which their produce was sold. The Boards were re-established after World War II and their role clarified in the Agricultural Marketing Act of 1958. In 1978 the EC adopted regulations to define the role of marketing boards. See also *Potato Marketing Board* and *Milk Marketing Board*.

marketing margin the difference between the price paid by a consumer for a commodity and the price received by the farmer. The margin covers the costs and profits associated with processing, packaging, storage and distribution.

marrow stem kale see *kale*.

marsh spot a condition in *peas* brought about by Manganese deficiency. The symptom is a brown spot on the under surfaces of the *cotyledons*. This deficiency occurs in association with high soil pH and on soils rich in organic matter. It can be corrected by application of Managanese sulphate either to the soil or to the crop.

mash a mixture of animal feeds which have been ground or crushed. Usually it is presented mixed with water as a soft pulpy mixture - wet mash.

Masham a hardy sheep originating from crossing a *Teeswater* ram on a *Swaledale* ewe.

mastitis inflammation of the *mammary gland* due to an interplay of managerial factors and bacterial infection. Mastitis may affect the female of any species but is most common in the dairy cow. Even in subclinical cases there is a reduction in *milk yield* from infected glands and in clinical cases the milk contains clots and is of abnormal composition. Mastitis leads to the culling of many cows from the UK dairy herd. Also called Garget.

maternal effect the part of the *environmental* effect controlled by the maternal *phenotype* for example.

mat grass see *nardus*.

mating system the principle according to which selected animals are paired for breeding e.g. *inbreeding, outbreeding, random mating*.

mayweed a *weed* of *arable* crops; several types are recognised. All have white, daisy like flower heads and finely divided leaves. They are members of the Compositae family and the types include Stinking Mayweed, Scentless Mayweed, Rayless Mayweed. They are not the easiest of *weeds* to control by *herbicide*.

MCA (Monetary Compensatory Amount) see *green currencies.*

MCPA a *translocated herbicide* which enables selective control of broad leaved weeds in cereal crops and grassland. It is a relatively cheap *hormone* weedkiller which effectively controls weeds such as *charlock, poppy* and *fat hen.*

meal a general term for finely ground animal *feedingstuff.* These may be single ingredients e.g. *fishmeal, soya bean meal* or a mixture.

measles a condition of *beef* or *pork* carcasses due to the presence of *tapeworm* cysts.

meat the edible, fleshy part of an animal's *carcass* consisting of the animal's *muscles.* The meat may also contain both *bone* and *fat.*

Meat and Livestock Commission (MLC) established under the Agriculture Act (1967), the Commission is financed by a levy per head of livestock at point of slaughter and by charges for some of its services. Its objective is to improve meat production and marketing in the UK. It supplies market intelligence and technical information to producers, slaughterers, wholesalers and butchers; provides a recording service for livestock and assesses breeding potential; its staff certify and classify stock at *auction markets* and carcasses at *abattoirs.* The MLC must also have regard to the needs of consumers. The *Intervention Board for Agricultural Produce* delegates functions to *MLC* in connection with support schemes for cattle and sheep. See *beef* and *sheepmeat regimes.*

meatmeal, meat-and-bone meal a *meal* used as an animal *feedingstuff* which is derived from waste *meat* (and *bone*) which has been steam cooked to bring the *dry matter* content to 90%. Excess *fat* is removed and the residue ground to produce a meal of high protein content. The main problem with these meals is their variable composition.

mechanical grazing See *zero grazing.*

meiosis a process of cell division in which the number of *chromosomes* are halved from the *diploid* to the *haploid* number. It is also called Reduction Division and is responsible for the formation of the *gametes* of both the male, *spermatozoa* and the female *ova.* Contrast *mitosis.*

melatonin a *hormone* produced by the *pineal* gland which is involved in the mediation of photoperiod effects on farm livestock e.g. control of the breeding season in seasonal breeders. Use of exogenous melatonin is showing promise for the artificial control of sheep breeding.

merchant credit see *trade credit.*

merchant's list those veterinary medicines, specified by the Medicine Act of 1968, which can be supplied by agricultural merchants to farmers without a prescription from a veterinarian.

meristem a growing point in plants: an area of active cell growth, division and multiplication.

metabolic disease one of a number of diseases arising due to a disturbance in the *metabolism* of an animal. Examples include *hypomagnesaemia, milk fever, ketosis.* Also called Production Disease.

metabolic profile a veterinary service, most commonly used for dairy cows, in which blood samples from representative animals in a herd are analysed for some of the important metabolites. Comparison of the actual levels against normal levels can provide an indication of the energy, protein and mineral status of the herd.

metabolisable energy (ME) ME is the proportion of the energy in a food which becomes available to the *metabolism* of an animal. It represents the *gross energy* of a *feedingstuff* minus the losses of energy in undigested feed (faeces) *urine* and *methane.* Systems of energy evaluation for *ruminants* and *poultry* are based on ME with both animal requirements and feed supply being expressed in joules.

metabolism the sum total of all the physical and chemical changes taking place in a plant or an animal. Examples include *photosynthesis* in plants and *internal respiration.*

methane a colourless, hydrocarbon gas which is produced as a waste product by the micro-organisms in the *rumen.*

methionine one of the *amino acids* essential for animal growth and production. In non-ruminant diets based on *cereals,* methionine is often one of the first limiting amino acids and therefore an animal's requirement for methionine, and the other sulphur containing amino acids (cystine and cysteine) is often specified in diet formulation.

metritis inflammation of the uterus. In the sow it may be found in conjunction with *agalactia* and *metritis* as MMA.

Meuse-Rhine-Ijssel (MRI) a dual-purpose breed of cattle originating from the Netherlands. It is a red and white breed and was one of the breeds used in the UK in the *dairy shorthorn* improvement scheme to increase milk production.

microbe any microscopic organism e.g. *bacteria, protozoa, virus.*

midden a heap of *farmyard manure.*

Middle White a white breed of pig, smaller than the *Large White* and characterised by a turned up nose. It is now a rare breed.

middlings See *wheatings.*

mildew foliar diseases affecting many crop plants. Different organisms are responsible for producing the white fungal hyphae on different plants. See *powdery mildew* and *downy mildew.*

mild mosaic a *virus* disease of *potato* crops caused by Virus X. The disease is almost symptomless but is responsible for yield loss. It is spread by contact, by person or machine.

milk the opaque, white liquid secreted from the *mammary glands* of a female during *lactation.* The average composition of cows milk (protein 3.3%, fat 3.8%, lactose 4.7%, minerals and vitamins 0.7% in the dairy cow) is well suited to the nutritional requirements of the young animal. Cows milk for human consumption is sold to the *Milk Marketing Board* who allocate it to either the liquid or manufacturing (butter, cheese, yoghurt etc.) markets.

milk clipping the *shearing* of lactating ewes which are suckling *lambs.*

milk compositional quality payment See *milk price.*

milk fever a *metabolic disease* of unknown cause which is characterised by hypocalcaemia, or low levels of blood calcium. It occurs in a number of species immediately following *parturition* and is particularly common in the dairy cow with its large output of calcium in the milk once *lactation* commences. It is characterised by muscular weakness and inco-ordination, tetany, loss of consciousness and death. There is no fever. Treatment is by the injection of calcium borogluconate. The disease also occurs during *pregnancy* in the ewe. Also called Parturient Paresis, Hypocalcaemia.

milking the removal of milk from the *mammary gland* of a lactating female either by hand or by *milking machine.* Whilst sheep and goats can be milked the technique is usually applied to *dairy cows.* It is important that milking is synchronised with the milk *let down* and follows a quiet routine.

milking machine a machine for milking cows. All types aim to mimic the sucking action of the calf and remove milk from the *milk sinus* of the *udder* of the cow. This is achieved by the application of an intermittent vacuum pressure on the *teat* causing milk to flow into each *teat cup* of the *cluster.* In most modern milking machines the milk then passes to a collecting jar or directly via a pipeline to the bulk tank. In older systems, often associated with *cowshed* rather than *parlour* milking, the milk passed into pails or churns.

milking parlour a specialised building containing a number of milking machines. Various layouts exist e.g. Abreast, Tandem, Rotary and Herringbone. Parlours may have either one or two cow places per milking unit: thus a 12:12 herringbone parlour would have a milking unit for each of 12 cow places, whilst a 6:12 would have 2 cow places for each milking unit and therefore a slower throughput of cows per hour. Often *concentrates* will be fed to cows in the parlour as it offers the opportunity to feed specific amounts to specific animals which are often housed, and therefore fed, as a group.

Milk Marketing Boards (MMBs) of which there are five in the UK, were originally established under the Agricultural Marketing Acts of 1931 and 1933. The Boards consist of a majority of members elected by producers and a small number of ministerial appointees. The Boards are required to purchase all milk consigned by producers and all producers must register with a Board and sell through it. The Boards resell it on liquid or manufacturing markets, or license producer-retailers to sell it direct to the consumer. The Government ceased to determine liquid *milk prices* in the UK in January 1985 (1978 in Scotland) leaving them to be negotiated, along with manufacturing milk prices, by the Boards. An important determinant of the producers price is the structure of prices for milk products determined under the CAP. The Boards undertake promotional schemes, through Milk Publicity and Dairy Councils, part of the proceeds from *co-responsibility levies* being available for this purpose. *Artificial insemination, recording* and *management schemes* are also provided by the Boards. See also *marketing boards* and *dairy regime.*

milk price milk producers are paid for the constituents of the milk they supply to the *Milk Marketing Boards*. Their average return per litre is thus a weighted average of these constituent prices. The structure of a producer's return for milk of a typical composition is determined as follows:

Constituent	Price per 1% of a litre (pence)	Composition %	Value per litre (pence)
Butterfat	2.012	3.96	7.968
Protein	2.044	3.29	6.725
Lactose	0.302	4.64	1.401
			16.094

This basic price would be adjusted to allow for seasonal and quality factors. Promotion, transport and administrative costs and *co-responsibility levies* would also be deducted in arriving at the final price to producers. These latter deductions averaged between 1 and 1.5 pence per litre, in the UK, in the 1980s.

milk producers outgoers scheme See *dairy regime* and *Dairy Herd Conversion Scheme.*

milk quotas were introduced by the EC in 1984. The UK quota scheme defines the individual producer's entitlement to deliver milk to market in terms of his volume of production in 1983. These 'reference quantities' are adjusted from year to year in line with the national adjustments determined in Brussels. *Super-levies* are payable on the excess of production over the reference quantity. Following a *Council of Ministers* decision in 1985, the levy is calculated retrospectively and at the regional level in the UK for each *Milk Marketing Board* area. Thus super-levy does not arise unless one of the board areas produces more than its aggregate reference quantity. The declared rate of super-levy is 100% of the *target price* for milk, but because it only applies to a small volume of over-quota production, the amounts collected have so far been small.

milk recording schemes for example the *Milk Marketing Boards* National Milk Records Schemes, provide producers with data on the quantity of milk produced by each cow, supplemented if they choose by information on milk fat and protein content on a monthly basis.

milk sinus the teat and gland cavities of the *mammary gland* into which milk passes from the secretory cells and from which it is extracted during suckling or milking.

milk vein one of the two large veins (the subcutaneous veins) which are clearly visible on the belly of a cow and which run from the *udder* to the *sternum.*

milk yield the amount of *milk* produced by an individual female over a specified time period e.g. a day or a *lactation*. For the *dairy cow* there is considerable variation in the lactation yield due to *genotypic* (especially *breed*) and *environmental* (especially *nutrition* and health) factors. The steady increase in dairy cow milk yields to a figure of 5,700kg in recorded herds in the early 1980s was halted by the introduction of *milk quotas* and the consequent reduction in feeding.

mill a machine, or the building containing such machinery, for grinding, crushing or rolling *feedingstuffs*, particularly *cereals*. See also *hammer mill* and *roller mill.*

milling wheat types of *wheat* which produce grain suitable for *milling* to produce flour for bread or biscuits and therefore of higher value. Whether or not a sample is suitable for milling depends upon a combination of *variety* and crop management.

mineral inorganic substances which occur naturally in rock or soil. Contrast *organic* matter which is derived from previously living material.

mineral deficiency an example of a *deficiency disease* due to an inadequacy in the supply of a mineral to a plant or an animal. Examples include Grey Leaf due to Manganese deficiency in *cereals* and *hypomagnesaemia* due to Magnesium deficiency in cattle.

mineralisation the biological process by which organically bound *nitrogen* is released in the form of *ammonium* and *nitrate* ions for use by growing plants. Mineralisation occurs by the action of micro-organisms in the soil, which in metabolising organic matter release ammonium ions as a by-product.

mineral lick a hard block or slab of a formulated *mineral mix* for animals to lick to appetite.

mineral mix a mixture of minerals, both major and *trace elements,* which has been formulated to supply a particular class of *livestock* with its mineral requirements for *maintenance* and production. It is often added to a complete diet or a *concentrate* or *cake* (especially for pigs and poultry). Alternatively it may be given loose in a trough or as a *mineral lick.* Often *vitamins* are combined with the minerals in a *vitamin-mineral mix.*

minimal cultivations systems of soil *cultivation* for crop production which involve only a very limited number of passes through the soil. Only one or two machines, for example *chisel plough, disc harrow,* are used to move the topsoil and, perhaps, the subsoil, to create a suitable *tilth* for crop seeds. The term usually refers to systems which do not rely on conventional mould-board ploughing.

minimal disease herd or flock a herd or flock of livestock which has a very low level of infectious diseases. Often this has been achieved by the purchase of replacement stock solely from minimal disease establishments and is followed by participation in one of various Health Control Schemes.

minimum import prices a policy instrument first introduced by the UK Government in 1962 for cereals, but not used since EC entry in 1973. Its effect is to raise the internal market price thus reducing the cost to the Government of operating the *deficiency payment* scheme. Minimum import prices differ from the EC's *variable levies* in that the latter are taxes imposed on imports whereas the minimum import price may give those exporting to the EC a higher price than they would otherwise seek. Minimum import prices do not yield revenue to the government.

Ministry of Agriculture, Fisheries and Food (MAFF) the main Government Department with responsibility for agriculture, headed by a Minister of Cabinet rank. Its activities include policy formation, in the UK and the EC, land management, advice to farmers (through the *Agricultural Development and Advisory Service*), administration of a range of controls over animal and plant disease, drainage, pesticide and other chemical use on farms. It employs some 14,000 civil servants, more than one-third of which are in *ADAS*. Some conflicts arise between its role in supporting farm incomes and its obligations to consumers with respect to the price of food. See also *agricultural policy, Experimental Husbandry Farms, DAFS* and *DANI*.

mite a subclass of the Arachnida and related to the *tick*. Mites are widespread *parasites* of animals and plants.

mitosis the series of changes through which the nucleus passes during ordinary cell division. It ensures that each of the two daughter cells formed by the division of a typical *diploid* cell are themselves diploid and each possess an identical copy of the genetic material on the *chromosome* of the original cell. Contrast *meiosis.*

mixed farm generally a farm with several *enterprises* on it. In *farm classification* schemes, mixed farms are those which do not show any notable degree of *specialisation.*

MMA (*mastitis, metritis* and *agalactia*) a condition in which the three diseases *mastitis, metritis* and *agalactia* occur together. Its occurrence is usually in the period immediately following *parturition* and is a major problem in some sow herds.

MOET (Multiple Ovulation and Embryo Transfer) is a technique principally applied to cattle, which aims to increase the numbers of genetically superior animals. The first stage is to increase the number of *ova* produced by a particular donor cow (either of a rare breed or an individual of high genetic merit) by superovulation using PMSG. These ova are then fertilised within the cow and the fertilised ova, often six-ten in number, collected. The *embryos* may then be frozen for later use or implanted into a recipient animal. Although still an expensive technique, MOET is being used to an increasing extent both by commercial farmers and animal breeders keen to increase the number of progeny which a superior female can produce.

moisture content the amount of water present in a sample of animal feed, cereal or forage. It is usually expressed as either a percentage or as g/kg.

Thus a dairy *concentrate* may have a moisture content of 14%. In *hay* making the aim is to reduce the moisture content of the cut grass from 80% to below 20% as quickly as possible. The moisture content is equivalent to 100 minus the *dry matter* percentage.

molar 1. The posterior or cheek teeth of animals. 2. The molarity of a solution is its concentration expressed as the number of moles of dissolved substance per litre of solution.

molasses a *by-product* of sugar refining which is similar to thick treacle having a *dry matter* content of 70-80%, high in sugars. A low level (e.g 5%) of molasses is often used in the pelleting of animal *feedingstuffs.* Higher levels may be fed to ruminant livestock by pouring over silage or as part of a *complete diet.* It is quite *palatable* and often leads to an increased feed intake. Molasses may also be used as a *silage additive* where its high sugar content provides a good substrate for fermentation.

mole drain a channel drawn in the soil by a specialised implement, a mole plough. The technique is only possible in some soil types, notably the heavier clay soils. Moles are formed by drawing a bullet shaped object through the soil at depth which leaves a channel of circular cross section down which water can flow. Mole drains can be used to augment other *drainage* systems.

Molinia (Molinia caerulea) a moorland grass occasionally called *purple moor grass.* It is a large tufted *perennial* grass typically found in wet peaty conditions, which is not very palatable to livestock except when in the very immature state. The leaves are *deciduous* giving a brown/white appearance to a Molinia dominant moorland.

molluscicide a chemical used to kill snails and slugs.

molybdenum a *trace element* which when present in excess can cause *scours* in *ruminant* livestock. *Legumes* are believed to have a specific requirement for molybdenum for *nodule* formation.

monensin an antibiotic originally used in the control of *coccidiosis.* It is now extensively used as a *growth promoting feed additive* in ruminants especially cattle. It acts on the microbial population of the *rumen* altering the fermentation pattern and giving a balance of VFAs. These are used more efficiently for growth and therefore feed conversion efficiency is increased.

monetary compensatory amounts (MCAs) under the CAP, MCAs are a system of taxes and subsidies on trade designed to offset the distortions in trade introduced by divergences of *green currencies* from central exchange rates.

monocotyledons members of the main series of flowering plants which have a single *cotyledon* in the *seed.*   Important examples include the *cereals* and *herbage grasses.*

monoculture 1. A collection of similar plants grown as a crop. 2. Growing the same crop on the same area for a number of consecutive years.

monogenic caused by a single *gene.*

monogerm the description of sugar beet *seed* in which the *fruit* coat encloses only one viable seed.   Normally in sugar beet, it is the fruit which is sown, and if more than one seed is present, this gives rise to a cluster of plants at one station. This *multigerm* habit is disadvantageous in modern systems of sugar beet production since the multiple plants would have to be *singled,* often by hand, to leave only one plant per station.

monosaccharide a carbohydrate which is a simple single molecule sugar e.g. glucose.

monozygous originating from a single fertilised *ovum* e.g. *monozygotic* or *identical twins.*

moorland land of generally low agricultural value, usually on thin upland soils. Moorland may also produce heather which is a valuable feed for both sheep and the larger *game* birds. Such land is prized by many for its open and spacious landscape qualities and abhorred by others for its bleakness and low *productivity.*

mor humus the type of *humus* which remains on the surface of the soil forming consecutive layers of undecayed vegetable matter, to rotted humus at greater depth, above the mineral soil. Usually more acidic than the contrasting *mull humus.*

mortgage a form of long-term *loan:* money is borrowed on the security of farm land or other property.

mould 1. The detectable signs of damage or injury to a crop or crop product caused by the presence of *fungal* growth. Hay and grain which has been attacked by *fungi* is said to be mouldy. 2. The upper layer of soil in cultivated land.

mouldboard plough an implement which, when drawn along, inverts the soil through which it has passed. This implement has formed the basis of *cultivation* techniques for crop production for centuries increasing only in size (i.e. number of furrows) as the power available has increased. Apart from exposing a clean surface of soil, the mould board plough has been used to bury *stubble* and *weed* material which remained on the surface after harvest.   Because of its importance and because it is frequently the first *cultivation* technique employed, ploughing is often referred to as *primary* cultivation. See *reversible plough.*

movement licence a licence to move animals in accordance with certain specified conditions. The licence is aimed at controlling animal movements and thus preventing the spread of disease. A movement licence is only required if animals are to be moved out of, or within an *Infected Area.* It must be obtained from a MAFF or Local Authority inspector.

mow the process of cutting down a crop by hand or by machine.

mower a machine used to cut down a crop. Originally these were based on a rapidly reciprocating bladed mechanism whereas now the more normal type depends upon rapidly rotating blades on a series of drums or discs.

mower-conditioner a machine which *mows* the crop and mechanically agitates it to leave a *swath* which will dry more quickly. Usually used for cutting *herbage* crops before *ensiling.*

muck See *farmyard manure.*

mulch a material which added to the surface of a soil to influence the behaviour of the surface layer of that soil. Mulches would include *straw,* composts, *farmyard manure* and more recently, plastic materials. Mulches may be used to provide control over wind erosion, prevention of excessive soil moisture loss, more even soil temperature conditions and some nutrient supply.

Mule 1. A cross bred sheep produced by crossing a *Swaledale* ewe with a *Bluefaced Leicester* ram. Various alternative breed combinations including use of a *Scottish Blackface* ewe and/or a *Border Leicester* ram may also be referred to as mules. 2. The infertile hybrid produced by crossing a female horse by a male ass.

mull humus the type of *humus* which is well-mixed with the mineral soil below. It is usually less acidic than the contrasting *mor humus.*

multigerm the description of sugar beet *seed* in which several plants arise from one sown 'seed'. The 'seed' in this instance is actually a *fruit* containing several true seeds. These multiple plants must be reduced to one per station for effective crop production. The process, known as *singling,* is usually carried out by hand. Contrast *monogerm.*

multiple suckling a system of calf production in which dairy or beef x dairy cows are used to suckle several (e.g. 4) calves at a time. It is an extension of *double suckling* which requires a 'milkier' cow with a higher *milk yield* to provide for the larger number of calves.

muriate of potash the chloride form of potassium often used as a *fertiliser* when only the potassium ion is required.

Murray Grey a breed of cattle which originated in Australia in the early 1900s from crossing an *Aberdeen Angus* on a very ligh roan *Shorthorn* cow. Colour ranges from chocolate to silver grey. The breed's attributes include easy calving, quick growth and the production of a good *beef carcass.*

mutagen a substance e.g. chemical or radioactive material, which causes *mutations.*

mutation a change in the chemical structure of the *gene.* Mutation is one of the important contributing factors to genetic variation and may lead to a change in the morphology or physiology of the resulting animal or plant which is referred to as a mutant.

mutation rate the frequency of *gene mutations* in a given species in each generation.

mycorrhiza the association between certain *fungi* and the roots of higher plants which can often be beneficial in terms of nutrient uptake by the host plant.

Nardus Nardus stricta a moorland grass sometimes called *mat grass*. It is a common *perennial* grass of wet mountain or moorland forming densely packed tufts of wiry, bristle-like leaves which are extremely unpalatable to livestock. It is a grass of very low grazing value.

National Farmers' Unions the main union is the National Farmers Union of England and Wales (NFU), founded in 1907.   Scotland, Wales and Ulster, each have a separate NFUs. The farmers unions represent the farming interest in public issues. A major function is to negotiate with MAFF about matters relating to farm prices, subsidies, taxes and other matters concerning *agricultural policies*. Since the UK joined the EC in January 1973 their role has become diffused, as they now operate both directly on the UK Government and directly or indirectly through COPA (the EC level equivalent organisation) with the European Commission and other agencies of the EC. In addition to negotiating on behalf of their members, the NFUs provide a range of services, including insurance.

National Institute of Agricultural Botany (NIAB) an organisation responsible for independent testing and assessment of new crop varieties in England and Wales.   Based in Cambridge but with testing centres throughout the country, NIAB carries out numerous comparisons of new varieties. Successful varieties will be admitted to the *National List* and may be sold. The best will be placed on the *Recommended List* and will therefore become more popular with farmers. Apart from the statutory variety testing, the NIAB also runs conferences, publishes a journal and is generally involved in the dissemination of useful information on crop production.

National list a list of crop *varieties* which it is permissible to buy and sell within the EC.

National Parks areas designated by the *Countryside Commission* under the National Parks and Access to the   Countryside Act 1949, with the aim of conserving and enhancing their natural beauty, and encouraging the public enjoyment of these areas. These objectives are pursued subject to the needs of agriculture and the local economy.   The Parks are managed by local planning authorities under the general supervision of the Countryside Commission.   There are ten National Parks in England and Wales covering 1.4M ha.

National Union of Agricultural and Allied Workers (NUAAW)   See *Farmworkers Unions*.

navel-ill a disease of young animals caused by a variety of bacteria and characterised by abscess formation in many organs and arthritis affecting notably the leg joints.   This gives rise to its alternative name: *joint-ill*.

neck rot a storage disease of bulb onions caused by the fungus Botrytis allii.

The stored onions soften and rot internally. There are no symptoms until the fungus on the infected bases of older leaves invades the neck. The fungus is carried internally in onion seeds. Control is by use of *clean seed*, by *curing* the crop prior to storage and by application of *fungicide* to windrowed crops.

neck tether a broad strap which fits around the neck of an animal securing it in a stall. Traditionally used for horses in stables and cows in *byres*. More recently they have been used with *dry sows* in *stall houses*.

necrobacillosis See *orf*.

necrosis death of a cell.

nematode See *roundworm*.

nematodirus disease a disease of lambs caused by parasitic *roundworms* of the Nematodirus species. Infection of pastures occur through eggs passing out in the *faeces*. The eggs hatch and pass through a number of larval stages before they are ingested and infect new *host animals* later in the season. Alternatively over-wintering can occur with lambs then becoming infected in the next grazing season. Infected lambs show reduced growth rates and diarrhoea. Control is by *clean grazing* and drenching.

nest box one of a number of boxes made available to poultry kept on a *deep litter system* in which they may lay their eggs.

net assets total *assets* less current *liabilities*.

net blotch a fungal disease, caused by Pyrenophora teres, of winter barley which has increased in importance with the tendency to grow continuous winter barley. Short brown stripes initially appear on the leaves. These coalesce to form irregular blotches. Control is by use of *resistant varieties* and *fungicide*.

net capital see *net worth*.

net current assets see *working capital*.

net energy (NE) the energy which is available to the animal at the tissue level for *maintenance* and *production*. It is equal to the *metabolisable energy* of a feed minus the *heat increment* of *feeding*. Evaluation Systems based on NE give a very good indication of the energy requirements of an animal for any particular purpose. However, because the ME is used with differing efficiency (k value) for different productive purposes, the NE values of feeds will vary accordingly.

net farm income is derived by adjusting the farm *net margin*. Notably, interest charges are excluded, a *notional* rent (cost) is charged on owner-occupied land, and a notional wage is charged on unpaid manual work carried out by any member of the family, except the farmer or spouse. Net farm income therefore represents a reward to management and the manual labour of the farmer and spouse as well as a return on the *tenant's capital* invested in the farm. This income measure allows the income from owner-occupied farms to be compared with that from tenanted farms. Contrast *management and investment income.*

net margin *gross margin* less *fixed costs,* usually calculated for the whole farm and sometimes less satisfactorily for individual enterprises. Many fixed cost items, such as *rent,* tractor *depreciation* and *interest* payments are not directly associated with individual enterprises, making their allocation imprecise and often meaningless for management purposes.

net present value a criterion calculated in *investment appraisal.* It is the *discounted* expected future *net cash flow* of an investment option summed to a *present value.* This sum is then subtracted from the initial capital cost of the project, to give the net present value.

net worth (or net capital, owner's equity, owner's capital) the total *assets* of a business less *liabilities* to third parties.

neutralising value the ability of a product intended to correct soil acidity to do so. A measure of the *lime* content of various materials.

Newcastle disease an acute, highly contagious disease of chickens and other domestic and wild birds. Symptoms include loss of appetite, diarrhoea and respiratory and nervous problems. Mortality rates are high, particularly amongst young birds. Historically, control was by *vaccination* but introduction of an eradication programme in 1981 led to the UK becoming disease-free and a ban on vaccination. Subsequently, periodic disease breakdowns have occurred. The disease is also known as Pseudo-Fowl Plague and *fowl pest* and is a *notifiable disease.*

New Forest Disease a contagious eye condition occurring in cattle. Most commonly caused by a bacterium Moraxella bovis.

NFU see *National Farmers Union.*

NIAB see *National Institute of Agricultural Botany.*

nicking in animal breeding, the combination of sire and dam with an unexpectedly good effect.

nitrification the process, occurring within the soil, in which ammonium ions are oxidised through nitrite to nitrate ions. There are a number of stages of this process in which soil *bacteria* play an important part. Because it is a biological process, it is influenced by temperature, being inhibited in winter but increasing in spring and summer.

nitrogen a colourless gas which forms four-fifths of the atmosphere. Important as one of the three major plant nutrients, nitrogen is an essential part of plant protoplasm. Nitrogen is taken into the plant from the soil where it is present in many different forms, both organic and inorganic. It enters the plant as either the ammonium or the nitrate ion. Shortages of nitrogen restrict plant growth and plants appear yellow and stunted. In order to avoid restricting yield, nitrogen *fertilisers* are applied to the soil.

nitrogen cycle the system describing the movement of nitrogen in the air, the plant and the soil. The nitrogen cycle gives both qualitative and quantitative consideration to the input and outputs of the system.

nitrogen fixation the process in which atmospheric *nitrogen* gas is transformed into nitrogenous compounds in the soil and therefore available for plant growth. Certain plants, notably *legumes,* have the ability to fix nitrogen by virtue of a *symbiosis* between *bacteria* on the *roots,* and the *host* plant. They are therefore relatively independent of soil nitrogen supply.

nitrogen-free extract the fraction remaining after a *proximate analysis* has been conducted to determine the *moisture content, ash, crude protein, ether extract* and *crude fibre.* The nitrogen-free extract consists mainly of soluble *carbohydrates.*

node 1. The part of a stem from which a leaf arises. 2. A thickening or swelling of an animal tissue e.g. *lymph* node.

nodule the outgrowth on the root of *legume* crops formed when nitrogen fixing bacteria, *rhizobia,* infect the plant and establish a *symbiotic* relationship. Effective nodules, in which nitrogen fixation is taking place, are pink in colour, where ineffective nodules are white.

non-protein nitrogen nitrogen present in a material in a form other than *protein.* Amongst the various forms of non-protein nitrogen are free *amino-acids, nitrates, nitrites, amines, amides* and *urea.* Non-protein nitrogen sources may be used as a *fertiliser* and some (e.g. *urea*) may be used in a limited way as a source of RDP (Rumen Degradable Protein) in the feeding of ruminant livestock.

Norfolk four course rotation an historically important crop *rotation* encompassing a sequence of crops which were complementary. Typically *turnips* or *swedes* would be followed by *spring barley.* That would be followed by *red clover* and then by *winter wheat.* The *cereals* would be cash crops where the two intervening crops, used in situ by livestock, helped to restore *fertility.*

normalised budgeting uses the fixed assumptions of prices, yields and technology to ensure that a true comparison can be made between *budgets* for future and the present farm plans.

North Country Cheviot See *Cheviot.*

notifiable diseases 1. Diseases of animals and poultry which under the Diseases of Animals Act 1950, must be reported to the police if either the owner or the veterinary surgeon suspects them of being on a farm. Amongst the 20 or so diseases listed are *anthrax, Aujeszky's disease, enzootic bovine leucosis, foot-and-mouth disease, Newcastle disease, rabies, sheep scab, swine vesicular disease* and *tuberculosis* in cattle. 2. Diseases of plants, and associated vectors, the existence or suspected existence of which must by law be notified to the MAFF. These include *wart disease* of potatoes and *Colorado beetles.*

notional costs assumed costs imputed in the absence of actual costs, e.g. the wage for manual work carried out by a farmer or spouse, or the rental value of owned land.

NPN See *non-protein nitrogen.*

NSDO the National Seed Development Organisation is responsible for marketing the new crop *varieties* which result from plant breeding programmes in the state funded institutes.

Nubian a breed of goat originating in NE Africa and which has been extensively used in cross-breeding with British goats to produce Anglo-Nubians.

nucleus the chief component of a cell which is surrounded by *cytoplasm.* The nucleus controls many of the activities of the cell. It also contains the genetic material of the cell, in the form of *chromosomes,* and determines the transmission of inheritable *traits* when the nucleus and cell divides. See also *mitosis.*

nucleus herd as part of the *Pig Improvement Scheme* run by the *Meat and Livestock Commission* there are 65 Nucleus Herds (and a number of reserve nucleus herds). These are the best pig herds in the UK and are subject to intensive *performance testing* and *selection.*

nucleus multiplier herd the Nucleus Multiplier Herds operate to multiply the improved genetic stock produced by the *nucleus herds* of the *Meat and Livestock Commission's Pig Improvement Scheme.* As such they form a middle tier in the pyramid structure of pig breeding in the

UK.

nurse cow a foster cow used to suckle the calf of another.

nut a small pellet or cube of compressed *meal* and fed to *livestock*.

oatmeal an animal *feedingstuff* consisting of a *meal* prepared from *oats* from which the *husks* (Z) have been removed to a greater or lesser extent.

oats (Avena sativa) cultivated cereals, the grain of which is used for animal feed and to a lesser extent for human consumption. Originally widely grown as a feed for horses; now because of the decline in the number of horses used for work, the demand is low and oats have become a minor crop. Contrast *wild oats*.

oesophagus the region of the *alimentary* system leading from the mouth to the *stomach*.

oestradiol one of the major group of *oestrogens*. One synthetic oestradiol (17β) has been *implanted* and used as a *growth promoter* in beef cattle until the recent EC ban.

oestrogens *sex hormones* produced by female animals mainly from the developing follicle in the *ovary* and the *placenta* of the pregnant animal. Oestrogens cause the altered behaviour characteristics of the animal at *oestrus* when she is *in heat*. Oestrogens are also involved in the growth and development of the *mammary glands*, the *reproductive tract* and various *secondary sexual characteristics*.

oestrous cycle the regular cyclical changes in the reproductive physiology of the non-pregnant female. The oestrous cycle is under *endocrine* control and consists of a follicular phase under *oestrogen* dominance culminating in *oestrus* when ovulation of the *ova* occur and mating may take place. This is followed by a luteal phase under *progesterone* dominance before another follicular phase is entered. The oestrous cycle of the cow and the sow lasts 21 days and that of the ewe 17 days. Oestrous cycles continue until the female becomes pregnant or, in the case of the ewe which is a seasonal breeder, until the end of the breeding season.

oestrus the period of *heat* when the female is receptive to the male and will stand to be mounted by him. It is a period of altered behaviour caused by the high levels of circulating *oestrogens*. The behaviour of the female becomes more like that of the male and she will mount other females and receive such mountings. She will show increased activity, polyurination, male searching and deviate from her normal well-established routine.

oestrus detection efficient detection of animals which are in oestrus is important, irrespective of whether natural service or *artificial insemination* are to be used, if a high reproductive efficiency is to be achieved. Oestrus detection may rely solely on the keeping of good records and observation of the behavioural changes associated with *oestrus*, or it may make use of various oestrus detection aids such as heat mount detectors, tail paint, milk temperature changes or pedometers.

offal low value parts of a slaughtered animal, including the viscera, liver, heart and parts cut off the *carcass.*

oils the *ether extract* fraction of *proximate analysis* consists of *fats* and *oils* which both consist of glycerides and esters of fatty acids. However, whilst fats are often found in a solid form, oils generally exist as liquids.

oilseed crops general name given to crops grown for their oil-rich seeds e.g. *linseed, soya, rape.* The oil is removed by crushing the seeds and the residual meal is often used for *livestock feed.*

oilseed rape a crop of the Brassica napus family with bright yellow flowers, grown for the oil contained in its seeds. Spring and autumn sown varieties of oilseed rape exist, but the most popular are the autumn sown types. Rape oil is used in the manufacture of margarines, for cooking and for lubrication. Because the crop can be grown and harvested with the equipment used for cereals, oilseed rape has become a very popular *break crop* for cereal growers. Most crops are grown on contract to merchants who are responsible for having the seed crushed to extract the oil (some 42%). The remaining meal of high energy and protein content can be used for animal feed, but only in limited amounts because of its undesirable *glucosinolate* content. Crops may be *dessicated* before harvest or may be *swathed* before combine harvesting.

oilseed residues the residues remaining following the extraction of *oil* from oilseeds. The oilseeds may be of UK origin (e.g.*oilseed rape, linseed)* or may be imported (e.g. *soyabean, sunflower, groundnut, cottonseed).* The oilseed residues are generally high in protein and have a moderately high energy content due to residual oil. They are generally processed to produce a *meal* which is included in livestock *feedingstuffs,* although traditionally they were often fed as *cakes.*

omasum one of the *stomachs* of the *ruminant* to which food passes after microbial fermentation in the *rumen* and *reticulum.* The structure of the omasum is similar to the leaves of a book and it has an absorptive role. It is also called the Psalterium or Manyplies.

omnivore an animal which eats both animal and vegetable material. The *pig* is an omnivore and contrasts with *herbivores* (e.g. cattle and sheep) and carnivores.

once grown seed a term applied to *potato tubers* intended for use as *seed.* They are the progeny of a *certified grade,* grown on the farm under normal conditions and intended for use as seed on the same farm in the following year. Once grown, seed cannot be sold as seed by law, and may be of a lower standard if affected by disease.

on-farm computing the use of a microcomputer in the farm office to assist with payroll, accounting, budgeting, and enterprise monitoring.

Contrast *bureau service.*

on-off grazing a term sometimes applied to *rotational grazing.*

on-the-hoof live animals for slaughter are sold 'on-the-hoof' and the farmer is paid for them on a *liveweight* basis.

on-the-hook animals which although sold live are slaughtered and the farmer paid on a *deadweight* basis dependent on the worth of the *carcass.*

oocyte female germ cell which matures within the *ovary* to form the female *gamete,* the *ovum.*

open cheque a cheque which can be cashed by anyone, but only at the payer's bank. Contrast *crossed cheque.*

opportunity cost see *cost.*

optimisation see *linear programming, production function.*

orf a disease of sheep although goats and cattle may also be affected. It is a contagious virus disease characterised by the formation of pustules on the skin especially in the regions of the lips, nose and feet. Commonly there is secondary infection due to a fungus. It is also called contagious pustular dermatitis and necrobacillosis.

organic to do with carbon containing substances. Usually the carbon is combined with hydrogen and often also with nitrogen and oxygen. Plant and animal tissues consist largely of organic substances e.g. *carbohydrates, fats, proteins.*

organic farming describes systems of agriculture which do not rely upon inorganic or synthesised organic chemicals for *fertilisers, crop protection chemicals, feedingstuffs* or drugs. Instead, the systems are based on *crop rotation* and other natural forms of pest and disease control, and on the use of *organic manures.* Products from such systems can often be sold at a higher price because of the popular demand for natural products, free from potential pollutants and additives.

organic fertilisers *fertilisers* of *organic* origin applied to improve soil fertility. The most important example is *farmyard manure* but others include bone meal, hoof and horn meal etc.

organo-chlorines the general name for a group of *insecticides* which have *contact* action. Examples include *DDT,* Aldrin and Dieldrin which are all of restricted use. *DDT* in particular is very persistent and its widespread use led to accumulation of residues in the *environment* which were widely acknowledged to be unacceptable.

organo-phosphates general name for a group of *insecticides* which are dangerous to use and which have both *contact* and *systemic* action. Examples of the non-systemic chemicals include malathion used for *aphid* control and the systemics include dimethoate which may be used against *aphid* and *wheat bulb fly.*

osmosis the diffusion of a solvent through a semipermeable membrane into a more concentrated solution, thus tending to equalise the concentrations on both sides of the membrane. Osmosis operates in a number of biological contexts: for example, water in the soil passes into the cells of root hairs of plants by osmosis.

outbreeding the mating of individuals which are less closely related than the average of the population to which they belong. Contrast *inbreeding.*

outfall with reference to *drainage,* the place where the main drain or drains discharge water into a water course.

out-of-parlour feeders feeders developed to dispense *concentrates* to selected cows outside the *parlour.* They vary in sophistication but many are electronic and by means of transponders can determine which cows are due to receive extra concentrates and how much each is to receive. Often the daily allocation of concentrates is split over the 24-hour period with theoretical advantages to the digestive physiology of the animal. Also called cow activated concentrate dispensers.

out-of-season breeding techniques which may be applied to seasonal breeders e.g. sheep so that they may be bred from when they would normally be *anoestrus* due to being outside their breeding seasons. Methods involve either the manipulation of light/dark ratios and/or the use of exogenous hormones.

output the physical or financial production from an *enterprise* or farm, arising from the application of variable *inputs* to the *factors of production.*

out-wintered animals, usually sheep or cattle, which are kept outside during the winter as opposed to inside under cover. Contrast *in-wintered.*

ovary 1. The gonad or reproductive gland of the female animal which is a combined exocrine gland producing *ova* and endocrine gland producing *hormones - oestrogens* and *progesterone.* 2. The part of a flower in which the *ovules* are found.

overdominance the superiority of a *heterozygote,* at any given *locus,* over both *homozygotes.*

overhead a *cost* which is not directly attributable to an individual enterprise. Contrast *variable cost.*

ovule the female germ cell which will develop into a *seed* if fertilisation by the male *pollen* cell occurs.

ovum (pl ova) the female *gamete* or egg. A *haploid* cell produced in the *ovary* following *meiotic* division. Fertilisation of the ovum by a *spermatozoan* results in the formation of a *zygote* which develops into an *embryo.*

owner's equity or capital see *net worth.*

own resources of the EC, the label applied to the three sources of finance which funds the *EC budget.* These are the *variable levies* charged on agricultural imports, customs duties on all imports from outside the EC and a share of the *value added tax* revenue in member states. This last element is the largest of the three components, amounting to some 70% of the total in 1988. In January 1986 its limit was raised to 1.4% of the EC *VAT* base. In February 1988, a further extension brought the effective limit up to 2.2% of the EC *VAT* base. See *financial solidarity.*

ox (plural, oxen) a general term for *cattle* of either sex, although it is more specifically used for *steers,* used for draught purposes.

Oxford one of the largest of the *Down breeds* of sheep which is largely used as a *terminal sire* for lamb production. It is characterised by a dark brown face with wool over the forehead and on the cheeks.

oxidation the combination of oxygen with another molecule. The oxidation of organic materials will lead to the evolution of carbon dioxide and other oxides of carbon. Slow oxidation of *fen* soils means that they are gradually disappearing. Oxidation of some farm effluents is necessary before they can be discharged into water courses in order to reduce their *BOD,* or pollution potential.

oxytocin a *hormone* secreted by the posterior lobe of the *pituitary* gland. It has two main physiological roles: one is associated with milk *let down* the other stimulates the contraction of the smooth muscle in the *uterus* at *parturition* to aid the ejection of the *foetus.*

paddock a field enclosed for livestock.

paddock grazing a form of *rotational grazing* in which the total area available for grazing is divided into smaller areas (paddocks) which are each grazed periodically through the season. The paddock subdivisions may vary from temporary fences to more permanent fences or hedges. Normally the aim is to make all paddocks of similar area.

palatability the degree to which an animal *feedingstuff* is attractive to the sight, smell and taste of an animal. Feeds which are palatable will be consumed in preference to unpalatable feeds and may lead to a greater overall feed intake.

palea the inner bract which, together with the *lemma* surrounds the flowering parts in each *floret* in the *inflorescence* of the *gramineae.*

palm kernel cake a *cake,* used as an animal *feedingstuff,* which is derived from the *oilseed residue* of the kernels of the oil palm. It is generally of lower protein and energy content than many of the alternative oilseed residues.

pan a layer within a *soils profile* with root development or water movement. Such a layer may be formed by physical damage during *cultivation* or by the redistribution of chemicals into an impermeable layer by the downward movement of water.

pancreas an organ located close to the *intestines.* Its endocrine function is the production of the *hormone insulin,* whilst its exocrine function is the production of pancreatic juice containing various enzymes which aid digestion.

panicle a form of *inflorescence* in the *gramineae* in which *florets* are loosely arranged. The most common example of a panicle is the inflorescence of *oats.*

paraquat a very popular *contact herbicide* which is active against any green plant material with which is makes contact. Its action is non-selective so it must only be applied to the weeds either by *band spraying* or by careful timing of application. Paraquat can be used as a total defoliant prior to *direct drilling.* Although deactivated on contact with the soil, paraquat is fatal if swallowed and a number of deaths have resulted from the drinking of this product.

parasite an organism which lives in or on another *host* organism from which it derives subsistence without rendering it any service in return. There are many parasites of agricultural importance affecting either animals or plants. Parasites of animals include external parasites (e.g. *lice, ticks)* and internal parasites (e.g. *roundworm, tapeworm).*

Parasites of plants include fungi and bacteria which cause disease such as *rust* or *mildew*, as well as a number of insects or their larvae (e.g. *aphids, eelworms*).

parasympathetic a subdivision of the *autonomic nervous system* which innervates a number of body organs and tissues and generally promotes a relaxed body state.

parent stock the individual plants or animals from which others have been bred and are descended.

park cattle See *British White.*

parlour See *milking parlour.*

parsnip (pastineca sativa) a *biennial vegetable* crop grown for the swollen tap root which is produced after one growing season. They are mostly grown on a market-garden scale for human consumption.

partial budgeting a method of budgeting in which only the costs and returns directly affected by a proposal are considered. It is used to appraise the effect of marginal changes on profitability. Contrast *whole farm budgeting.*

partnership a contractual relationship between individuals collectively carrying on a business with a view to profit. Such a grouping of persons constitutes a firm.

part-time farmer either the occupier of a *part-time holding* or a farmer who has a source of livelihood additional to his farm. Contrast *full-time farmer.*

part-time holding one which provides less than enough work for one person in a year. The amount of work is usually measured in *standard man days* (and the threshold is set at 250) but other measures of business size are also possible. Contrast *full-time holding*, see also *farm size.*

part-time worker a regularly employed worker who completes less than 40 hours per week for an employer. Contrast *full-time worker.*

parturient paresis See *milk fever.*

parturition the act of giving birth to young at the end of *pregnancy.* Parturition is referred to as *calving* in cattle, *farrowing* in pigs and *lambing* in sheep.

passive immunity natural passive immunity is the temporary acquired immunity which a young animal acquires by passage of *antibodies* across the *placenta* or in the *colostrum.*

pasteurellosis the group name for diseases caused by the Pasteurella genus of bacteria. The diseases are often characterised by septicaemia and pneumonia and include fowl cholera, swine plague and haemorrhagic septicaemia of sheep and cattle.

pasteurisation the heat treatment of milk in order to kill the majority of bacteria present without affecting its *palatability* to the consumer. The most commonly used pasteurisation treatment is the HTST method (High Temperature, Short Time) whereby milk is heated to 72°C for 15 seconds and then rapidly cooled to 10°C or less. Most milk is pasteurised at central dairies although some on-farm pasteurisation is undertaken by *producer-retailers.*

pasture a field consisting of a mixture of *grasses* and/or *herbs* being grown for animal consumption. Frequently used to describe fields of long-term grassland which have not been ploughed and reseeded for several years. The *botanical composition* of these pastures tends to be varied and to reflect the management of the field and the nutritional status of the soil, rather than the seeds sown.

pathogen any disease causing micro-organism.

pay-as-you-earn (PAYE) the method of collecting employees' *income tax.* Employers are required to administer the collection of income tax on behalf of the Inland Revenue, at the time wages are paid. All employees, including casual workers, earning more than a given amount, are included in the scheme. Tax adjustments may be made, if necessary, at the end of the tax year.

pay-back period a rule of thumb measure used to appraise investments. The pay-back period is the time taken for the net income generated by a project to pay back the initial capital outlay. The shorter the period, the less risk attached to the investment. There are two major criticisms of the measure. The costs and returns beyond the pay-back period are ignored, and no consideration is made of the time value of money. See also *investment appraisal, discounting.*

pea (Pisum sativum) an *annual legume* crop cultivated primarily for its *seeds* which are used for human and animal consumption but also cultivated for *forage* when the whole crop would be harvested. Pea seeds may be harvested and eaten fresh when immature or they may be harvested immature and *deep frozen* to store for later consuption. See *vining.* They may also be allowed to grow to maturity before harvesting as dried peas. These can then be rehydrated before consumption. The type or variety of pea grown will depend upon the objective of growing the crop. Those for seed production may have a minimum of foliage (see *leafless* *peas*) whereas those for *forage* will be more leafy.

pea cyst nematode Heterodera goettingiana a nematode pest responsible for poor performance of *pea* and *bean* crops which have been grown too frequently. Plants are stunted, yellow and *senesce* prematurely, pods are also yellow and their marketing is impaired. Host crops should not be grown more than one year in four to avoid the problem.

pea moth an insect pest of *peas.* Larvae enter pods and feed on the peas until fully grown causing excessive damage. They pupate in spring, the adult emerging in summer. Control is by *insecticide,* where timing of treatment is very important.

peat an *organic* growing medium formed from the partially decayed remains of vegetation under moist conditions. Peat soils result in areas of flooding e.g. the wet uplands or in the *fens.* In remote areas the high organic content of peat is utilised by burning as a household fuel.

pea weevil insect pest responsible for conspicuous U-shaped notches cut in the margins of leaves of infected plants. During early spring, eggs are laid on the soil near plants. *Larvae* feed on roots, causing crop check whereas adults feed on leaves. Control by *insecticide.* See also *bean weevil.*

pecking order the *social hierarchy* in a group, especially of poultry but also of other animals. The term is derived from the behaviour of dominant individuals pecking subordinate individuals which are below it in the pecking order. Also called the Bunt Order.

pedigree a record of the ancestry of an animal which forms a genealogical tree. Such details of a pedigree animal are registered in a *herdbook.*

pedigree selection the selection of animals for *breeding* on the basis of desirable features or qualities e.g. *type,* of their ancestors.

pedology the scientific study of the soil.

pellet animal *feedingstuff meal* which has been extruded through circular holes of a *cuber.*

pelvic girdle the skeletal framework comprising the *ilium,* ischium and pubis which is attached to the sacrum of the *vertebral column* and forms the firm basis of articulation for the hind limbs.

pen a small enclosure, either indoors or outdoors, in which livestock are kept. The term is also used for those animals kept in the pen and which are sufficient to fill it. Often pens have species specific names e.g. a *fold* for sheep or a *sty* for pigs.

pencil a form or *pellet* of small diameter which is often fed to young animals.

pen mating a mating system where only one male is allowed to run with and mate the females in a specified area, group or pen. Contrast *flock mating.*

pepsin one of the enzymes of *gastric juice* which helps break down insoluble *proteins.*

peptide a substance resulting from the breakdown of *proteins* following the action of *pepsin.* Peptides consist of two or more *amino acids* linked together.

perennial long lasting. In relation to plants, those which remain active for several years.

perennial rye grass (Lolium perenne) is the most popular sown grass in the UK, forming the basis of nearly all grass seeds mixtures. It is a native perennial, renowned for its ability to produce high yields of good quality herbage and to respond to additions of fertiliser nitrogen. A wide range of types of *cultivars* are available from those which are prostrate in habit, well-adapted to grazing, to those which are more erect and better suited to cutting. These facts, together with the relative ease of establishment from seed, account for the popularity of this grass. *Permanent pastures* may also contain varying amounts of perennial rye grass.

performance test a direct comparison between the individual performance or production of a series of prospective parents. It is particularly important in the evaluation of livestock for breeding.

permanent pasture the name given to long-term *grassland* which has not been, or is not to be, ploughed for some years.

permeability of a soil describes the rate at which water enters it. Sometimes called *infiltration rate,* it depends on the proportion of larger pores in the soil surface.

pest any of a range of animals, insects, etc. which are troublesome and cause damage to livestock or crops. The term is sometimes extended to include *bacteria, weeds* and *fungi.*

pesticide one of a range of poisonous chemicals used to kill a specific type of plant or animal *pest.* Thus there are rodenticides for killing rats, *insecticides, herbicides, fungicides* etc. Many of the pesticides are organic chemicals which may have persistent and damaging effects on the environment.

petiole the stalk on which a leaf is carried.

petty cash small amounts of cash, used for cash transactions.

phage See *bacteriophage.*

phagocyte a cell which exhibits amoeboid phenomena and is able to engulf foreign bodies e.g. bacteria as part of the defence mechanism of an animal's body.

pharynx the part of the *alimentary tract* between the mouth cavity and the *oesophagus.*

phenotype the appearance and/or performance of an individual which results from the influence of the *environment* (4) on a particular *genotype.*

phenotypic correlation a correlation between two measurements on the individuals of a population. It may be separated into *genetic* and *environmental correlations.*

phenotypic selection the selection of animals for breeding on the basis of their *phenotype.*

phloem in plants, the tissue in which organic substances are transported from one part to another. Part of the *vascular system.*

phosphate See *phosphorus.*

phosphorus an element which is essential to plants and animals. Phosphorus is applied to the soil in the form of phosphatic fertilisers and is necessary for the root development of plants. It is involved in many other aspects of plant development including crop ripening. Phosphorus is involved in the general body *metabolism* of animals as well as being directly involved in the formation and maintenance of bones and teeth. Good dietary sources of phosphorus are Di-calcium phosphate, *meat and bone meal, milk* and *cereals.*

photoperiodism the response of a plant or animal to changes in day length. Photoperiodism may induce flowering in certain plants and controls reproduction in sheep and poultry which are seasonal breeders.

photosynthesis the primary process in plants in which carbon dioxide from the air is combined with water to produce the carbohydrates needed for plant growth and development. This process is supported by the energy from sunlight, transferred into a usable form by *chlorophyll.* The *carbohydrates* thus produced form the major sources of the diets of humans and farm animals.

pH value a logarithmic index for the hydrogen ion concentration in an aqueous solution. It is used as a measure of the acidity/alkalinity of a solution. On a scale from 0-14, less than 7 is acid, 7 is neutral and greater than 7 is alkaline.

physiology the study of the way in which living organisms, both animals and plants, carry on their life processes.

pick your own a direct sales method where farmers allow their customers to pick fruit and vegetables on the farm.

piebald a term used for animals whose coat consists of two colours, black and white, in patches.

piecework work rewarded by earnings related to measured amounts of work. Many manual jobs on farms have traditionally been done on this basis, and it has been the normal form of employment for casual workers in arable areas. Work examples include hand hoeing sugar beet, hand harvesting potatoes and picking brussels sprouts.

Pietrain a Belgian breed of pig which is being used in *cross breeding* programmes in the UK pig industry because of its good carcass quality.

pig a domesticated *ungulate* descended from the wild boar (Sus Scrofa). Although pig production is conducted throughout the UK there is a tendency towards fewer, larger units and these are mainly located in Eastern England. Total pig numbers are in excess of 8 million with the majority being kept in intensive housing systems. The main pig breeds are *Large White*, *Landrace* and *hybrids* based predominantly on these two breeds.

pig breeding company one of a number of commercial companies involved in the production of *hybrid* pigs, based on the *Large White* and *Landrace* breeds, for the UK pig industry.

piggery any place where pigs are kept. This may range from extensive systems where the only buildings are movable arks or sheds, through strawed yards to intensive buildings with controlled environments. Examples of types of piggery include: *danish, flat deck, harper adams, solari, sweat box, verandah house.*

Pig Improvement Scheme started in 1971 by the *Meat and Livestock Commission*. This scheme is aimed at the genetic improvement of pigs. The scheme is based upon *nucleus* and *nucleus multiplier herds*, and involves extensive performance testing.

pin bones the projections of the pelvis either side of the tail of the cow. Often used as a site for body *condition scoring*.

pine a disease of cattle and sheep caused by a dietary deficiency of cobalt. Often it is characterised by emaciation and *anaemia*. Also known as *bush* *sickness.*

pineal an outgrowth of the *brain* which responds to *photoperiodic* changes and produces the *hormone melatonin.*

pioneer crop a hardy crop used as part of the preparation of land to receive more susceptible seeds. For example, *forage rape* may be sown on land intended eventually for grass. The growth and subsequent *grazing* of the pioneer crop helps to achieve a degree of *cultivation* and improved soil *fertility.* A grass crop would be sown in the following year.

pituitary the major *endocrine* gland of animals, which is situated beneath the *hypothalamus* region of the *brain.* The posterior pituitary which consists of modified nervous tissue produces the *hormones oxytocin* and *vasopressin.* The anterior pituitary produces *prolactin, growth hormone, luteinising hormone, follicle stimulating hormone, thyroid stimulating hormone* and *adrenocorticotrophic hormone.*

placement of *fertiliser* refers to various techniques of application which do not spread the *fertiliser* material uniformly through or over the soil but which concentrate it in strips or layers at specific locations with respect to the crop. For example in a *potato* crop, the fertiliser may be placed below, and to the side of the *seed tubers.*

placenta 1. The apposition of foetal and maternal tissue which acts as the organ for the exchange of gases between the foetus and the dam. It allows for the blood supply of the two to come into close contact without actually mixing. The placenta is shed as the afterbirth in the third stage of parturition. 2. The part of the *carpel* wall to which the *ovules* are attached in plants.

plant growth regulators (PGR's) substances, usually containing *hormones,* which when applied to crop plants in small amount influence the physiology and/or morphology of the plants to the benefit of yield or quality. Examples include *chloromequat* which when applied to *cereals,* reduces *straw* length, helps prevent *lodging* and improves the *harvest index.*

plant population the number of plants per unit area. Usually expresed as plants per m2 or plants per hectare.

plastic drains long lengths of perforated plastic pipe used to transport water in field *drainage* systems. An alternative to *tile drains,* plastic drains are lighter to transport and to handle, and easy to install mechanically.

plate mill a mill used for coarsely grinding grain. It consists of two circulate plates, one fixed and the other rotating. The gap between the two can be adjusted to determine the fineness of grinding.

pleiotrophy the manifold effect of *genes* whereby one gene often influences more than one *character.*

plough the process of turning over or disturbing the surface of the soil in preparation for crop production: also the name of the equipment used to achieve this purpose. See also *mouldboard plough, chisel plough.*

plough pan a layer of smeared soil at plough depth created by regular cultivation to that depth. It impedes water movement and root development.

plumule the rudimentary shoot in the *embryo* of a *seed.*

PML a veterinary preparation on the PML (Permitted Merchant's List) is one which comes within Schedule 1 to 'The Medicines (Exemptions from restrictions on the retail sale or supply of Veterinary Drugs) Order 1984' as amended, and can thus be sold by a retail pharmacy or an agricultural merchant. Contrast *POM.*

PMSG Pregnant Mares' Serum Gonadotrophin is a *hormone* collected from the blood of *pregnant* horses. As a gonadotrophin, it has the endocrine properties of both *follicle stimulating hormone* and *luteinising hormone,* and is used as an *exogenous hormone* for increasing the reproductive efficiency of a number of species of farm livestock, especially *sheep.*

poaching 1. The damage caused by the action of animals' hooves during *grazing* of *pastures* in excessively wet weather. When the soil is made soft by heavy rain, animals' hooves penetrate the surface causing smearing and compaction of the soil. *Herbage* plants may be buried or be smeared with mud. This problem is usually more severe where large numbers of animals congregate for example near gateways, troughs etc. 2. The theft of *game.*

point of lay the state of a *pullet* when it is about to lay its first egg: about 22 weeks of age for modern egg laying *hybrids.*

Poll Dorset a breed of sheep identical to the *Dorset Horn* except that it lacks horns.

polled the descriptive term for an animal which naturally lacks horns. To poll an animal is to dehorn it.

pollen produced by *meiosis* in the male parts, the *stamens,* of the flowering plants, pollen is transferred onto the female parts where it begins the process of *seed* formation.

pollination the process of transfer of *pollen* from the *stamens* of a plant to the *stigma*. *Self-pollination* is said to occur when pollen from the stamens of one flower moves to the stigma of the same flower whereas *cross-pollination* occurs when pollen moves from one flower to another.

polygene a *gene* whose individual effect is small and cannot be recognised in the *phenotype* because it is obscured by other variation.

polyploid the condition of plants which have more than twice the single (*haploid*) number of chromosomes. Plants may occur naturally as polyploids or they may be induced as part of a plant breeding programme. See also *diploid* and *tetraploid*.

polysaccharide a group of complex *carbohydrates* made up of many condensed simple sugar molecules. Examples include *starch*, the main energy storage form of plants, *glycogen*, the main energy storage form for animals and *cellulose*, an important structural material of plants.

POM a Prescription Only Medicine is a veterinary preparation which can only become available for use to farm livestock when prescribed by a veterinary surgeon. Contrast *PML*.

poppy a *weed* of *arable* crops. A member of the Papaveraceae, Field or Corn Poppy (Papaver rhoeas) is a common annual *weed* frequently found in *cereals* before the introduction of effective *herbicides*. Bright red petals make this a prominent weed which flourishes by prolific seed production.

population in animal breeding a group of interbreeding individuals sharing a common gene pool. This may be large - a breed, or small - a closed herd.

porcine of, or pertaining to *pigs*.

pork the meat of *pigs*.

porker a *pig* being reared for *pork*. More specifically a pig being rapidly grown for slaughter at a *liveweight* of 50-65 kg - considerably lighter than the alternative weight classes of pigs. Contrast *cutter, baconer, heavy hog*.

porosity of soils describes the existence of air spaces or pores within the soil. The presence of larger and continuous pores in the soil confers more rapid *drainage* characteristics, allowing more rapid water movement. Porosity depends on *soil texture, aggregation* and the stability of aggregates.

pot ale a by-product from the Scottish whisky making process used for animal feed. It is a syrup resulting from the first distillation and has a high *energy* content. It is generally fed either as part of a *complete diet* or simply poured over *forage* for *ruminant* livestock.

potash a very important plant nutrient and one which is frequently in short supply. Although it is not a constituent of the plant fabric, potassium is important in the synthesis of *proteins* from *ammonium* ions. Crops differ in their response to potash but it is often applied as one of the three major nutrients.

potassium See *potash.*

potato (Solanum tuberosum) a crop cultivated for the *tubers* produced on underground stems. Potatoes are normally *vegetatively propagated* from other *seed tubers* and should therefore be genetically identical. Potatoes are subdivided into groups depending on the likely date of harvest into *early potatoes* or *maincrop potatoes.* The produce may be sold fresh, or it may be canned or dehydrated for later consumption.

potato blight a serious disease of potato crops caused by the fungus Phytopthora infestans. Badly infected crops lose their foliage and cease to grow. *Tubers* may also be infected by spores, especially at harvest time, rendering them unsatisfactory for consumption. Control is achieved by spraying with a *fungicide* at regular intervals through the growing season and especially after a lengthy period of warm, moist weather. See *Beaumont period.*

potato cyst nematode (Globodera rostochiensis or G. pallida) a serious pest of *potato* crop. Small cysts are formed on the roots of infected plants affcting both water and nutrient uptake. The field symptoms appear as patchy areas within the crop where stunted and weakened plants are growing often with wilted foliage. The organism is spread on soil which may adhere to machinery and on infected tubers. Some control may be achieved by *varietal resistance* but the main method is by observing *rotations* involving long period between successive potato crops. *Crop protection chemicals* are available but are expensive and toxic. This pest is sometimes called potato cyst eelworm or simply *eelworm.*

Potato Marketing Board (PMB) set up in 1955, under the *Agricultural Marketing Acts,* the PMB runs a marketing scheme for potatoes, controls the area planted and operates a support buying scheme. Producers are allocated a 'basic area' and quotas are expressed as a proportion of this. The PMB may buy up to 0.5M tonnes of potatoes, marketed after 1st July, in order to support prices. Most support buying is by pre-season *contract,* but there is some scope for direct intervention in regional markets, if prices fall below a specified trigger price. The Board is funded by a levy of £75 per ha on growers, and fines on those who exceed their quota hectarage. The PMB no longer has the right to ban imports.

poult a young *turkey,* specifically one less than 8 weeks of age.

poultry domestic fowl or *chickens, ducks, geese* and *turkeys* kept for *egg* and *meat* production. The term is often used specifically for domestic fowl which are descended from the jungle fowl. Although a number of breeds were of considerable historical importance they have largely been superceded by distinct *hybrid* lines of *layers* and *table birds.* Aided largely by genetic improvement but accompanied by improvements in nutrition and general husbandry all sectors of the poultry industry have increased markedly in efficiency in recent years. The UK industry now numbers approximately 55M table birds, mainly *broilers* killed at about 10 weeks of age and 40M *layers*, largely housed in *batteries,* with an average egg production of 260 per year. The industry is characterised by a small number of large producers.

poussin *poultry* killed for the table at very light *liveweights* e.g. 1kg. Contrast *broilers.*

powdery mildew 1. A widespread fungal disease affecting cereals and grasses. The organism Erysiphe graminis consists of many races, each affecting different crop species. Leaves and stems of affected plants have a white powdery appearance and older infections turn brown. Mildew is commonly found on wheat ears but not on barley ears. The organism tolerates many environmental conditions but infection becomes more severe in dry weather. Infection can be reduced by using *resistant varieties* from different *diversification groups* and by the use of *fungicides.* 2. A fungal disease of *sugar beet* which is commonly found on foliage in dry weather in late summer. The organism reponsible is Erysiphe betae. 3. A fungal disease of *brassica* crops. Erysiphe cruciferarum causes leaf infections of *turnip* and *swede* and other *brassica* crops. White patches are found on the upper surfaces of leaves which may completely cover the leaf and lead to *senescence.*

power harrow a form of *cultivation* equipment in which the vertical tines which make contact with the soil are driven from the *tractor* engine such that they rotate or reciprocate. This action, combined with forward motion of the equipment means that vigorous soil movement takes place and a *seedbed* can be produced in a few operations.

precision chop harvester a type of *forage harvester* in which the *herbage* is finely chopped before being blown into a trailer. The 'precision' derives from the fact that the length of chop can be varied by changing the rate of feed through the secondary cutting mechanism and to a lesser extent by changing the number of blades in that mechanism. These machines have a high power requirement.

precision drill a piece of agricultural machinery used to introduce *seeds* into the soil. Distinguished from other seed drills by the fact that the depth of sowing and the distance between consecutive seeds within the row are precisely determined, precision drills are slower to operate and often more costly. *Sugar beet* and *turnips* are usually precision drilled, but precision drilling of *cereals* has not become popular.

pre-emergence herbicide a *herbicide* which is applied before the emergence of the crop. Such materials may have contact action, killing *weeds* which have grown between the sowing and emergence of the crop or they may have residual action, remaining in the soil to prevent weed *seedling* emergence.

pregnancy See *gestation*.

pregnancy diagnosis the detection of pregnancy or *gestation* in a female. This may be by simple observational methods e.g. the absence of *oestrus* or change in the shape of the *abdomen.* Alternatively techniques using the analysis of *hormones* in milk or blood or *ultrasonics* may be used.

pregnancy toxaemia a *metabolic disease* of unknown cause which affects *ewes* towards the end of pregnancy or *gestation.* It is acute, often fatal and is characterised by a number of nervous symptons and the accumulation of *ketones* in the body tissues, the urine and on the breath. It is associated with a low energy intake in late pregnancy, often when twin lambs are being carried: hence its alternative name *twin lamb disease.*

premium farms those with a considerably higher than average business performance. Such groups are commonly identified in survey reports produced by the *Farm Business Survey* and others.

prepotency the capacity of one parent to transmit more *traits* to the offspring than the other parent.

present value the value now of a sum of money to be received in the future, calculated by *discounting.*

PRID A Progesterone Releasing Intrauterine Device which is used for *oestrus* synchronisation and controlled breeding of cattle. The PRID is impregnated with *progesterone* and *oestrogen,* and is placed in the uterus of a cow in order to manipulate her *oestrus cycle.*

prill approximately spherical particle of *fertiliser* made by allowing a molten solution to fall through the air, solidifying as it falls. Both ammonium nitrate and *urea* are available as prills for use as a fertiliser. *Urea* may also be used in this form for incorporation into animal diets.

primary cultivation the initial *cultivation* of the soil following the harvesting of a crop. Traditionally this involved inversion of the soil using a *mouldboard plough.*

primary host in the *parasites* which require two *hosts,* the primary host is the one in which sexual maturity is reached. Contrast *secondary host.*

producer-retailers term used by the *Milk Marketing Board* for milk producers who do not sell their milk to the Board but sell it directly to the public. The term may be used for the producers of commodities other than milk who similarly sell direct to the public.

production disease See *metabolic disease.*

production function an expression of the technical relationship between the inputs used by an enterprise and the output it produces.Such a relationship can be estimated statistically from survey or experimental data. If prices and costs are known it can be used to find the input levels which maximise profitability.

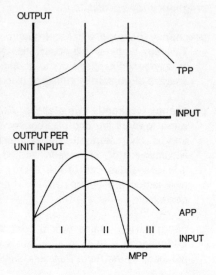

The diagram shows a theoretical relationship between a single variable input and output, labelled Total Physical Product (TPP).Additional information can be derived defining the rational range of input use, which together with knowledge of the price of the product and the cost of the input allows the optimal or profit maximising level of input to be found. It would be irrational to produce in Stage I where the Average Physical Product (APP) is increasing, or to produce in Stage III where the TPP is declining. The optimal, or profit maximising input level, is within Stage II. It is at the point where the cost of one extra unit of input equals the resulting marginal change in the value of the product. It should be noted that the function shown in the diagram exhibits the law of diminishing returns, that is, the marginal physical product (MPP) declines above a given input level (e.g. throughout Stage 1).

production grants direct subsidies paid to farmers to reduce the cost of the inputs they use. The term was particularly applied to the subsidies paid by the UK Government before 1973. Examples were the lime and fertiliser subsidies, drainage and ploughing grants, the Farm Improvement Scheme. Similar subsidies are now used within the CAP under the general title, assistance with *agricultural structures.* The cost of them is shared between the UK Government and the EC budget. See *Agricultural Improvement Scheme, structural policy.*

productivity See *agricultural productivity.*

profile a vertical cross section of a soil which allows the different layers to be identified. See *soil profile.*

profit the total *revenue* from sales of products or the provision of services, less the amount of *assets* and resources consumed in earning the revenues, in a given time period.

progeny offspring or descendants from particular parent plants or animals.

progeny test an evaluation of the *breeding value* of an animal from the performance of its progeny. It is often used when the *traits* on which selection is being conducted can not be seen in the live animal, e.g. carcass traits or lactation performance of bulls.

progesterone one of the female *sex hormones.* It is a *steroid* produced by the *corpus luteum* of the *ovary* during the luteal phase of the *oestrus cycle* when it is concerned with preparing the *uterus* to receive the fertilised *ovum.* If fertilisation occurs then progesterone production from the *corpus luteum* is maintained throughout *gestation* and is supplemented by progesterone produced by the *placenta.* As well as its effects on reproduction, progesterone together with *oestrogen* controls *mammary gland* development.

prolactin a *hormone* produced by the anterior *pituitary gland* which controls the production and secretion of *milk* by the *mammary gland.*

prolific description of a female animal which produces a large number of young.

propagation the multiplication of plants or animals from parent stock. In crop production this term is often used to describe the growing of plants from *seedlings* in a controlled or sheltered *environment,* prior to planting out in the field. Forms of vegetative propagation are used to ensure that small amounts of plant breeders materials are multiplied up to quickly produce more plants for investigation.

prophylactic an agent which tends to prevent or protect against disease, especially against infectious disease. Compare *therapeutic.*

prostate a gland associated with the reproductive tract of male animals and which is involved in the production of *seminal plasma.*

protein essential constituents of living cells (both animal and plant) which are complex organic compounds consisting of carbon, oxygen, hydrogen and nitrogen, which are combined together to form *amino acids.* In turn the amino acids are arranged in polypeptide chains which make up the protein. Some of the proteins are simple, containing only amino acids, whilst other are conjugated or combined with other compounds e.g. fats (lipoproteins) or carbohydrates (glycoproteins). Plant proteins are found in many plant tissues, especially the seeds. When fed to animals these are digested by *proteolytic enzymes* into their component amino acids which are then used within the animal's body to synthesise animal protein such as *casein* (milk protein) or *albumen* (egg protein). Proteins are essential components of animal diets and may be provided from either vegetable sources (e.g. *forage, legumes, oilseed residues)* or animal sources (e.g. *fishmeal, meat and bone meal).* Generally animal proteins are of a higher quality with a better balance of amino acids, especially the *essential amino acids* such as *lysine* or *methionine,* however they tend to be more expensive. See also *crude protein.*

proteolytic said of *enzymes* which act as catalysts to the breakdown of *proteins* into simpler substances - *amino acids.*

protoplasm the cellular contents of all living plants and animals.

protozoa the subkingdom of small unicellular animals of varying shape and complex microstructure. Amongst the protozoa of agricultural importance are those within the *rumen* which bring about microbial fermentation of feed.

proud a term meaning excessively developed or advanced. It may be applied to either crops or livestock. Thus a winter proud crop is one which has come through the winter having made more growth than would be considered usual.

provender an historic term for dry *feeds* used for livestock.

proven sire a *sire* which, as a result of a *progeny test,* has been shown to produce progeny of high potential be it for milk, meat or wool production. The term may be applied to any of the farm species, thus proven boar, bull, ram etc.

proximate analysis the chemical analysis conducted on samples of material e.g. animal *feedingstuffs* which yields information on the amount of six fractions present: *moisture content, ash, crude protein, ether extract, crude fibre* and *nitrogen free extract.*

psalterium See *omasum.*

pseudorabies See *Aujeszky's disease.*

pullet a female fowl in the first laying year.

pullorum disease also called Bacillary White Disease, it is a disease of young chicks caused by Salmonella pullorum. Affected chicks appear drowsy, may develop diarrhoea and often die.

pulpy kidney disease an acute and fatal toxaemia of lambs due to an enteric infection by the bacterium Clostridium perfringens.

pulsator a piece of apparatus attached to a *milking machine* which causes alterations in the vacuum pressure on the cow's *teats* when in operation.

pulses the collective name for the edible *seeds* of *leguminous* crops such as *peas* and *beans.*

pupa the resting stage in the life cycle of an insect. The *larvae* which have been feeding voraciously pupate, and during this stage they undergo a large scale reorganisation from which the adult insect emerges. During the pupal stage the insect does no damage to crops but is difficult to check because of the protective coat.

purchases the value of goods and services bought, excluding any *value added tax* which can be reclaimed.

purebred an animal whose breeding has been pure within a particular breed. Often it is a *pedigree* or registered animal.

pure line a group of animals distinct in *pedigree* over several generations.

purple moor grass see *molinia.*

quarter 1. A butcher's term for the limb of an animal's *carcass* and the adjacent body parts. Thus in cattle following slaughter the carcass is generally halved by cutting along the backbone and then each side is cut into two. Thus each carcass yield two forequarters and two hindquarters. 2. One of the four divisions of a cow's udder, each being a distinct *mammary gland* with its own *teat*.

quarter ill See *blackleg*.

quicklime see *lime*.

quotas physical quantities of production or deliveries which are imposed upon suppliers by some central authority. They may relate to output at the individual farm level (e.g. milk, cereals) or to quantities of product delivered by exporting countries to a particular market (e.g. sugar imports into the USA). The best known quota system in the UK relates to milk production which has been regulated in this way since 1984. Quotas also apply in the UK to potato and sugar production under national or EC regimes. See also *super-levies*.

rabbit a rodent which has been present in the UK since the eleventh century. It's agricultural importance is twofold. Either as a *pest* by grazing cultivated crops e.g. *grass* or *cereals* or as domesticated livestock being reared intensively for meat production.

rabies a *notifiable disease* which affects many animals and is due to infection with a virus. The UK is currently rabies free but elsewhere it is communicable to man by the bite of infected animals.

race 1. A passageway along which *livestock* may be moved, often towards the site of some operation, e.g. an animal weigher or a sheep dip. 2. A vague term used in plant and animal breeding to signify a *breed, variety,* group or class. Generally it implies a common ancestor and the possession of common *traits* or characteristics.

rachis the central axis in the *inflorescence* of a member of the *gramineae* such as *grasses* or *cereals.*

rack 1. A wooden or metal frame from which livestock, especially *cattle* and *sheep,* can obtain *fodder,* especially *hay.* 2. A butcher's term for the neck and spine of the forequarter of a *carcass.*

raddle 1. A harness complete with a colouring or marking device which is attached to a *ram* during the breeding season so that when he mates a *ewe* she is marked on her rear quarters. Different colours can be used to designate either different rams and/or different time periods of the breeding season. Also called a ruddle. 2. A flexible piece of wood used in the construction of hurdles.

radicle the rudimentary root in the *embryo* of a *seed.*

ragwort (Senecio jacobaea) a common *weed* of grassland which has a short thick taproot and flowers produced in the second year. The weed is poisonous to animals, especially when included in hay made from weedy pasture. It can be controlled by *herbicide* but animals must not be allowed to eat wilting plants.

rake 1. To move a *flock* of *sheep* from pasture to pasture e.g. up and down a hill during the day. 2. A pasture. Also called a raik.

ram an entire or uncastrated male sheep. Also a Tup.

Ramblers Association a pressure group which represents those who wish to walk in open space in the countryside. It works to keep open ancient rights of way, by ensuring that they are walked regularly. It takes an interest in all matters of access to open space for recreation purposes.

random mating a situation in which every possible mating in a *population* has the same probability of occurring. It is unlikely to occur in farm animals where controlled *mating systems* are used.

rape (Brassica napus varieties) crops grown for *forage* and for the oil contained in the seeds. Forage rapes are quick growing and provide animal food in late summer and autumn. *Biennial* plants, the leaves and stems produced in the first season are generally grazed off by *folding*. Some regrowth may occur and this too may be grazed later. These crops are lower yielding but quicker growing than *kales*. See also *oilseed rape*.

Rare Breeds Survival Trust an organisation formed with the aim of preserving and encouraging renewed use of breeds of farm livestock the numbers of which have reached such low levels that the survival of the breed is endangered. They see the maintenance of the old breeds as providing a reservoir of genetic material which may be valuable in the future.

rates a form of taxation levied on the occupation of landed property, collected and used by local authorities. Farm homes and cottages are rated, but since the Local Government Act 1929, agricultural land and buildings have been exempt from rates.

ration the feed allocated to an animal often calculated as a summation of its requirements for maintenance and production.

RDP Rumen Degradable Protein is the protein in the diet of a *ruminant* animal which is degraded in the *rumen* to *urea* and *ammonia* and thus becomes available to the *rumen micro-organisms* for their *metabolism*. The RDP becomes incorporated into the micro-organisms but subsequently becomes available to the host animal as microbial protein.

real rate of interest the *nominal rate of interest* corrected for inflation. A real rate of interest should be used in budgeting, to be consistent with the usual practice of ignoring general price inflation.

reap to cut a crop either of *cereals* or of *herbage* prior to gathering it in.

receipts all monies received for the sale of produce, the provision of services such as contracting, and from *subsidies* and grants.

recessive gene the one of a pair which will not be manifested when both are present as it is masked by the *dominant gene.*

reciprocal cross a type of animal breeding where if A and B are breeds, A x B is the reciprocal of B x A. Thus in cattle breeding if the two breeds under consideration are the *Hereford* and the *Friesian,* a Hereford x Friesian is the reciprocal of a Friesian x Hereford, with in the first case the Friesian being the *dam* and in the second case the *sire.*

Recommended List a list of crop *varieties* compiled and published by the *NIAB* for the benefit of farmers. The recommended lists contain details of the main yield and quality characteristics of the varieties based on the results of tests carried out at several locations throughout England and Wales. Only those varieties of outstanding merit are placed on the recommended list.

reconciliation in book-keeping, a process of verifying that the cash transactions (including *standing orders* and *direct debits)* recorded in the office are the same as those recorded on bank statements.

rectum the terminal part of the *alimentary canal* leading to the *anus* through which *faeces* are voided.

red clover (Trifolium pratense) herbaceous *legume* used for *forage.* It has trifoliate leaves and purplish red flowers from which it derives its name. Its growth habit is most suitable for cutting for hay or silage. It has declined in popularity in the UK despite the introduction of improved *diploid* and *tetraploid* varieties.

red meat *meat* is often classified into red and white. Red meat includes *beef, lamb* and game meats e.g. *venison.* Contrast *white meat.*

Red Poll a hornless breed of red cattle which originated in East Anglia as a *dual-purpose* breed but which is now uncommon.

Red Rubies a popular name in SW England for *Devon* cattle due to their colouration.

reducing balance See *depreciation.*

reducing balance loan a *loan* whereby the capital is repaid in equal installments, and interest is charged on the outstanding balance. For example, if £10,000 is borrowed over a period of 10 years, then the annual capital repayment would be £1000 each year. If interest is paid in arrears at 12% per annum, then the interest payable at the end of the first year would be £10,000 x 0.12 = £1200, giving a total repayment of £2200. At the end of the second year, the interest payable on the reduced balance of £9000 capital would be £1080, (£120 less than the first year) giving a total repayment of £2080, and so on in each of the remaining repayment periods.

redwater a disease of *cattle* caused by infection of the red blood corpuscles by the *protozoon* Babesia bovis which is transmitted by a *tick.* The disease is characterised by fever, anaemia and diarrhoea.

reed stomach or rennet stomach See *abomasum.*

rennin an *enzyme* found in *gastric juice* which causes the clotting of the proteins in *milk*. A commercial preparation of rennin (rennet) is prepared from the mucous membrane of a calve's *abomasum* and used in making junket and/or cheese.

rent 1. Generally it refers to the contract rent paid by a *tenant* to his *landlord* on a per hectare basis. 2. There is also *economic rent,* a theoretical concept attributable to Ricardo, who used the term to mean the extra earnings required from a particular piece of land, to bring it into production. See also *share-farming.*

rent review negotiations which take place every three years between *tenant* and *landlord* to fix a rent. If no settlement is agreed, the dispute is taken to a rent tribunal for arbitration. See also *Agricultural Holdings Act 1984.*

repeatability the correlation between repeated performances (e.g. lactations yields) of the same animal.

reproduction the process of generation of new individuals which thus ensures perpetuation of the species. In farm animals reproduction is by sexual means in which the male and the female *gametes* come into contact and fuse to form a *zygote.* In plants, reproduction may be either sexual or asexual (e.g. *vegetative)*

resazurin test a test employed to determine the hygiene status and thus the keeping quality of milk.

reseed to re-establish grassland using proven *varieties* of *herbage* plants in an effort to improve productivity. The term usually applies where established grassland is *ploughed* and *cultivated* to make way for new *pastures.* The term reseed also applies to the process of introducing the seeds.

reserve nucleus herd the tier of the pig breeding pyramid immediately beneath the *nucleus herd.* See *pig improvement scheme.*

residual herbicide a *herbicide* which remains active over an extended period, preventing *weed seedlings* from emerging. Often these materials remain loosely attached to the soil particles near the surface of the soil although some may be *cultivated* into the upper layer of the soil to increase their effectiveness.

residual value of *fertilisers* and *manure* is the longer-term value of nutrients applied but not used by the crop in the season of application. Fertilisers which have a high residual value are those in which the nutrients are present in an organic or other slowly available form. Often they have to be broken down further by soil micro-organisms to release the plant available nutrients.

resistant varieties crop plants which have been bred to show resistance to a particular pest or disease. The resistance may be conferred through physiological or morphological adaptations but the main factor is that, even in the presence of the pathogen, plants do not become infected. The resistance may be specific to only one or a few races of the pathogen concerned. Other races of the same pathogen may exist or may develop which are not restrained by the resistance mechanism.

respiration a physiological process which involves two main stages. External repiration is the process by which living organisms take in oxygen from their surroundings and give out carbon dioxide. In animals this is referred to as breathing. The second stage is referred to as internal or tissue respiration.

restitution See *export refund.*

reticulum in *ruminant* animals the second division of the stomach. The reticulum functions as a microbial fermentation chamber in a similar way to the first stomach, the *rumen.* It is sometimes called the honeycomb stomach as the lining membrane has a honeycomb structure.

retting the process of soaking and separating the fibres from the stems of *flax* plants.

return a term used for a female animal which having been mated has not conceived to that mating but returned to *oestrus.*

return on capital See *financial ratios, rate of return.*

return on tenant's capital a commonly used indicator of farm profitability. It is the ratio of *management and investment income* to *tenant's capital* expressed as a percentage. It is a *financial ratio.*

returns revenues adjusted for *valuation* changes between the beginning and end of the accounting period or production cycle (*revenue* plus closing valuation less opening valuation).

revenue *receipts* adjusted for trade *debtors* at the beginning and end of the accounting period (i.e. receipts plus closing debtors less opening debtors).

reversible plough a form of *mouldboard plough* in which the direction of inverting the furrow can be changed by simple operation of a switch or lever. Thus at the end of a row of ploughing, the tractor can be turned around and can plough in the opposite direction whilst still turning the soil in the same direction as before. This saves time and obviates the need to plough in blocks or sets.

reversion the phenomenon in which, by missing a generation, a particular *trait* in the offspring is unlike the corresponding trait in the parents but resembles the corresponding one of grandparents or more distant relatives. Also called *atavism* or popularly referred to as *throwback.*

rhinitis See *atrophic rhinitis.*

rhizobia bacteria responsible for the formation of root *nodules* on *legume* plants. Different species of Rhizobia infect different legumes but all live in a state of *symbiosis* with the host plant. Carbohydrates from *photosynthesis* by the plant are used by the rhizobia which in turn, are able to fix atmospheric *nitrogen* in a form which can be used by the plant. When not in association with a legume, rhizobia can exist for extended periods in the soil. In those situations where legumes have not been grown before or, in the case of *lucerne* where the appropriate rhizobia are relatively short-lived, *seed* may be *inoculated* with rhizobial spores before sowing.

rhizome a horizontal underground stem produced by some species of plants. The mechanism by which some plants reproduce *vegetatively.* Because the stems can produce both roots and shoots at each *node,* individual new plants can grow from any short section of stem which includes a *node.*

rhynchosporium (leaf blotch) a foliar disease of barley caused by the fungus Rhynchosporium secalis. It is most common in wet seasons and high humidity areas. Infected leaves show pale brown lesions with a dark brown margin, often in the leaf *axil.* Control is achieved by use of *resistant varieties* and/or *fungicides.*

rick a *stack.* Hence rickyard which is a stackyard.

rickets a nutritional disease of young animals characterised by defective ossification and softening of the bones such that the long bones tend to bend and develop swellings near the joints. It is due to deficiency of *vitamin D* and the associated failure to absorb and utilise *calcium* salts.

ridge the name given to the raised line of cultivated soil in which crops such as *potatoes* and *celery* are grown. They are also known as baulks or drills. The term may also refer to the pasture ridges in the *ridge* and *furrow* system. They are visible as regular undulations in the land surface in many old long-term grasslands which may have been produced for *drainage* or may be the result of *cultivation* practices in the Middle Ages.

ridge and furrow see *ridge.*

rig a male animal in which either one (unilateral) or both (bilateral) *testes* have remained in the *abdomen* and not descended into the *scrotum.* The testes retain their normal *endocrine* function and the animal will exhibit normal *secondary sexual characteristics*. However, the bilateral rig will be infertile as the higher abdominal temperatures prohibit *spermatogens*. Also called Cryptorchid.

right of way the public right to pass across land, usually on foot. These, often ancient, rights are being clarified as footpaths and bridleways.

ring 1. A metal circle placed through the nose of an animal for a variety of purposes e.g. a *bull* may be ringed in order that it may be roped and led, or a pig may be ringed to prevent excessive *rooting* behaviour. 2. At a market, a combination of dealers who have a prior arrangement not to bid against one another in order to keep prices down.

ringworm a contagious disease characterised by the formation of ring-shaped patches on the skin of animals, with young *store* cattle being most commonly affected. It is caused by a number of species of fungi.

RNA ribonucleic acid, one of the nucleic acids which play a central role in protein synthesis and in the transmission of hereditary *traits*.

roan the colour of an animal's coat. Most usually a mixture of white and coloured hairs, especially red.

rogueing the process of removing by hand unwanted plants of the wrong type from a crop. It applies to seed potato crops where plants of different *phenotype* are removed to maintain seed purity and to the removal of *wild oats* etc. from cereal crops before they mature to prevent the spread of weeds/seeds.

rolled grain *grain*, especially *barley*, which has been passed through a *roller mill* in order to break the surface of the grain before it is fed to *livestock*. The rolling of grain aids its digestion by *ruminant* animals whilst grain for *pigs* and *poultry* requires greater processing before it is fed and is usually ground or milled to a *meal*. Also called Crushed Grain.

roller mill a machine which prepares *rolled grain* for feeding to *livestock*. *Grain* is partly crushed by passing it between two rotating metal cylinders rotating in close proximity to each other. Also called a Crushing Mill.

roll-over relief See *capital gains tax*.

Romney a breed of polled sheep developed in the Romney Marsh area of Kent, and which is also called the Kent breed. It is a long-wooled breed which is often crossed with a *Southdown* to produce lambs for slaughter. The breed has been widely exported - especially to New Zealand.

Romney halfbred a *cross-bred* sheep produced by crossing *Romney* ewes with North Country *Cheviot* rams.

root 1. The underground parts of plants which provide anchorage and enable water and nutrients to be taken up from the soil. 2. To turn up earth, straw or other materials with the snout. A behaviour often seen in pigs. Also called rootle.

root crops those crops grown specifically for the storage products in swollen roots. Examples include *sugar beet, fodder beet, swedes, turnips.* Although not strictly root crops, *potatoes* are often described as such by the farming and gardening community because the swollen stems form underground storage organs.

rotary cultivator a machine used for *secondary cultivation* of soil to produce a *seedbed.* The tractor power is transmitted to a set of blades attached to a rotor. The soil is then subjected to vigorous chopping action of the blades. The fineness of the *tilth* can be determined to an extent by the relative speed of rotation of the rotor and the forward movement of the machine. Such machines usually have a high power requirement.

rotary parlour a type of *milking parlour* which may be arranged as an Abreast, Tandem or Herringbone but which is characterised by the fact that the cows stand on a raised platform which moves or rotates slowly, with the operator working inside the circle in the case of a *tandem* or *herringbone* but outside with an *abreast.*

rotation of crops. The regular alternation of crops in a particular field to avoid the build up of pests and diseases and the depletion of soil fertility.

rotational crossing a form of cyclical crossing of three or more breeds where each is used in turn to provide the crossing sire.

rotational grazing a form of grazing management in which animals are allocated to a limited part of the total area available. The forage is eaten down rapidly, animals are then removed to allow it to regrow for a period of weeks before being defoliated again. Groups of animals rotate around the area available. Examples include *paddock grazing* and *strip grazing.*

roughage any bulky animal *feedingstuff* which is characteristically low in *energy* but high in *fibre.* Roughages, such as *silage, hay* and *straw,* are important in the *diets* of *ruminant* in that they stimulate normal *rumen* functioning and movement. Roughages may be considered as poor quality *forages.*

Rough Fell a hardy breed of hill and moorland sheep found in Cumbria and N Yorkshire. Their wool, which has to serve a protective function in the harsh environment, is coarse and their face is characteristically dark coloured.

rough grazing unimproved grazing land of poor value which supports a low animal *stocking rate*. It is particularly associated with upland and hill farming, and joins the more productive *in-bye land* surrounding the farmstead. Rough grazing provides grazing for sheep and to a lesser extent beef herds. See also *adjusted forage area.*

round a circular stone wall found in hill and upland areas where it has been constructed to provide shelter for sheep against snowdrifts.

roundworms the nematoda class of worms which includes free-living and parasitic forms. They are parasites of both plants (e.g. *eelworms*) and animals where they may be variously found in the stomach, small intestine or lungs of the *host* giving rise to a number of conditions including gastro-enteritis and *husk.*

roup a general term applied to the symptoms associated with a number of respiratory diseases of *poultry*. It is often used specifically for the contagious bacterial infection, Infectious Fowl Coryza.

row crops those grown in widely spaced rows which enable the passage of men and machinery for the larger part of the season. *Turnips* and *potatoes* are two examples of row crops which traditionally allowed for mechanical *weed* control between the rows.

rumen the first stomach of a *ruminant* which acts as a large microbial fermentation chamber. Morphologically it is an extension of the lower end of the *oesophagus* and is used for the storage of food. However, whilst in the rumen the food is acted upon by the rumen micro-organisms which together with the ruminal movements and the process of *rumination*, aid in breaking down the ingested feed. Some of the nutrients thus made available (e.g. volatile fatty acids) are absorbed through the mucous membrane of the rumen wall, whilst others are digested further along the *alimentary canal.*

ruminant an animal which characteristically exhibits *rumination* e.g. *cattle*, *sheep* and *goats*. They possess a specially adapted, complex digestive system consisting of four *stomachs;* the *rumen*, the *reticulum*, the *omasum* and the fourth or true stomach, the *abomasum*. Because of the cellulase enzymes of the microbial populations within the rumen, ruminants are able to utilise large amounts of fibrous *forages* and *roughages* the nutrients of which are largely unavailable to non-ruminants such as pigs and poultry.

rumination the regurgitation of food that has already been swallowed and its further mastication (chewing the *cud*) before reswallowing. A characteristic of *ruminants.*

runt generally, any small, undersized or stunted animal. More specifically the smallest *piglet* in a *litter.* There are many regional names for a runt piglet.

rural development boards under this general title a number of agencies have been established to attempt to draw together the various public policies pursued in rural areas. The Highlands and Islands Development Board operates in the northern half of Scotland. Another, Mid-Wales Development, operates on a narrower range of policy activities in Mid-Wales. For two years (1970 & 1971) there was a Rural Development Board covering specifically agricultural development in the North Pennines.

Rural Voice a confederation of pressure groups who came together in 1980 to promote their common interest. Participants include the *National Farmers Union,* the *Country Landowners Association,* the *Council for the Protection of Rural England,* the Federation of Women's Institutes, the Agricultural and Allied Workers National Trade Group, the National Association of Local Councils, the National Council for Voluntary Organisations, the Federation of Young Farmer's Clubs and the Standing Conference of Rural Community Councils. Despite the diversity of its membership, Rural Voice has produced agreed policy statements on various matters concerning living conditions and development in rural areas.

rushes plants of the family Juncaceae which are to be found in wet *pastures* and moorlands especially on acid soils. Leaves are cylindrical, spiky and of little nutritional value to livestock. Examples include the common rush, Juncus effussus and soft rush, Juncus conglomeratus.

rusts foliar diseases of plants due to fungal organisms. See *yellow rust, brown rust.*

rut 1. The seasonal period of breeding and associated sexual arousal and activity in male animals of species which are seasonal breeders (e.g. deer). 2. The deep tracks made by machinery wheels in soft ground.

rye (Secale cereale) a crop grown for both grain and *forage* production. It is adapted to grow in slightly acidic, low fertility conditions. The grain can be used to produce flour for rye bread which is of relatively low quality. The *straw* is useful for animal bedding but not for feed. Because of its hardiness, dense tillering and early growth in spring, rye is also used as a *forage* crop for large crops of *silage* or for *early bite.*

ryegrass See *perennial ryegrass* and *Italian ryegrass.*

Ryeland a small, close-wooled breed of sheep which is not very common.

Saanen a white Swiss breed of goat used for milk production.

sac a bag or pouch, within a plant or animal which is often fluid filled.

Saddleback See *Essex* and *Wessex Saddleback.*

sainfoin (Onobrychis viciifolia) a *herbage legume* of minor importance in the UK, found largely in the south and associated with calcareous soils. Two main types of sainfoin exist, a heavy yielding but short lived type and a lower yielding but *perennial* type.

sale and leaseback see *leaseback.*

sales 1. The value of produce sold, net of *value added tax.* See also *receipts.* 2. The occasion when a quantity of goods are sold, for example livestock sales, farm sales.

saliva the watery secretion, produced by the salivary glands, the function of which is to lubricate the passage of ingested food and to aid in its digestion due to the presence of starch digesting amylase *enzymes.*

salmonella a group of *bacteria* all of which are pathogenic to animals, giving rise to a grouping of infectious diseases - salmonellosis. S. dublin and S. typhimurium affect cattle and give rise to a variety of symptoms including fever, diarrhoea, loss of appetite and associated reduced performance. Infection is easily spread by a variety of routes e.g. animal to animal, in *faeces* or *slurry*, contaminated *feedingstuffs* or by healthy *carriers.* Many types of salmonella are associated with food poisoning in man.

salvage value the value of an item of *capital* at the end of its useful life.

saprophyte a *fungal* organism which lives on dead and decaying *organic* matter. Saprophytic organisms in the soil help to break down plant remains into *humus.*

saw toothed grain beetle an insect pest of stored grain. Eggs are laid on stored grain and the larvae feed on damaged grain. The grain heats rapidly in store, becoming caked and mouldy. *Insecticide* can be applied as the grain is placed in store.

scab 1. See *sheep scab.* 2. See *common scab.*

scabies a contagious skin disease caused by a *parasitic mite,* the female of which burrows into the horny layer of the skin. It is commonly called Itch as it often causes the animal to scratch.

scaly leg a form of mange affecting the feet and legs of fowl. It is caused by a *parasitic mite* burrowing in the skin.

sclerotia *fungal* structures which enable an organism to survive difficult environmental conditions. Sclerotia are dense masses of fungal *hyphae* enclosed in a hard coat. Being dark, and spherical, they may occasionally be present in samples of *seed* of similar appearance e.g. *clovers.*

Scottish Blackface a numerically important breed of hill and mountain sheep which are dominant in the hill and moorland areas of Northern England and Scotland. They are small and characterised by a mottle black face which is devoid of wool. It is a horned breed and *rams* have spiral horns. They are very hardy and possess a coarse fleece which is used for carpet making. Flocks are often bred pure in the hills but ewes are then *drafted* to the lowland after approximately 3 lamb crops where they are commonly crosses with either a *Border Leicester* ram to produce the *Greyface,* or with a *Down Breed* (e.g. a *Suffolk*) as a *terminal sire.*

Scottish Half-Bred a type of *cross-bred sheep* which is the result of crossing a *Border Leicester ram* on to a *Cheviot ewe.* The resulting cross has a white face and long ears, with the ewes often being mated to a ram of a *Down Breed* (e.g. *Suffolk*) for lamb production.

scours the common term for diarrhoea which may result from nutritional or infectious causes.

scrapie a chronic nervous disease of *sheep* which is caused by a virus and characterised by various nervous symptoms including an uncontrolled gait. The virus is slow acting but the symptoms become increasingly more pronounced as the disease develops, with death often occurring after a few weeks or months of the onset of the symptoms. Often widespread wool loss occurs wih large areas of skin being exposed and often becoming ulcerated due to repeated rubbing.

scrotum in male animals the sac-like extension from the ventral body wall which contains the *testes.*

season the period of *heat* or *oestrus* when a female animal is receptive to the male.

secondary fermentation in the process of *ensilage,* undesirable secondary fermentation may occur if conditions do not favour the desirable *lactobacilli* but instead other organisms. If this happens, other organisms such as *clostridia* begin to metabolise both the sugars and the lactic acid produced by the primary fermentation. The necessary fall in pH is arrested and may even be reversed causing increased loss of nutrients. Clostridia also metabolise plant proteins, producing undesirable amines and ammonia. The presence of free ammonia in *silage* is indicative of secondary fermentation.

secondary host in those *parasites* which require two *hosts,* the secondary host is the one in which much of the life cycle is completed. See also *primary host.*

secondary sexual characteristics characteristics of an animal which are specific to that *sex* and are due to the actions of the *sex hormones.* Thus in the male, *androgens* promote the development of the accessory reproductive organs, growth and development of hair, developments of the musculature, lowering of the voice and male behaviour. Whilst in the female *oestrogens* and *progesterone* promote the development of the accessory reproductive glands including the *mammary glands,* reduction in growth of the long bones, promotion of fat deposition, reduction in muscle growth, and female behaviour.

security see *collateral.*

sedges (Carex species) plants which are predominantly found in wet places, beside water and on *grassland* soils. They are perennial plants which develop from *rhizomes* and have grass-like leaves. Because they are of low value, they are considered undesirable. They may be controlled by improvemnt of *drainage, liming* and the application of *fertilisers.*

seed in flowering plants the basic unit from which new plants develop. Seeds formed after the fertilisation of flowers in the previous generation, contain all that is required to produce a new plant. The typical seed will consist of an *embryo,* which will develop into the *seedling,* and a store of reserves which will support the seedling in the early stages of growth before it becomes independent. The reserves are usually compact sources of energy and/or protein in a relatively dry, non-perishable form. Such seeds therefore have high nutritional value for humans and other animals. In the case of *potatoes,* the unit often referred to as the seed tuber, is not a true seed but a collection of growing points on a swollen *stem* used for *vegetative propagation.* Some other agricultural 'seeds' remain enclosed in the fruit coat e.g. *sugar beet* and are therefore not true seeds.

seedbed the condition of a soil into which seeds are sown. Normally the aim is to produce a finely divided crumb structure at the surface to provide a satisfactory rooting medium for the developing *seedling.*

seed certification under EC regulations, all seed sold to farmers must be officially controlled, certified, tested, sealed and labelled. For each type of crop, the standards of purity, trueness to type, freedom from pest and disease, presence of *weeds* and other contaminants are specified. Depending on the levels achieved, seed will be sold with particular certification grades. The responsibility for operating the system is shared between *MAFF* and *NIAB.*

seed dressing 1. a material applied to a seed before sowing intended to improve its chance of survival or to increase the rate of growth of the seedling. *Pesticides* are frequently applied either to reduce the risk of soil or seed borne pest or disease attack. They may be applied as a dust which adheres to seed or perhaps as a solution. 2. the cleaning of a seed sample for sale or use. The removal of *chaff,* weed seeds, etc.

seeding rate the weight of seed sown per unit of ground area, generally expressed as kilogrammes per hectare.

seedling a young plant in the early stages of development from a seed. Often consisting of the *cotyledons* and the first true leaves.

seed royalties sums payable to the breeders of registered plant varieties by those holding a licence to reproduce seed. Their existence provides plant breeders with direct incentive to develop new varieties.

seeds mixture the blend of *herbage seeds* used to produce a new *ley.* Unlike most crops, grasslands rarely consist of a single *species* or *variety* but a mixture of several of these. They may include several *grasses* and also some *legumes.* Different mixtures will be chosen depending on the purpose for which the *ley* is required, its expected life, the soil type ,etc.

segregation the separation of the genes, on their chromosomes, of maternal and paternal origin at *meiosis.*

selection in animal breeding the systematic choice of animals from a population to be the parents of the next generation.

selection differential the difference, in a particular *trait,* between the mean of the animals selected for breeding and the whole population to which they belong.

selection index a breeding technique which aims to combine several *traits* (e.g. growth rate, feed conversion and carcass characteristics) into an index. This can be used to guide selection for overall economic improvement.

selection intensity the proportion of the animals of a given generation which are selected to be parents of the next.

selective herbicide a *herbicide* which can be applied to a mixture of crop plants and *weeds* but which only kills the weeds. The selectivity may be achieved because the chemical runs off crop plants but remains on the weeds or because of physiological differences between the plants which mean that only the weeds are destroyed.

self-pollination the process in which *pollen* from one plant fertilises the flowers on the same plant. *Wheat, barley, oats, peas* and *flax* are examples of self-pollinating crops.

self-sown applied to plants which have developed from seeds naturally dispersed.

self-sufficiency at the national level, the concept refers to the extent to which a country feeds itself from the food it produces. Several measures of self-sufficiency are available and in the UK two definitions are used.   First, expressing the value of home food production as a percentage of all food consumed (in 1987 this was 57%).   Secondly, it may be measured as home produced food as a percentage of consumption of indigenous type foods. With this measure the UK was 73% self-sufficient in 1987 compared with 62% in 1974/75.   This increase in self-sufficiency is attributable to the stimulus of higher prices within the EC and the new technology available. See *community preference*. At the commodity level, self-sufficiency is measured by weight. The term may also be applied at the individual farm level to denote the extent to which a farm produces the animal feedingstuffs required for its own livestock or the replacement for its herd, flock etc.   Sometimes applied at the regional level in considering the movement of animal feed from one part of the country to another.

semen the fluid formed by the male reproductive tract which is ejaculated from the *penis* during copulation. It consists of the *spermatozoa* suspended in *seminal plasma*.

semi-leafless peas see *leafless peas.*

seminal plasma the secretions of the accessory sex glands of the male which form the bulk of *semen.*

seminal vesicle one of the accessory sex glands of the male which produces some of the constituents of *seminal plasma.*

seminiferous tubules the tubules, within the *testes* of the male, in which *spermatogenesis* occurs.

senescence the natural ageing of plants which may be accentuated by pest or disease attack. In crops this is often associated with leaf loss.

sepals the *bracts* of a flower which are outside the petals.

separated milk See *skimmed milk.*

septicaemia the invasion of the blood system by *bacteria* and their multiplication therein.   It is often associated with fever, chills and haemorrhaging.

septoria fungal organisms which are important causes of disease in cereal crops. Septoria tritici and Septoria nodorum are the cause of leaf blotch and *glume* blotch. Patches of dead tissue with yellow margins may be seen on leaves later in the season. Spread is favoured by wet conditions. Organisms tend to spend the winter on *volunteer crops* before moving to winter and spring cereals. Control is achieved by a combination of *crop hygiene, clean seed, tolerant varieties* and *fungicides.*

serum 1. The watery fluid which, on coagulation, separates from blood. 2. Blood serum containing *antibodies,* taken from an animal that has been innoculated with *bacteria* or their *toxins.* It is used to immunise animals.

serum agglutinatin test a blood test which tests for the presence of *antibodies* to a disease in an animal's blood. The presence of antibodies gives a positive result to the test i.e. a grouping together of the organisms (agglutination). The test is used to detect *carriers* of *brucellosis* in cattle and pullorum disease in chickens.

serve to copulate with a female (said of a male animal). Also called to *mate* with or to *cover.*

service the act of a male animal copulating with, or covering, a female in *oestrus.*

service crate or service pen a special piece of apparatus or a designated area in which *matings* of farm animals take place. For example, service crates are sometimes used when the male is too large or heavy to be supported by the female.

set an alternative name for the *seed tuber* in *potatoes.*

set-aside a method of reducing agricultural surpluses by paying farmers to remove land from agricultural production. The system has been used in the United States and has been proposed in the EC as a means of managing cereal supply. The limitations of this policy instrument are that it requires specification of the land to be taken out of production and monitoring of the participating farms. Its effectiveness has been questioned in the United States, where farmers have tended to remove their worst land from production, and to use the payments to apply more inputs to the land remaining in production. However, set-aside might help resolve the problem that production *quotas* and *super-levies* cannot deal with, namely that a major share of the cereal production is fed to livestock on the farm on which it is grown. See *Common Agricultural Policy, Extensification Scheme.*

set-on to foster an orphaned young animal onto another female. For example an orphaned lamb may be set-on to another ewe; such a lamb may then be referred to as a set-to.

set stocking a form of *grazing* management in which animals are allowed to graze, throughout the growing season, on the total area of *herbage* available without the use of subdivisions or rationing. Traditionally such systems were operated at low *stocking rates* and with constant *stocking rates* through the season. Now this is often used to describe systems with *continuous stocking* which are more intensive and which allow animal numbers to vary. Contrast *rotational grazing, strip grazing, paddock grazing.*

severe mosaic a virus disease of potatoes caused by potato virus Y. It is transmitted by *aphids* and is very prevalent in some areas causing total loss of yield in diseased plants. Control is by *resistant varieties,* use of *certified seed* and *insecticides* to limit the spread of the aphid *vector.*

sex the sum total of the *traits* or characteristics both structural and functional, which distinguish male and female organisms, especially with regard to the part played in reproduction.

sex chromosome the *chromosome* which is responsible for the initial determination of *sex.*

sex hormones *hormones* produced by the *gonads* e.g. the male sex hormone, *testosterone* produced by the *testes* and the female sex hormones *oestrogens* and *progesterone* produced by the *ovaries.*

sex-limited a term used for *traits* which are expressed phenotypically, in one sex only. An example would be *lactation* which is only exhibited by the female.

sex linked a term used to describe *genes* located on the *sex chromosome.*

sex ratio the ratio of males to females in an animal population.

shank the lower or distal part of the foreleg, from the knee to the foot.

share farming has become a popular form of land holding falling outside the provisions of agricultural holdings legislation. Such arrangments are often reached between a landowner and a share-farmer to avoid the security of tenure provisions contained in the *Agricultural Holdings Act1984.* Unlike *partnerships,* each party runs a separate business, with their own bank accounts, book-keeping and tax returns. The landowner provides the land and usually most of the fixed equipment, agreed proportions of livestock and *working capital.* Growing crops are owned by the landowner but the share-farmer farms the land and harvests the crops. Returns from the produce belong to each party in some proportion to the inputs provided. The farm machinery is usually provided by the share farmer. No *rent* is paid and exclusive right of possession is not given to the farmer.

shear 1. To remove the *fleece* from a *sheep* by clipping or cutting. 2. A term used to approximately describe the age of a sheep in relation to the number of times it has been shorn. Thus a four-shear ewe is between four and five years of age having been shorn four times.

shearing the process of removing the *fleece* from a *sheep* either by hand shearing or usually by machine. Shearing is often carried out by gangs of shearers who start with lowland flocks in Southern England in May and move up through the upland flocks before finishing with the hill and mountain flocks in August.

shearling a young sheep which has been shorn just once.

shed 1. A farm building which may be used for livestock or implements. 2. To separate out one or more animals from a herd or flock. 3. Crops, such as *cereals* or *oilseed rape,* are said to *shed grain* or *seed* when wind or rain causes them to fall to the ground from the ears or pod.

shedder a form of *race* incorporating a swinging gate which assists sheep or cattle to be *shed* (2) from the flock or herd-mates.

sheep sheep (Ovis aries) are small *ruminants* kept throughout the UK under a wide range of environmental and management conditions for *meat* and *wool production.* The total sheep population of the UK is shown as approximately 34M by the *Agricultural Census.* This figure includes lambs and *shearlings* as well as the *ewes* which number about 13M. There are a large number of sheep breeds (approximately 50) and many cross-breds which leads to a very complex industry. However, distinct categories of breeds exist: the Long-wooled breeds, Short-wooled breeds (including *Down* breeds) and the mountain breeds. Many of these are linked together by the *stratification* system which exists. Often, sheep tend to be found in geographic locations when the land is less suitable for alternative enterprises.

sheep carcass classification a marketing service by the *Meat and Livestock Commission.* The aim is to describe carcasses in common terms to provide information to all those interested in sheepmeat trading; farmer, wholesaler and butcher. Carcasses are described by sex, weight, fat level and conformation. Fat classes run from 1 (leanest) to 5 (fattest) with some classes being subdivided (H or L). Conformation classes run from E (extra) to Z (very poor). Classification is used in assessing eligibility for the variable premium of the *sheepmeat regime.*

sheep dip one of a number of approved chemicals used in a *dip* in which sheep are immersed to disinfect them as a control measure against *ectoparasites* such as *sheep scab.*

sheep ked a bloodsucking, wingless fly which lives on the wool and skin of sheep.

sheep maggot fly a type of blowfly which lays its eggs in wounds and the fleece and areas of the sheep's body where *faeces* have collected (e.g. on the wool around the *anus*). When the maggots hatch they bore into the flesh causing a condition known as *strike.*

sheepmeat regime the policy instruments applicable to sheep production, through the CAP. The two main instruments are the Variable Premium and the Ewe Premium. The Variable Premium works in the same way as a *deficiency payment,* bridging th e gap between th e weekly average market price for lambs of required quality and a predetermined weekly Guide Price. The Premium is returnable on sheepmeat which is exported. The Ewe Premium, which is determined annually, is payable on all ewes (including those in LFAs). Twenty-five percent of the cost of payments made is received from the *EC budget.* See also *administered prices.*

sheep pox a highly contagious disease of sheep caused by a *virus* and characterised by eruptions of the skin and mucous membranes of the respiratory tract and *alimentary canal.* It is a *notifiable disease* and infected animals, which often have difficulty feeding and breathing are compulsorily slaughtered.

sheep scab a mange of sheep caused by the *mite* Psoroptes communis ovis. The mite lives on the skin feeding on *serum* from the animal's blood system. The sites of serum removal become inflamed and covered by scabs. The mites secrete a poison which is a powerful irritant which causes the animal to rub itself against any available object. This rubbing causes part of the *fleece* to be lost, often in patches, which exposes the scabs which are then rubbed and become ulcerated. Sheep scab was once eradicated from the UK but re-appeared in 1973. It is a *notifiable disease* and attempts at control and eventual re-eradication are based on a thorough double-dipping programme over the summer to kill the mite.

sheeps fescue (Festuca ovina) a *grass* used for *herbage* production predominantly in *upland* regions. Characterised by fine, needle-like leaves, it is a hardy but relatively productive species which provides good quality *grazing* in comparatively harsh *environments.* Although rarely sown, sheeps fescue is a constituent of many of the better quality upland *pastures.*

sheep sick said of land on which sheep no longer thrive, as through being continuously used for sheep over a number of years there has been an associated build-up of various sheep diseases e.g. *roundworms.*

sheep tick See *tick* and also *ked.*

sheep variable premium See *sheepmeat regime.*

shelter belt a small area of woodland planted and managed to provide shelter for crops or stock. Shelter belts work by reducing wind speeds on land adjacent to them and thus preventing heat loss from soil, plants and animals.

Shetland 1. A breed of rare, largely unimproved *sheep*. Its *fleece* is dense and composed of a fine soft wool which is traditionally used in knitting in the Shetlands where the breed is mainly found. 2. A black and white, dual-purpose breed of cattle originating and now mainly confined to the Shetlands. Although it is hardy it is not a breed of high productive potential.

shippen or shippon an old-fashioned term for a *cowhouse.*

Shorthorn a breed of *cattle,* characterised by short horns, which came about by controlled inbreeding of the *Durham* breed. With time it spread throughout the UK and gave rise to four separate breeds of which the most important are the *Beef Shorthorn* and the *Dairy Shorthorn,* both of which are of considerably less importance than previously.

short-wooled sheep a grouping of sheep breeds which includes the *Down Breeds.*

shots small, young *lambs* which are often *culled.*

Shropshire one of the less important breeds of *Down sheep* although in the past large numbers were exported (especially to North America) from the Welsh Borders where the breed originated. The breed is of medium size and is characterised by its black face and close growing *fleece.*

shrub a *perennial* plant which produces several woody stems at ground level. Some shrubs may provide useful *grazing.* Contrast *herb.*

shut up a *pasture* or *meadow* is said to be shut up if *livestock* are prevented from grazing it in order that sufficient grass growth occurs that it may be subsequently cut for conservation as *hay* or *silage.*

sib a shortened form of sibling: a full brother or full sister i.e. an animal with the same sire and dam as another.

sib test an evaluation of the *breeding value* of an animal from the mean performance of his *sibs.*

side a butcher's term for half of a carcass having been cut along the backbone.

silage a partially fermented forage, stored under anaerobic conditions for winter feeding ruminant livestock. See *ensilage.*

silage additives materials added during the making of silage with the aim of improving the quality of the stored product. Such materials include sources of sugar (molasses to improve the amount of substrate for fermentation), acids (formic or sulphuric to hasten the fall in pH), or inhibitors (formaldehyde to restrict bacterial activity) and inoculants of desirable bacteria (organisms to improve the chances of a good fermentation).

silo a structure used for the storage of crop products. In some instances silos may be adapted to enable the storage environment to be controlled for the benefit of the product but more often they simply offer dry conditions. For example, silos for the storage of grain may have perforated floors to allow for some circulation of air to complete the drying process in the store. Silos are also used to store *silage.* These may be simple *clamps* or more elaborate *tower silos.*

Simmental a breed of dual-purpose cattle from Switzerland. Colouration varies from red to yellowish-brown, usually with a white head and outward and forward curving horns. In the UK the breed has been used both as a cross-bred *suckler cow* and also as a *terminal sire.*

single or singleton an animal born to a female without any *sibs* at the particular *parturition.* Contrast Twin or Triplet. The term is most often used when referring to *lambs.*

single-suckling a system of beef production involving a *suckler cow* in which calves are allowed to suckle their mothers - usually as *singles* (unless she gave birth to twins). Contrast *double-suckling* and *multiple suckling.*

singling the process of reducing the *plant population* in a crop by removing unwanted plants. Specifically in *sugar beet* grown from *multigerm seed,* singling is the process of reducing to one the number of plants at each point in the row. Because of the delicate nature of this work it is usually carried out by hand.

sinking fund provision for the repayment of debt. Regular payments are made to a fund, which is invested to accummulate interest, and is used ultimately to settle the debt.

sinus generally a hollow or lake in an animal tissue which often contains fluid.

sire the father of an animal or the act of fathering an animal.

Sites of Special Scientific Interest (SSSIs) areas designated for conservation by the Nature Conservancy Council (NCC) under the *Wildlife and Countryside Acts.* Local Planning Authorities may not give planning permission for development and MAFF may withhold certain agricultural grants on SSSIs. In the latter case owners or occupiers may receive compensation through a *management agreement.*

six-tooth sheep a sheep which is usually between its third and fourth shearing.

skimmed milk milk from which the cream has been removed. It is sometimes used an an animal *feedingstuff,* either in liquid feeding systems or more usually as a dried powder. Dried skimmed milk powder forms the basis for milk substitutes for early weaned calves and lambs. It may also be used in *creep* diets for piglets or in chick diets. It is a high *protein* feed. Also called *separated milk.*

slaked lime see *lime.*

slaughterhouse See *abattoir.*

slink an animal born prematurely or removed from the *uterus* of a slaughtered female. The term is most commonly used for calves: hence a slink calf. The meat form slink calves is termed slink *veal* and may be used for products such as meat paste.

slip to *abort* or miscarry. Thus a cow which slips her calf is one which has aborted.

slugs pests of many agricultural crops, causing damage by grazing of foliage and consumption of seeds placed in the soil. Mainly affects cereals, grassland, potatoes. Control can be achieved by the use of pellets containing poison.

sluice gate price see *administered price.*

slurry a mixture of animal faeces, urine and water collected from housed animals and normally stored over winter for disposal or use as a fertiliser in the following year. Slurries will differ mostly in moisture content depending on the amount of extraneous water from rain, drainage and parlour washing. They also differ in nutrient value depending upon the type of animals and their diets. Rates of slurry application may be limited by potential contamination of crops such as grassland, and by the environmental nuisance value of the unpleasant smells. Distinguished from *farmyard manure* by the absence of *straw* or *litter.*

smallholding generally a small farm: more specifically smallholdings are provided as farms to rent by county Local Authorities in England and Wales. The number of smallholdings grew rapidly after the two World Wars but the number is thought to be decreasing now. As small rented farms they were intended to provide a way into farming for those with limited access to capital.

smedi an anacronym for a complex of viruses which affect pigs and are associated with stillbirths, mummified foetuses, embryonic death and subsequent infertility.

smuts *fungal* diseases of the *cereals, wheat, barley* and *oats* caused by Ustilago species. The symptoms of loose smuts are that infected ears become a mass of black spores which, when dispersed by the wind infect healthy ears. Covered smuts produce brown or black spore bodies instead of grain in the ears. When infected grain is planted, seed and fungus germinate together and young plants become infected. Seed dressings can be used to achieve control.

Soay a small, primitive breed of sheep originating from the Outer Hebrides. The fleece consists of a mixture of wool and hair, and is of a variety of colours.

social hierarchy the situation within a group in which some individuals are superior (or dominant), some intermediate, and some inferior (or subordinate), this being shown by their behaviour to other individuals within the hierarchy. It is suggested that the social hierarchy operates to confer social stability on a group and ensure that if resources are limiting that their use is maximised from the viewpoint of the species. Also called Bunt Order, Dominance Hierarchy, Pecking Order.

sodium an element which is essential for animals and helpful for crop growth. Some crops e.g. *sugar beet* give higher yields when sodium is applied, even if they have sufficient *potassium,* whereas in other crops, sodium may be substitute for inadequate potassium. If required, sodium can be supplied cheaply as agricultural salt.

software control programs written for a computer. Contrast *hardware.*

soilage See *zero grazing.*

soil profile a description of the various layers of horizon of a soil with increasing depth. Knowledge of a soil profile provides evidence of a soil's present condition but also provides some indications of its development.

soil structure the aggregation of soil constituents into structural units or crumbs. The size, shape and persistence of these crumbs can influence the ability of a soil to support crop growth by affecting water and nutrient supply and by influencing root penetration.

soil texture the result of varying proportions of the different materials which constitute soil e.g. coarse sand, fine sand, silt, clay. Soil texture affects the physical behaviour of a soil e.g. its response to *cultivation,* and the ability to supply a crop with nutrients.

Solari piggery a *piggery* for fattening pigs with pens arranged either side of a central feeding passage within an open-sided Dutch barn. Each *pen* usually has an inner 'kennel' with a hinged roof which can be opened or closed to affect temperature and ventilation control.

solids-not-fat the constituents of *milk* excluding water and *butterfat*. Solids-not-fat thus consists of the milk proteins (*caseins*), *lactose, minerals* and *vitamins*.

solvency a business is solvent, as opposed to insolvent, when its total *assets* are greater than the *liabilities* owed to third parties. See also *balance sheet, financial ratios.*

somatic of the body. Thus a somatic cell is one of the normal cells of an organism's body as distinct from a reproductive cell.

sopralin *soya bean meal* which has been treated with formaldehyde in an attempt to reduce its rumen degradability when fed to *ruminants* and thus increase its feeding value.

South Country Cheviot See *Cheviot.*

South Devon the largest of our native breeds of cattle which are a light red colour. Although originally a *dual-purpose* breed they are now mainly regarded as a *beef* breed being used as *terminal sires.*

Southdown the smallest of the *Down Breeds* of sheep. It is characterised by a campact body covered by a dense fleece of high quality wool. It is early maturing and provided excessive fatness is avoided, produces high quality *carcasses.* The breed has continued to the genetic make-up of many of the other Down Breeds including the important *Suffolk* and *Dorset Down.*

sow 1. An adult female pig from the time she has *weaned* her first *litter.* 2. The process of introducing seeds into the soil which may be carried out by hand but is more usually achieved by *drilling* or *broadcasting* by machine.

sow yards a system of sow housing in which sows are kept in yards often on straw. It is a less intensive and more welfare acceptable system of sow housing than *stalls* or *tethers.*

soya bean (Glycine max) grown for oil and protein for both human and animal feed. The oil for human consumption is removed by crushing, leaving a residue of protein rich meal which is highly valued as an ingredient of ruminant diets. Internationally it is a very important crop although it is not grown in the UK which is outside the limit of its climatic tolerance and must therefore be imported. Nevertheless, the price and availability of soya bean on the world market tends to dictate the price of alternative sources of oil and protein e.g. *oilseed rape, beans, peas.*

soya bean meal an *oilseed residue,* resulting from the extraction of oil from the *soya bean,* which has been ground into a meal. It is high in *protein,* particularly the *amino acid lysine,* and is used as a *feedingstuff* for both *ruminant* and non-ruminant livestock, often in conjunction with cereals which are a major energy source. Most of our soya bean meal is imported from North America.

spay to remove the *ovaries* of a female animal to prevent it breeding or to remove associated *secondary sexual characteristics.*

specialisation the concentration of a business on a few enterprises. In this way economies of size can be exploited through large machinery, simplicity of management is possible, and the comparative advantage of exploiting management and practical skills. It does however increase risk. Contrast *diversification.*

species a term used in the classification of plants or animals to denote a group of closely allied, mutually fertile individuals, showing constant differences from allied groups.

spectrometry the technique of measuring wavelength or energy distribution in radiation. It is used in a number of analytical techniques applied to agriculture.

sperm a common and shortened form of *spermatozoon.*

spermatic cord the 'cord' consisting of the *vas deferens* and associated nerves and blood vessels which passes from the *testes* into the abdomen of a male animal's body.

spermatocyte a stage in development of the male germ cell. It arises by division from another spermatocyte or from a gonocyte and develops into a spermatid which in term develops into a *spermatozoon.*

spermatogenesis the formation of *spermatozoa* through a number of stages from *spermatocytes,* through *spermatids* to the mature *spermatozoa.* Spermatogenesis occurs within the *seminiferous tubules* of the *testes.*

spermatozoa the male *gametes* or sperm. They are *haploid* cells produced in the *seminiferous tubules* of the *testes* following *meiotic* division. Fertilisation of an ovum by a spermatozoon results in the formation of a *zygote* which develops into an *embryo.* (Singular: *spermatozoon).*

sphincter a muscle which by its contraction closes or narrows an orifice or opening.

spikelet in the *gramineae,* the term used to describe the arrangement or grouping of *florets* in the *inflorescence* which always consists of a series of spikelets. The structure of a typical spikelet is shown in expanded form below.

Grass Spikelet

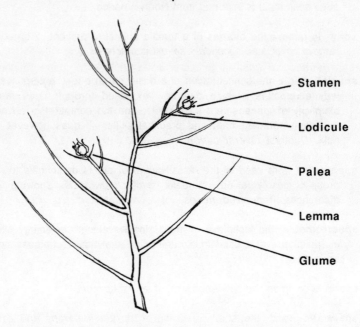

- Stamen
- Lodicule
- Palea
- Lemma
- Glume

spine the spinal column or backbone of an animal which consists of a number of *vertebrae* forming the *vertebral column*.

spot price the current market price of an agricultural commodity. Contrast *forward contract.*

spraing a viral disease of potatoes causing internal marking of *tubers,* which is not visible till tubers are cut. It prevents the sale of infected tubers.

spray a technique and/or a formulation of a chemical which ensures effective application to the crop. Chemicals, e.g. *herbicides, fungicides, fertilisers* may be suspended or dissolved in a large volume of water then applied as small droplets from a set of nozzles to the soil or the crop. Droplet size and the pressure of expulsion may be varied to ensure the most effective dispersal of the chemical. This may be further enhanced by the use of a *wetter.*

spray drift the accidental contamination of *hedges* and adjacent crops which occurs when fine droplets of a *spray* are carried laterally away from the target crop. This may result in damage to susceptible crops and may have considerable nuisance value. For this reason, spraying should not be carried out on windy days. *Controlled droplet* application may also help.

spray irrigation the system of applying *irrigation* water by sprinkler from above the crop. This contrasts with other forms of water application in which channels are used to direct water onto the soil surface from rivers or canals.

spreadsheet a versatile computer worksheet. As on paper, budgets, plans and other numerical problems can be laid out. Its advantage is that it allows easy comparison of a wide range of options. When any specified value is changed recalculation of the entire worksheet is automatically done.

springer a cow almost ready to calve. More commonly called a Down Calver.

stable fly a fly which breeds in rotting organic matter. They are a serious pest of livestock in warm summer months when they bite them, particularly on the legs, in order to obtain blood. This causes restlessness and irritation to cattle, horses and pigs particularly when housed.

stack a large pile of either loose or baled *straw* or *hay.* Hence a stackyard is where stacks are located.

stag a male deer or male turkey.

staggers the common name for symptoms such as giddiness, loss of balance and loss of consciousness in animals. Specific examples include *grass staggers* or *hypomagnesaemia* and *louping ill.*

stalls partitioned compartments in a livestock shed e.g. for cattle, horses or sows.

stamens the male organs of flowering plants consisting of the *anthers* which contain the *pollen* and stalks, the filaments.

standard gross margin (SGM) a financial measure used in the EC farm classification system to classify farms by size and type. SGMs are enterprise *gross margin* norms, estimated by region, expressed per hectare of crop or per head of livestock. Farm business size is defined by aggregating individual enterprise SGMs. Farm type is classified according to the proportion of total SGM derived from main enterprises. See also *European size unit.*

standard man day (SMD) eight hours of work. Norms of SMD requirements for crop enterprises are published, on a per hectare basis, or per head of livestock. Farm labour requirements can be assessed by summing SMDs, but this does not take into account seasonality or the special features of a farm, such as soil type, skill of the work force, desire to work overtime hours, the extent of mechanisation, or the layout of buildings. More detailed approaches to labour planning are the construction of *labour profiles* and the construction of *gang work day charts.* SMDs are also used for *farm classification* purposes.

standard quantities have been used by Governments to limit their liability to farmers through particular subsidy schemes.   In the UK during the 1960s and 1970s, the Government defined a standard quantity to which government support applied and beyond which farmers received only the market price. Standard quantities were revised each year at the *Annual Review.* The method was mainly used for cereals and milk. Under the CAP a similar concept is applied as the threshold quantity.

standing crop a partially grown crop, often *cereals.* The term is used in the context of applications of *crop protection chemicals* being applied to the standing crop or valuations for *tenant right.*

standing order a regular automatic payment made by a bank to a business or individual on behalf of the payer.

staple the staple length of wool is an indication of the average length of wool fibres.

starch a polysaccharide *carbohydrate* which consists of a number of glucose units. Starch is the main energy storage substance of plants being formed as an end product of *photosynthesis.* It is stored in the form of starch granules in various sinks e.g. the seed in *cereals* or the tuber in *potatoes.* Because of the high starch content of many plants which are important animal *feedingstuffs,* starch is an important energy source in animal diets. On digestion, starch is broken down through maltose to glucose. Animals do not store carbohydrates in the form of starch but as *glycogen.*

Starch Equivalent an historic system of *energy evaluation* in which all animal *feedingstuffs* were given a SE value which represented their energy content for fat deposition relative to that of starch. SE systems have now been replaced by systems based on *metabolisable energy.*

steading farm buildings, often including the farmhouse.

steaming up the practice of increasing the plane of nutrition of pregnant dairy cows during the *dry period* as *calving* approaches.   Current nutritional advice favours a more gradual attainment of body condition than that achieved with high levels of *concentrate* feeding by steaming up.

steer a castrated male ox which is over one year of age.   Also called a bullock.

stell an open enclosure built of stone or metal on hill land as a shelter for cattle and/or sheep.

stepped feeding a system of *concentrate* allocation to *dairy cows* which approximates to a Feeding to Yield system in that the level of concentrate fed is increased as milk yield increases in early *lactation* and then is reduced by steps as lactation proceeds and milk yield declines.

stereotype in animal behaviour a response which is shown by an animal, regardless of whether it produces reward or punishment, often being shown to an insoluble problem situation. Stereotypes may be seen with intensively housed farm livestock e.g. bar biting, teeth grinding and head rolling of sows housed in *stalls* or *tethers.*

sterilised milk milk which has been subjected to prolonged heating (e.g. 30 minutes at 110-150°C) in sealed airtight containers to kill off bacteria and prevent further contamination.

sternum the breast bone of animals to which the ribs are attached.

steroid a group of organic compounds which include the steroids, *bile* salts, *sex hormones* and hormones of the *adrenal* cortex.

stigma the part of a plant which receives the *pollen.*

stilbene organic compounds known as phenylethylenes. Two synthetic stilbenes, hexoestrol and *DES* (Di-ethyl-stilboestrol) were used as growth promoters, particularly as implants in steers, until they were taken off the market following concern as to their safety.

stillbirth a young animal which is not alive at the time of *parturition.*

stint a traditional term denoting the number and kinds of animals a common right holder is entitled to put on a *common.*

stock 1. The animals on a farm (*livestock*). 2. The various stores, implements and other equipment on a farm (*deadstock*). 3. The source material or *race* from which a plant or animal has been bred.

stockfeed *feed* intended as a *feedingstuff* for *livestock.*

stockfeed potatoes potatoes, surplus to requirements or a lower quality than required for human comsumption, which are to be fed to *livestock.*

stocking rate the relationship between the number of animals and the size of the area available to feed them. It indicates the intensity of the system. Although not always stated, the term also has a time component i.e. number of animals per hectare per year (or per month). A rather imprecise term, often used loosely by farmers and advisers, since it does not adequately define the type of animal or the potential of the area available for feed. See also *grazing livestock units.*

stockman man in charge of the feeding, bedding and general care and attention of *livestock.*

stolon a stem produced by certain types of plant which is prostrate, at or near ground level. Such stems can produce roots and new shoots from *nodes* which are in contact with the soil. This is therefore a form of vegetative proliferation of spreading. One important plant which produces stolons is *white clover.*

stomach the sac-like portion of the *alimentary canal* between the *oesophagus* and the *intestine.* The site of *gastric* digestion. In *ruminants* the *abomasum* is equivalent to the true stomach of non-ruminants.

stomata the pores on the leaves and other structures of higher plants through which gaseous diffusion can occur. An increase in hydrostatic pressure within the guard cells of stomata will cause the pore to open while a loss of pressure will allow it to close. Stomata are thus very important in controlling the rate of moisture loss from the plant by *transpiration* as they close as a plant begins to *wilt* and open when supplies of moisture are adequate.

storage drying the drying of crop products e.g. grain or hay whilst they are in store. This is usually achieved by forcing drying air through the stored products by a system of ducts or through a perforated floor. They may be in an adapted *barn* or a specifically designed *silo.*

storage feeding a system of feeding occasionally used for *dairy cows* in which the cows are housed all the year round and fed on conserved *forage* usually *silage.* It is a high cost system which allows a high use of resources with a high overall *stocking rate* due to the efficient indirect utilisation of grass by *conservation.*

store cattle cattle grown at a moderate or zero growth rate often on a relatively cheap *ration,* during the winter period, prior to a period of *compensatory growth* following *turn-out* to grass in the spring or introduction to a higher quality diet.

store lamb a lamb fed on a low level of nutrition to achieve zero or low growth rates prior to a phase of more rapid growth during a final finishing period.

stover various types of fairly coarse poor quality *forage* which may be used as an animal *feedingstuff* e.g. cereal stubble, clover hay.

straight an animal *feedingstuff* or a *fertiliser* composed of just a single ingredient.

straight line depreciation See *depreciation.*

strain a *line* of animals within a breed which has been produced with only limited *inbreeding.*

straw with reference to cereals, the stems of the cereal plant together with some parts of the leaves and floral structure, which remain in the field after *combine harvesting.* Straw from the *barley* crop may be used as a low quality feed for livestock and for bedding. *Wheat* straw is normally only suitable for bedding.

straw burning a system of straw disposal in which the straw remaining in the field after a cereal crop has been combine harvested is burnt. Straw burning has been subject to considerable criticism and debate.

straw yard a loose-housing system used for cattle or pigs where the animals are group housed with straw as the bedding material.

strike an infestation of the skin of sheep, especially in the anal region, caused by *blowfly* larvae. Prevention is attempted by *dagging.*

strip to take the last few drops of available milk from a cow's *udder* at the end of *milking.* This last milk is referred to as the strippings and is high in butterfat.

strip cup a small container into which a few drops of foremilk are drawn, by hand, from each of the *teats* of a cow before *machine milking* starts. It is a statutory requirement to take the foremilk in order to check that the milk is not of an abnormal appearance due for example to *mastitis.*

strip grazing a form of *rotational grazing* in which animals are restricted to a small part of the total area available by a temporary (often electrified) fence. New allocations of feed are made available by moving the fence further into the growing crop.

structural policy 1. Initially the policies designed to directly encourage the amalgamation of small farms, to produce an increase in the average size of farm. 2. Under the CAP, the same term relates to all agricultural subsidies and supports, except those maintaining market prices. It thus includes measures designed to promote agricultural cooperation, support for the building of rural roads, investment grants and the like. See *structures policy of the EC.*

structures policy of the EC a Group of Regulations, Directives and Decisions (see *Common Agricltural Policy*) aimed at improving the efficiency of agricultural structures in a number of ways. Directive 797/85 includes farm improvement schemes, assistance to young farmers (under 40), aid for keeping accounts, for farmers' mutual aid groups, for replacement services and for farm management services. The Directive provides further encouragement for training, assistance for *Less Favoured Areas,* for farm forestry development, for environmental improvement in *Environmentally Sensitive Areas.* It also adjusts the previous Directive (355/77) relating to Marketing of Agricultural Produce. The latest Directive (1760/87) introduced the possibility of agricultural *Extensification Schemes.*

stubble the lower stem and root material remaining on a field after the harvesting of crops such as *cereals, oilseed rape, peas* and *beans.*

sturdy a nervous disease of sheep caused by the presence in the brain of a cystic stage of the *tapeworm.* It is also called coenuriasis and has many popular names.

sty a *pen* in which pigs are housed. It is a traditional form of housing consisting of a covered area together with an open run or dunging area. Sties have largely been replaced by more intensive systems of pig housing.

style a stalk-like support on which the *stigma* of a flowering plant is carried above the ovary.

sub-cutaneous situated just below the skin. Thus the sub-cutaneous fat or *adipose tissue* is situated just below the skin of an animal.

subsidy in agriculture any payment by a government to an individual which is not part of the price for goods or service being purchased. The purpose may be to encourage a particular activity or possibly to maintain an individuals income. Agricultural subsidies include those paid to farmers to encourage investment; to exporters, to encourage disposal of stocks; and, less commonly, to consumers to encourage particular consumption (for example the butter subsidy administered from time to time by the EC). See also *farm income problem, direct income transfers* and *production grants.*

subsoil that part of the soil which remains below the normal depth of cultivations but which, nevertheless, is exploited by crop roots. Subsoil frequently begins at a depth of 25cm. The boundary between topsoil and subsoil may be indistinct or it may be clearly marked by the presence of physical damage due to regular cultivation to the same depth. See also *plough pans.*

subsoiler a piece of cultivation equipment with rigid tines which penetrate below the normal depth of cultivation into the soil to break physical or chemical boundaries or *pans.*

succulent feeds animal *feedingstuffs* which have a high *moisture content*, typically 80-90%. However the *dry matter* is often high in *energy* although low in *crude protein* and *fibre*. Examples include the *roots* and *tubers* e.g. *swedes, turnips, potatoes* and certain green *brassica* crops such as *cabbages*. They are often used as a component of the winter diet of *ruminant* livestock.

suckle the act of a young animal removing *milk* from the *mammary glands* of the female.

suckler cow a cow which is kept with the sole intention of producing milk to rear her own calf (as in *single suckling*) or other calves (as in *miltiple suckling*). This contrasts with the *dairy* cow which produces milk for human consumption. Also called a *beef* cow.

suckling pig a young, unweaned, milk-fed *piglet*.

sucrose a storage sugar present in many fruits, sugar beets, sugar cane and *molasses*. It is also called cane sugar.

Suffolk or Suffolk Down one of the larger of the *down breeds* of sheep which was developed in E Anglia and is now the most important being extensively used as a *terminal sire* for cross-breeding and the production of finished lambs. It has a black face and legs which lack any wool cover. It's long body is covered by a close, short *fleece*.

sugar generally, any of the sweet, soluble monosaccharide or disaccharide *carbohydrates* e.g. *glucose, fructose*. More specifically it is the term applied to *sucrose* which is obtained from *sugar beet* and Sugar Cane.

sugar beet a cultivated form of Beta vulgaris grown specifically for the sugar which can be extracted from its swollen root. A member of the Chenopodiaceae family. Sugar beet plants are essentially *biennial* but the agriculturally important harvest occurs after one season of growth when the reserves of these plants have been diverted into swollen tap roots. The roots are harvested in autumn and sent for processing to extract the sugar (16-20% of the weight) to factories run by the *British sugar corporation*.

sugar regime the complex rules under which EC production of sugar is regulated. Production quotas are established and differential levies charged on them. The A quota (1040 thousand tonnes in the UK) yields a producer levy of 2% of the *intervention price*, and the B quota 39.5%. The revenue from these levies is used to fund storage and disposal of the remaining C production. The sugar regime was the first to embody the so-called principle of *co-responsibility*. EC sugar imports are subject to variable levies but preferential arrangements exist under the Lome Convention, for imports of cane sugar from certain African, Caribbean and Pacific (ACP) countries. The sugar regime is self-financing from producer levies, except for the equivalent levy revenue on imports under the Lome Convention, which is funded from the *EC budget.*

sulphate of ammonia an important inorganic source of *nitrogen* used as a *fertiliser.* Ammonium sulphate can be supplied in *granular* or liquid form for application to a wide range of crops. It is becoming less popular now because more concentrated sources of *nitrogen* are available, for example *ammonium nitrate* and *urea.* In addition, ammonium sulphate is recognised as having an acidifying effect on the soils to which it is applied.

sulphur a nutrient required in modest amounts by plants. Until recently, atmospheric pollution from the burning of sulphur-containing fuels provided sufficient for the requirements of crops in Britain. However, levels of such pollution are now falling and some requirements for additional sulphur as *fertiliser* have been demonstrated in the more remote areas.

sulphuric acid a mineral acid used on the farm as a *silage additive.* Although unpleasant and dangerous to use, sulphuric acid is effective at achieving rapid acidification of *silage.*

sunflower (Helianthus annuus) a tall annual plant which is not particularly suited to the UK climate. Mainly cultivated elsewhere as an *oilseed crop,* it may be grown for *fodder* in the UK. However, imported *oilseed residues* may be included in animal *concentrates* particularly for *ruminants.*

super-levy a tax on *surplus* production which sharply reduces market receipts from expanding the sales of particular commodities. Super-levies were introduced with *milk quotas* in 1984 as an essential part of the mechanism. They are set, for the UK, at 100% of the *target price* for milk, but because they are calculated for large marketing board areas, those producers exceeding quota are largely cancelled out by those producing less than quota and the resulting levy revenue is small.

superovulation a hormonally-induced excess *ovulation.* Often the *exogenous hormone* used is *PMSG* either to increase the ovulation rate of sheep or as part of a *MOET* programme in cattle.

superphosphate a chemically manufactured *phosphate fertiliser* made by treating ground rock phosphate with sulphuric acid. The treatment renders the phosphate soluble in water and therefore immediately available for plant uptake.

supplementary rations a term used for *concentrates* fed to *livestock* in addition to their *bulk* feeds. The concept of silage or hay for *maintenance* and supplementary rations of concentrates for *production* has now largely been superceded by an integrated approach to rationing.

supply the quantity of a commodity offered for sale at a given price.

supply schedule the relationship between the price (P) of a commodity and the quantity (Q) offered for sale. It may be represented graphically as shown: the upward slope indicates more will be offered for sale as price increases. Generally, the slope of the curve will be less steep as the period of response increases, i.e. in the long-term greater increase in sales would follow a small increase in price than in the short-term. See *elasticities* and *market equilibrium*.

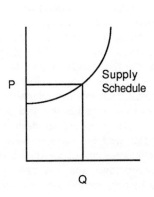

surplus generally, production in excess of the requirements of a particular market. In the EC, surpluses are usually defined, more narrowly, as the stocks of commodities held in *intervention* at a point in time. The term structural surplus is sometimes used to denote a surplus which arises because of the application of too many resources to a particular commodity. See *self-sufficiency, diversification* and *extensification schemes*.

Sussex a breed of red cattle which originated in SE England as the draught breed and which are related to the *Devon* breed.

Swaledale a hardy breed of hill sheep originating in the N Pennines. They have a *fleece* comprising long outer coarse wool over an inner layer of dense fine wool. They are horned with black faces, grey noses and mottled legs. The ewes are used to produce *crossbreds* when mated with either *Bluefaced Leicester* (- *mule*) or *Wensleydale* (- *masham*) rams.

sward the population of *herbaceous* plants which constitute a *pasture*.

swath a row or line of cut plant material. Applies to *herbage* crops which may be cut and allowed to dry in rows (swaths) in the field before storing and to *oilseed rape* which may be dried a little in the field before combine harvesting.

swayback a nervous disease of new born and young lambs characterised by degenerative changes in the brain, causing inability or difficulty in standing or walking. It is associated with a low copper content of tissue in the lamb and its ewe and is preventable by administering copper to the pregnant ewe.

sweatbox a type of *piggery* used for fattening pigs. Groups of up to 20 pigs are housed in closed pens with limited ventilation and thus a high temperature and humidity. Not commonly used in the UK.

swede a *fodder* and *cash* crop of the Brassica genus, they are part of the Brassica napus family. They are grown for the swollen storage 'root' produced in the first season. In fact, it is the upper part of the root which is swollen and much of the storage tissue is above ground. Mature swedes vary in flesh colour from white to yellow, in skin colour, from purple to green and in shape. Normally grown during one season for human or animal consumption during the following winter. Being frost tolerant, they can be left in the field until required but may be lifted and stored in a *clamp*. A popular *fodder* crop in the northern counties of England and in Scotland but reducing in importance because of the improvement in techniques for conserving grass. The crop is normally grown in widely spaced rows and this permits *cultivation* for weed control, so it was traditionally regarded as a *cleaning crop*.

sweet corn a form of *maize* (Zea mays) in which the endosperm in the seed remains sugary to a late stage. This type is used as a *vegetable* for human consumption when the immature cobs are cooked.

swill waste food from kitchens, restaurants and institutions which, following thorough boiling, is fed to pigs. Particular care must be taken with the boiling to ensure that proper sterilisation is achieved as previous outbreaks of *foot-and-mouth disease* and *swine fever* have been linked to swill feeding.

swine of, or pertaining to *pigs*.

swine erysipelas an infectious disease of pigs which in its acute form is a *septicaemia* characterised by fever, patches on the skin and lameness due to arthritis. Also called Diamond Skin Disease.

swine fever a highly contagious disease of pigs caused by a *virus* but usually complicated by secondary bacterial infection. Symptoms are variable but many include fever, diarrhoea, pneumonia and nervous symptoms.

swine influenza an acute viral infection of pigs characterised by fever, coughing and general respiratory distress.

swine paratyphoid a disease of pigs caused by Salmonella cholera suis, and characterised by *septicaemia* in the acute form.

swine vesicular disease (SVD) a *notifiable disease* of pigs which first appeared in 1972. It is caused by a *virus* and the symptoms are identical to those of *foot-and-mouth disease.* SVD is controlled by compulsory slaughter of infected animals and the establishment of *infected areas* to control the movement of animals. Some outbreaks have been associated with *swill feeding* which is still under suspicion as a method of transmission.

symbiosis a situation in which two organisms exist in close association, jointly benefitting from each others presence. An example is the association between *legumes* and *rhizobia.*

sympathetic nervous system the branch of the *autonomic nervous system* which innervates many of the organs of an animal's body including the medulla of the *adrenal* glands and tends to promote a response of Fight, Flight and Fright.

syrup feeds any of the *by-products* of the whisky distilling industry which may be used as animal *feedingstuffs* e.g. *pot ale.*

systemic generally the action of a substance dispersed to all parts of a plant or animal specifically used to describe the action of some *crop protection chemicals.* Once applied, systemic materials often remain active for considerable time periods.

table bird *poultry* reared for *meat* production as distinct from *layers* kept for *egg* production.

tail biting an abnormal behaviour or vice which may be exhibited by *pigs*. Its cause is not known but its incidence appears to be higher in poorly ventilated *piggeries* at high *stocking rates* and is said to be related to boredom. It is suggested that its incidence can be reduced by Tail Docking.

take all a fungal disease of *cereals.* The causative organism, Gaeumannomyces graminis remains on stubbles and roots to infect the next generation of plants. Therefore the disease is most evident when long successions of susceptible cereal crops are grown without a break. The consequent progressively greater drop in crop yields has become known as the Take-all decline. It is difficult to control except by crop *rotation.* It is also known as *whiteheads* because infected plants ripen early, before the grain has filled.

Tamworth a hardy breed of pig which has become quite rare in the UK. It has a characteristic golden-red colouration.

tandem parlour a type of *milking parlour* in which the *stalls* are arranged end to end on either side of a pit in which the milker stands. Thus the cows stand head to tail.

tandem selection a method of selection in animal breeding which involves selection for two alternate *characters* in alternate generations or periods of time.

tapeworm parasitic flatworms which possess hooks or suckers with which they attach themselves to their *host* in the region of the *intestines.* As they grow a chain of segments reaching several feet in length is formed.

tapioca See *manioc.*

taproot a well developed vertical main root which bears *lateral* roots. In agriculturally important plants, the taproot may be swollen as a reserve food store e.g. *carrots, sugar beet.* In *weeds,* the swollen taproot may act as an important means of survival and hence success.

target price see *administered prices.*

target yield the expected level of crop or animal production which is assumed for budgeting purposes.

tariff a tax on imports charged at the frontier. Tariffs may be expressed as an absolute sum (e.g. £5 per tonne) or as a percentage of the value of the item (ad valorem). See also *variable levy.*

TDN an energy evaluation system based upon a summation of the energy contents of the various digestible nutrients. The Total Digestible Nutrient system was quite widely used but has now been replaced by systems based upon either *digestible energy* (pigs) or *metabolisable energy*(poultry and ruminants).

teaser an entire male animal which has had his *vas deferens* surgically cut so that he is no longer fertile but still displays normal male reproductive behaviour. Teasers may be used to hasten the onset of the breeding *season* in ewes, to synchronise *puberty* in gilts or to aid in the detection of *oestrus.*

teat projection on the skin through which the duct system of the *mammary gland* opens. Thus the *udder* of the cow possesses four teats as there are four mammary glands.

teat cup one of the four tube-like projections forming the cluster of a *milking machine.* Each cup consists of a metallic shell containing a rubber liner which is fitted over the teat during milking. A vacuum is applied to the teat end within the teat cup liner by a *pulsator.* The pressure difference between the teat sinus and the open liner results in the opening of the teat sphincter and milk flows out from the streak canal.

teat dipping a method of applying disinfectant to a cow's teat following milking as a precaution against the spread of *mastitis.*

tedder a machine used to agitate a *swath* of cut herbage in order to accelerate the process of drying for *hay* or *silage.*

Teeswater a breed of sheep which is not now very common. Its main use is as a crossing sire to put on to *Swaledale* ewes to produce the *Masham cross-breds.*

teletext see *videotext.*

tenancy succession See *Agricultural Holdings Acts 1984.*

tenant the person who holds the right by *contract* to use land or property for specified purposes, in return for a stated *rent* payable to the *landlord.* See also *Agricultural Holdings Acts 1984.*

Tenant Farmers Association a specialist *National Farmers Union,* formed in 1981, to represent the interests of tenants. It was active in the debate on the *Agricultural Holdings Acts, 1984* and assists members in their dealings with *landlords.*

tenant right the compensation to which a tenant farmer may be entitled at the end of a tenancy. Compensation may be due, from the landlord or sometimes the incoming tenant, for improvements that have been made by the outgoing tenant to buildings, roads, fences etc. See also *dilapidations.*

tenant's capital capital traditionally owned by a tenant rather than landlord (see also *landlord's capital*). Tenant's capital comprises machinery, *breeding livestock, working capital.* It may now also include improvements to buildings, roads etc. contributed by the tenant.

tender a written bid submitted by a prospective purchaser for an item which is offered for sale. Sale by tender is, in effect, a secret auction. It is used in the sale or letting of agricultural property in which the vendor is nevertheless not obliged to accept the highest bid. Alternative methods of sale are by *auction,* or by private treaty. Also a written quotation to provide goods or services.

tenderometer a device for testing the tenderness of peas for processing. Essentially it measures the amount of pressure needed to crush a specific sample. Peas for freezing are only accepted within a very narrow range of tenderometer values because they quickly become too mature. Similar devices exist for measuring the tenderness of meat.

tendon a strong band of fibrous connective tissue which attaches a *muscle* to a bone. It consists mainly of the protein collagen. In meat, tendons are often referred to as sinews.

tendril a slender organ, common in *legumes,* which helps to support a plant by twisting around neighbouring stems or other possible supports. This may be a modified stem, leaf or leaflet.

terminal sire a sire used in *cross–breeding* to produce the slaughter generation of animals. Irrespective of species, a terminal sire should confer the *traits* of high growth rate, good feed conversion and good carcass quality on his *progeny.*

testa the outer covering of a *seed.*

testes the male gonads which have both exocrine and endocrine functions. The exocrine function is *spermatogenesis* and the production of *spermatozoa.* The endocrine role is the production of the male *sex hormones, androgens* of which the main one is *testosterone.* The singular form of the testes is testis or testicle.

test mating a specially arranged mating of a male to either related or *carrier* females in order to detect specific *genes* such as *lethal genes.*

testosterone the main *androgen* or male *sex hormone* which is produced by the Cell of Leydig in the *testes.* It stimulates the accessory sex organs of the male and is responsible for the *secondary sexual characteristics* of the male.

tetanus a disease due to infection with the tetanus bacillus, Clostridium tetani, of which the *toxins* secreted cause painful spasms of muscles, initially in the region of the jaw (hence the alternative name Lockjaw). Death usually follows. Infection usually results from the entry of the bacterium through open wounds from the soil.

tether a halter, either of rope, chain or material which is used to restrain an animal. Thus in a tether house a *dry sow* may be restrained by a tether around either her neck or her girth. There are growing objections to such intensive confinement systems of sow housing on animal welfare grounds.

tetraploid a condition of plant cell nuclei when they contain four sets of chromosomes, i.e. double the normal chromosome number. A tetraploid plant is often larger and more vigorous than the diploid equivalent but otherwise, it is similar in appearance.

Texel a Dutch breed of sheep which is reputed to be a good milk producer but which has been used in the UK mainly as a *terminal sire* because of its lower content of *carcass fat* than would be predicted at a given *carcass* weight.

therapeutic of, or pertaining to, the treatment of disease. Compare *prophylactic.*

thorax the part of an animal's or insect's body between its head and its abdomen.

thousand head kale see *kale.*

thousand seed weight the weight of one thousand seeds from a particular sample. A standard used by farmers and merchants to define the size of seed or plumpness of grain. It may affect the price obtained for seed and is considered when deciding upon a *seeding rate* to use for sowing.

three point linkage the system of attachment of implements to the rear of a *tractor.* It consists of two points of attachment, at or near ground level, one each side of the tractor, and a central point above the other two, connected to the tractor by the top link. Implements can be raised or lowered on this linkage by the hydraulic system of the tractor.

threshing the process used to remove the seeds from the remainder of the mature plant. It involves striking the plant to dislodge the seed and may be done manually in primitive systems or by machine in more developed systems. See *combine harvester.*

threshold price See *administered prices.*

threshold quantity See *standard quantity.*

thrifty a vague term applied to animals which are doing well in production terms.

throwback See *reversion.*

tick-borne fever a disease associated with fever in sheep and cattle which is caused by infection by the organism Rickettsia phagocytophila which attacks the white blood cells of the *host.* It is transmitted by the sheep *tick* (ixodes ricinus).

tick fever See *Redwater.*

ticks a suborder of relatively large bloodsuckling insects which are serious *parasites* of farm *livestock.* Generally they can cause worrying of *stock* and lack of *thrift.* More specifically they can transmit diseases such as *louping ill,* or *Redwater.* Ticks are controlled by the use of insecticides in sprays, dips or as washes.

tied housing a traditional form of tenure for farm workers, who are provided with a house by their employer. The tenancy is defined particularly by the circumstances under which it may be terminated. Roughly half of the full-time male hired agricultural workforce in the UK lives in what is described loosely as tied housing and more formally as service housing. Depending upon the rent which is agreed, the landlord, who is also the employer, may have an obligation to find alternative housing for an employee who wishes to work for him. In this he may be assisted by the ADHAC. Certain types of service tenancy have the full protection of the Rent Act of 1977.

tile drains pipes made of baked clay and used in field *drainage* systems. Supplied in short sections, the tiles are laid end to end to produce a continuous but loosely jointed pipe in the bottom of the trench. The older traditional tiles are being replaced by *plastic drains* in some places and situations.

till to *cultivate* the soil.

tiller the shoots which develop from the buds in the *axils* of the leaves of *cereals* and *herbage* grasses. Tillers become independent and can themselves produce secondary tillers which may produce tertiary tillers. Because the stems are extremely short, this leads to the formation of a rosette or tuft of leafy shoots. In grasses and cereals, the tiller is the basic unit of population.

tillering the process of branching in *cereals* and *grasses.* In cereals tillering occurs over a relatively short period in spring whereas in grasses it is a longer period.

tilth a description of the condition of a topsoil when it is finely divided but firm and in a suitable condition to accept crop seeds. When a tilth is satisfactory, the seed to soil contact will be such that developing seedlings will have a good supply of water, nutrients and air.

time sheet an employee's record of hours worked and job details, used by the employer to calculate wages.

timothy (Phleum pratense) a grass grown for *forage* in the UK. It is a high yielding *perennial* grass often sown and also present in many *permanent pastures.* Timothy is regarded as a palatable grass of high nutritional value, often favoured in *pastures* grown for *hay.* It is often late to start growing in spring and tends to be late flowering producing most of its *yield* in summer and autumn.

tissue respiration See *internal respiration.*

tolerance the ability of an animal or plant to endure adverse environmental conditions or the development of a parasite without showing signs of impaired performance.

tolerant varieties crop varieties which have been bred to continue growing reasonably effectively even when attacked by pest or disease. The variety is not *resistant* to the pathogen and may therefore be invaded, but the biological and economic consquences of the invasion are minimal.

top cross the mating of a male of a particular family to a female of another family of the same breed. The term is also used to refer to the *progeny* of such a mating.

top dressing the application of fertiliser to a crop as it grows rather than to the soil at the time of *seedbed* preparation. Top dressing is used to provide for the nutrient needs of a plant at particular times of the year or stages of growth e.g. *tillering* in *cereals.*

tops the common name for the foliage of crops such as *sugar beet* which may be harvested as a by-product for feeding to livestock. Sugar beet tops may be fed fresh or they may be *ensiled* for feeding later.

topsoil the layer of the soil which normal *cultivations* affect and in which most crop *roots* are found.

total farm area includes the areas of crops, grass, *rough grazing,* woodland, buildings, roads and waste land. It is measured in hectares or acres. See also *adjusted farm area.*

total farm output the sum of enterprise *output,* plus sundry *revenue.*

tower silo a tall, airtight container constructed from metal or concrete sections in which *silage* can be made and stored. The transport of herbage into, and *silage* out of these *silos* is usually automated. The silage is usually relatively dry (approximately 35% Dry Matter) and is chopped into short lengths to facilitate the mechanisation. High quality silage often results, but the cost of tower silos is high and many farmers prefer the cheaper alternatives of *pits* or *clamps*. See also *haylage*.

toxic a term applied to a chemical which is capable of damaging or killing an organism.

toxin a poisonous substance produced by micro-organisms either within an animal's body or in a *feedingstuff* which the animal then ingests.

trace elements nutrients required in extemely small amounts for healthy plant and animal production. Examples include Selenium, Cobalt, Manganese and Boron. Deficiencies or excesses of these elements may lead to plant or animal disorders.

trachea the windpipe of animals which leads from the glottis at the back of the throat to the lungs.

tractor a vehicle used to provide the motive power for transport, *cultivations, drilling, spraying* etc. on the farm. It must be sturdy and able to travel over uneven terrain. Most wheeled tractors have two larger wheels on the rear which provide the power but some have four-wheel drive in which both front and rear wheels are powered. Alternatively, tractors may have tracks instead of wheels. These provide better traction on soil and produce less compaction but are not suitable for use on the roads. Over the years, the average size and power of tractors used has continued to increase.

trade credit a form of short-term credit granted by a supplier. The term is usually payment within 28 days otherwise the price discount is forfeit.

trading and profit and loss account displays opening and closing *valuations, expenses, receipts,*and *profit* (or loss).

trading livestock livestock not kept for breeding purposes. Examples include *store* cattle and *fat lambs*.

trait a term used to designate any form, feature or function of an organism, particularly those which may be part of a breeding programme.

tramlines wheel tracks deliberately created within a growing crop such that all operations involving tractors can be carried out along these same tracks. This has the advantage of minimising crop damage and aids accurate application of *fertilisers* and *crop protection chemicals*. Equipment must be standardised to conform to the chosen distance between consecutive tramlines.

translocation   the transport or movement of materials through the *vascular system* of plants.   Thus a translocated   *herbicide* is one which does not only act on the plant at   the point of contact, but which is taken into the plant and   transported to all plant parts.   This systemic action results in the death of problem *weeds* (e.g. *couch, docks*)   which may normally survive because of underground storage organs.

transpiration   the process by which water is lost from the   leaves and upper parts of a plant into the surrounding air,   largely through the *stomata.*   In the transpiration stream,   water is drawn up through the root system, passes up through the shoot system and is finally lost to the atmosphere by evaporation.

Treaty of Rome   the Treaty signed by Germany, France, Italy, Netherlands, Belgium and Luxembourg which established the *European Community* in January 1958. See *Common Agricultural Policy.*

trichinosis   a disease, particularly of pigs, but other animals including man, can also be infected, in which the larvae of a *nematode* worm, Trichinela Spiralis migrate from   the intestine and become encysted in the muscles of the body.

triticale   a *hybrid* between *rye* and *tetraploid   wheat.* A *cereal,* intermediate in characteristics to its two parents.   Considered a 'new' crop of potential, it is grown in only   small amounts at present but may have a role as a feed grain.

trough space   the amount -of space required by each individual   in a group feeding situation.

true protein   a measure of the actual *protein* content of a material which is obtained by subtracting the *non-protein   nitrogen* from the *crude protein.*   The term true protein is sometimes useful as a number of animal *feedingstuffs* e.g. *silage* contain considerable amounts of *non-protein nitrogen.*

trypsin   an *enzyme* present in *pancreatic juice* which   breaks down *proteins* to *peptides.* The seeds of some grain legumes e.g. *soya beans* and kidney beans contain trypsin inhibitors which inhibit the action of trypsin with the   result of severe digestive disorders.   Trypsin inhibitors are destroyed by heat treatment.

T-sum   a *grassland* management aid, aimed at predicting the optimum time for the application of spring *nitrogen fertiliser* to grassland.   Daily records of temperature are   used to calculate the extent to which temperature exceeds a base of $0^\circ C$. Daily values are accumulated from 1 January.   The optimum time for application is said to be when a total of 200 day/degrees have been accumulated.

tuber the swollen tip of an underground stem of the potato plant (Solanum tuberosum) which is rich in starch. Because it is underground, often incorrectly referred to as a root.

tuberculosis infection of the body of many animals by Mycobacterium tuberculosis, especially of the lungs, lymphatic glands and joints. Of the farm species, cattle and pigs are particularly affected and show a characteristic development of tubercules in body tissues, fever, loss of appetite and loss of body weight.

tup 1. An uncastrated adult male sheep. Also a ram. 2. The act of the ram mating the ewe.

tupping time the mating season for sheep: the part of the breeding season when the tups are allowed to run with the ewes and mate them.

turkey a large type of *poultry* native to N America which is kept for its meat production mainly by specialist large scale producers.

turn-out the time, usually in the spring, when *ruminant* animals which have been housed during the winter, largely on *conserved* feeds are turned outside on to a fresh grass, rye or other fresh forage.

turnover the total *income,* derived from sales and other sources, received by a business during the *accounting period.*

twin lamb disease See *pregnancy toxaemia.*

twitch see *couch grass.*

two pasture system a farm of *grazing* management appropriate for upland farms in which a relatively small area of good quality grazing pasture is used to provide high quality *herbage* to animals at critical stages in their life cycles e.g. *sheep* after *lambing.* At other less critical times, lower quality moorland vegetation is sufficient to provide the nutritional needs.

two sward system a form of grassland management on lowland farms where the areas of crops for cutting are kept separate from those to be used for *grazing.* This allows specialist crops to be grown or management practices to be adopted and contrasts with situations where areas of *grassland* are used for both cutting and grazing on some occasions.

type a subjective assessment of *conformation* in the live animal, particularly those being assessed as potential breeders. Type has been important in the choice of parents in farm *livestock* breeding often at the expense of reduced genetic progress in production traits. The *linear classification* of the MMB aims to make type more objective and quantitative.

udder the sac-like structure which contains the four *mammary glands* of the cow.

UDP Undegradable Protein is that fraction of the *crude protein* in the diet of a *ruminant* which when it enters the *rumen* is not degraded to become available to the rumen micro-organisms but which passes through to the *abomasum* and small intestine for normal proteolytic digestion to occur.

UKASTA an association of agricultural supply industries representing their interests at the national level. See also *farmers groups.*

ulcerative stomatitis See *orf.*

ultra heat treated milk UHT milk has been flow heated to 130°C so that it is thoroughly sterilised and all *bacteria* and other micro-organisms are killed.   It is sold in   sterile cartons and can be stored, unopened indefinitely.   There are suggestions that the heat treatment may destroy some vitamins and proteins and affect palatability.

ultrasonics the study and application of ultrasonic sound and vibrations. Ultrasonics, frequencies above the upper limit of man's normal hearing, have a number of agricultural uses e.g. *pregnancy diagnosis.*

undersow to sow a *herbage* crop along with another *forage* crop or a cash crop in order that both should develop simultaneously.   Early removal of the *cover* crop allows the herbage crop to develop later in the season. The advantage of undersowing is that the low productivity during the establishment of the herbage crop is compensated by the yield of the cover crop.

undulant fever a disease of man characterised by recurrent fever which is caused by the same organism Brucella obortus that is responsible for *brucellosis* in cattle. Man may contract the disease either by contact with infected cattle   or by drinking unpasteurised milk and thus farm workers are exposed to greater risk than the general public. Undulant fever may also be caused by the related organism B. melitensis.

ungulate a term which covers a multitude of hoofed grazing animals whose common features (e.g. grinding teeth, muscular, articular and alimentary adaptations, long   necks and social organisation) probably arose independently in response to the same conditions. Cattle, sheep, goats, deer, pigs and horses are all ungulates.

unit an imperial measure of weight applied to *fertiliser* ingredients. A unit is equivalent to one hundredth of one hundredweight or 1.12lb. Purchased fertilisers usually   carry the details of the three major nutrients *nitrogen, phosphate* and *potash* expressed as unit values. This enables farmers to calculate easily the amount of each element being applied.

upland farms a broad categorisation of farm type, distinguished from hill farms by a higher proportion of *in-bye* land to *rough grazing* land, a lower reliance on sheep production and higher stocking densities. Production is mainly from livestock rearing. See also *Less Favoured Areas.*

urban fringe a loose term to define the area of land surrounding substantial urban settlements in which there is likely to be some impact of the urban population on farming and land use. Urban fringe land which is not designated as *green belt* is likely to be taken over for building. In parts of the urban fringe problems of trespass and vandalism may limit the forms of agricultural activity which can be carried out.

urea an organic compound rich in nitrogen (46%), available in either *prilled* or liquid form it may be used as a *fertiliser* or as a source of non-protein nitrogen in livestock feeds.

urine the excretory fluid produced by the kidneys, stored in the bladder and then passed to the exterior through either the *penis* (in the male) or the *vulva* (in the female).

uterus the muscular part of the reproductive tract of the female between the oviduct and the cervix. The walls of the uterus are capable of considerable expansion. It is in the uterus of the *pregnant* female that a *placenta* forms following the implantation of the *zygote* which develops into an *embryo* and *foetus.*

vaccination the inoculation of an animal with a preparation (or *vaccine)* containing either dead or attenuated (living but weakened) *antigens* so that the animal produces *antibodies* to protect itself against the disease specific to the antigen in question.

vaccine a preparation of any micro-organisms or virus, either killed or treated so as to be weakened (attenuated), for introduction *(vaccination)* into the body of an animal in order to stimulate the production of *antibodies* to the micro-organisms introduced. This confers immunity against any subsequent infection by the same type of micro-organism.

valuation the valuing of *assets* for accounting purposes. Three concepts are used in making farm valuations: 1. Net realisable value, which is the current or future expected market value less any marketing and storage costs still to be incurred. 2. Historic cost which is the initial price less *depreciation* to the date of valuation. 3. Replacement cost which is the current cost and particularly appropriate in times of high inflation. The basis of valuation chosen depends on the specific purpose for which it is made.

value added tax (VAT) an indirect tax borne by the final consumer of a product or service, but collected by businesses on behalf of the government. The standard rate of VAT is 15%, but most farm produce is zero rated whereas wages, land and building sales are exempt. VAT paid by businesses for inputs used to produce standard rated and zero rated output can be claimed back from the Customs and Excise, but VAT on inputs used to produce output which is exempt cannot be claimed.

variable costs vary with the level of production and with the size of *enterprise.* Characteristically, they can readily be apportioned to individual enterprises. Examples include the costs of seed, fertiliser, sprays, feedingstuffs and casual labour. See also *fixed costs, gross margin.*

variable levy a tax applied to imports into a country, which varies in order to bring the import price up to a given level. Such a levy has been used by the UK under its own agricultural policies before 1973 and has been a major instrument within the EC. Under the CAP the revenue from such levies is collected by EC member states and is then transmitted to Brussels as part of the Community's *own resources.* See also *administered prices.*

variety in agricultural terms a distinctly different and unique type of crop plant, which breeds true to give like individuals. Plant breeders seek to develop new varieties of the common crop plants which have improved yield or quality characteristics.

vascular system a finely divided set of tubes through which important fluids are transported. In plants, the *phloem* and *xylem* vessels constitute the vascular system through which water and nutrients are transported. In animals the *veins* and *arteries* perform a similar function in the transport of *blood.*

vas deferens a duct leading from the *testes* to the ejaculator organ of the male, the *penis.*

vasectomised See *teaser.*

vasopressin a *hormone* produced by the posterior *pituitary* which is involved in the control of water balance in an animal's body by its anti-diuretic action.

veal *meat* from calves slaughtered at young ages, often less than 15 weeks of age. Traditional systems of veal production involved the keeping of calves on intensive systems in *crates* which restricted movement and with reduced lighting and iron free diets in the belief that this kept the meat white. Today, systems of veal production are more welfare acceptable.

vector an agent of transportation of transfer. Frequently this term applies to the organisms responsible for the spread of pests, disease or weed seeds. Many vectors perform this function inadvertently as a result of some other primary activity. For example, *aphids* may spread *virus yellows* of *sugar beet*, as they move from infected to clean plants to feed on the cell sap.

vegetable crops crops grown for direct human consumption. These include *peas, beans, carrots, turnips, cauliflowers, potatoes.* Many of these may also be grown for animal feeds.

vegetative propagation the development of new plants by a process which does not require the production of *seed.* Vegetative propagation enables some plants to spread and to increase in number, as well as to survive from one generation to the next. It may be achieved by adaptations of the stem or root system which enable considerable lateral spread. Examples of crop plants which benefit from vegetative propogation are *potatoes*, and *white clover* and examples of *weed* plants include *couch grass.*

vein a vessel conveying blood back to the heart from one of the various organs of an animal's body.

venison the meat of deer.

ventricle generally, any chamber or cavity. In an animal's body important ventricles are located in the *brain* and in the heart where they form the main contractile chambers.

verandah house a type of *piggery* used for weaned pigs between the ages of

4 and 12 weeks. It consists of an umbrella roof over a central feeding passage with kennel accommodation each side.

vernalisation the induction of a flowering response in plants exposed to cold conditions. Certain *biennial* plants have a specific requirement for cold temperatures before they will flower. Premature flowering due to accidental vernalisation is called *bolting.*

vertebral column the backbone of an animal's body which is composed of a number of vertebrae which are small, irregular, median, unpaired bones.

veterinary surgeon a vet is a person qualified in veterinary science (the study of animal diseases) and is thus able to diagnose diseases, carry out surgery and prescribe medicines.

VFAs Volatile Fatty Acids, particularly the short chain fatty acids, *acetate, propionate* and *butyrate* which are produced by the *rumen* micro-organisms and absorbed by the *host* animal and used as an important energy source.

videotext a general term describing services available from television receivers capable of displaying pages of text and simple graphics. The services available to the farmer include current market information, weather forecasts and technical data.

vining the process of mechanically harvesting fresh *peas,* especially for processing. The whole crop is cut then separated by machine into peas and *haulm.* The haulm is returned to the field.

virus a particulate, infective agent smaller than *bacteria* and only capable of multiplying in susceptible living cells which are often subsequently damaged. They are the causative agents of many important diseases of plants (e.g. *virus yellows, mosiac disease*) and animals (e.g. *foot-and-mouth disease, swine vesicular disease*). Often the viruses are transmitted between plants by insects (e.g. *aphids*) and between animals by animal to animal contact and the associated inhalation of infected mucous droplets expelled by coughing and sneezing.

virus yellows diseases of sugar beet caused by beet yellows virus (BYV) and beet mild yellowing virus (BMYV). The foliage turns yellow and both yield and quality may be reduced. Viruses are spread by *aphids* from infected sources (old *mangold clamps* or remains of previous beet crops). Control is by *crop hygiene,* the use of *insecticides* to restrict *aphids* and some varietal *tolerance* is apparent.

viscera a general term for the abdominal organs of an animal e.g. *stomach, intestine, liver,* etc.

vitamin A or Axerophthol, which animals can obtain from its precursor, or pro-vitamins, the carotenes. It is required for vision, and the general good health and maintenance of epothelial surfaces e.g. the respiratory tract, reproductive tract.

vitamin B complex a group of water soluble vitamins which include thiamin, riboflavin niacin, pyridoxin, pantothenic acid and folic acid. The B vitamins are involved in a range of body processes including amino acid and carbohydrate metabolism and various oxidation processes.

vitamin C or ascorbic acid. Lack of vitamin C leads to scurvy but as grass and other green materials are high in vitamin C, deficiency is unlikely in *ruminant* animals. It is usually supplied to the *diet* of pigs and poultry.

vitamin D a fat soluble vitamin which is involved in calcium uptake from the intestine and its subsequent metabolism. A number of substances, including calciferol, have vitamin D activity. Livestock kept outside in the sun during summer are able to manufacture vitamin D through the irradiation of their skin.

vitamin E or tocopherol, a fat soluble vitamin which appears to be required for normal reproduction.

vitamin K a fat soluble vitamin which is required for the production of prothrombin and the normal clotting of blood.

vitamin-mineral mix a mixture of *vitamins* and essential *minerals,* in a form available to the animal, which is fed to farm *livestock* either included in a *concentrate* or *meal* or provided free access.

vitamins organic substances required in small amounts for the proper functioning of animals. They, or their immediate precursors, must be present in the animal's food (although because of the rumen micro-organisms, *ruminants* do not need to be provided with some of the B vitamins). Lack of vitamins leads to certain specific deficiency diseases which are curable by administration of the appropriate vitamin, partial lack may cause a lack of *thrift*. It is suggested that some vitamins have a valuable *therapeutic* action when given in large doses. As they were discovered, vitamins were distinguished by letters (A, B, C, etc.) but were later given names as their chemical structure was determined. They are often classified into fat soluble (A, D, E and K) and water soluble (C and the vitamin B complex) vitamins.

volunteer plants crop plants which develop from seed shed by the previous crop. They are therefore *weeds,* being both out of place and perhaps out of sequence with the existing crop. Hence volunteer *oilseed rape* plants may occur in *cereals* or vice versa. These plants are both unsightly and can provide an environment suitable for the survival of certain pest and disease organisms.

wafer a type of *nut* or *pellet,* produced by forcing *meal* through a *cuber,* which is used to feed farm *livestock.*   A wafer tends to be larger than the other cubed forms, often containing some processed forage and is somewhat less dense.

wages book used to record the wages of employees, overtime hours, bonuses and holiday pay, deductions for employee and employer National Insurance Contributions, and employee income tax.

warble fly one of two species of botfly (Hypoderma bovis or H. lineata) which worry and irritate grazing cattle in spring and summer as they lay their eggs on the legs (especially the fetlocks) of the cattle. Often cattle rush about to try to avoid attack by the flies - this behaviour is known as gadding. Once the eggs hatch the maggots penetrate the skin and migrate through the body of the *host* animal causing damage to body tissues as they go. By spring of the following year they have reached the back of the animal where they form chrysalises in swellings (or   warbles) immediately beneath the skin. Once mature the maggots escape through a hole in the hide of the animal and fall to the ground as pupa. The presence of warble flies causes severe inflammation and irritation to the animal which looses body condition; young animals may die. In addition the holes in the hide reduce its economic value   when the animal is slaughtered. Treatment is by pouring insecticide along the back of the cattle to kill the maggots.

ware potatoes   tubers which are of the correct size and quality for direct sale for human consumption.

warp   to give birth, especially prematurely.   The term is often used in relation to a miscarriage or abortion.

wart disease a fungal disease of the potato crop which is potentially serious but which is controlled by legislation and by the use of immune varieties. The causative organism, Synchytrium endobioticum may remain active in the soil for 30 years and can be spread on farm implements.   Tubers and stolons become affected producing a shapeless, warted mass. Most varieties are now immune. A *notifiable disease.*

waterlogging the condition of a soil when all spaces between soil particles are filled with water rather than air. Waterlogging occurs in conditions of heavy rainfall and where natural *drainage* is impeded. Soils with relatively small pore spaces e.g. clays and silts tend to become waterlogged more quickly than those with larger spaces e.g. sands. Waterlogging, if prolonged, causes reduced plant growth because roots cannot survive and remain active in the absence of air.

wayleave the right to use a defined area of land for purposes unrelated to its primary use.   For example, wayleaves may be granted by a land owner to electricity authorities to allow them to erect pylons. In return for granting a wayleave the land owner may receive payment.

weaner a young animal which has been weaned. The term is often specifically used for a young pig between weaning, at 3-5 weeks of age, and 10-12 weeks of age.

weaning the removal of young animals from their *dams* and therefore from their supply of milk from the *mammary glands,* marking the transition from a liquid diet to a solid diet in piglets, lambs and suckler calves. With calves from dairy cows, which are taken from their dams at or near to birth and reared on *milk substitutes,* weaning is generally referred to as being the cessation of feeding the milk substitute after which the animal only receives solid food.

weeds plants which are growing in the wrong place. Hence any other plant, either wild or cultivated, growing in a *monoculture* may be considered a weed. Weeds may reduce yields and quality and may be controlled by *rotations, cultivations* and *herbicides.*

Welsh a white, lop-eared pig which is similar in appearance to the *Landrace.* It is used in some *cross-breeding* programmes and in the construction of some of the *hybrid* lines of the Pig Breeding Companies.

Welsh Black a *dual-purpose* breed of cattle which has developed in the harsh conditions of the Welsh mountains and is thus able to thrive in harsh conditions. Under hill conditions, *cross-bred* calves sired by Welsh Black bulls grow particularly well. The cows produce a good milk yield, well spread out over lactation, making them very good suckler animals.

Welsh Half-Bred a cross-bred sheep arising from crossing a *Welsh Mountain* ewe with a *Border Leicester* ram.

Welsh Mountain one of the smallest of the British sheep breeds which is extensively found in the Welsh mountains. It is a very hardy breed which can tolerate adverse climatic conditions and poor quality grazing. It has a grey-white face and legs, whilst the fleece is soft with occasional red hairs.

Wensleydale a long-wooled breed of sheep which originated in N Yorkshire. It has a blueish-grey face, ears and legs and a finely purled, lustrous fleece. It is a breed of large mature size and is sometimes used as a sire to produce lambs which can be taken to heavy weights. However, its main use has been to cross onto *hill breeds* to produce *cross-bred* ewes e.g. the *Masham.*

Wessex Saddleback a *dual-purpose* breed of pig which has been amalgamated with the *Essex Saddleback* to form the *British Saddleback.* It is a black pig except for a white saddle covering the front legs and extending over the shoulder. Also, the hind feet and tail are white. The breed has traditionally been used in the production of *cross-bred* sows particularly for outdoor sow keeping systems.

wet feeding the feeding of *livestock,* especially pigs, of *meal* mixed with water. Wet feeding may be conducted simply by tipping water over meal in a trough or via an automated pipeline liquid feeding system.

wether a castrated male sheep.

wetter a chemical agent added to a *crop protection* chemical to improve its dispersion on the leaves of target plants. Many wetters act by reducing surface tension.

wheat (Triticum aestivum) an extemely important cultivated *cereal.* Wheat exists in both autumn and spring sown types, the autumn sown types being much the most important in the UK. Grain is used for milling, for bread or biscuits, and for animal feeding depending on quality. Recent advances in plant breeding have produced improvements in yield and quality, enabling much British wheat to be used for bread making.

wheat bulb fly (Delia coaretala) an important insect pest of winter wheat and barley. Damage caused by larvae feeding in the base of infected *tillers.* The central shoot of the plant turns yellow and dies in early spring. The fly may be controlled by *insecticides,* especially in combination with early drilling.

wheatfeed the offals of *wheat* which result from flour making and which are used as an animal *feedingstuff.* It consists of a mixture of *bran,* wheatgerm and both coarse and fine middlings and typically has a *crude fibre* content of 7-9%. Also called wheatings, pollards or sharps.

whey the residue from milk after cheese making has removed the majority of the fat and protein. Whey is often fed to pigs via liquid feeding systems.

white clover Trifolium repens, an herbaceous *legume* used for *forage.* White clover is a perennial plant with trifoliate leaves and white flowers. It has a stoloniferous growth habit which enables vegetative propagation and allows white clover to withstand grazing by livestock. Because of this, white clovers can be found in many lowland pastures both as a native and as introduced plants. They contribute to the *nitrogen* economy of the pasture and to its nutritional qualities.

whiteheads see *take-all.*

white meat *meat* is often classified into red and white. White meat includes *veal, poultry, rabbit* and usually *pork.* Contrast *redmeat.*

white muscle disease a disease of calves and lambs in which muscular degeneration occurs due to *vitamin E* or *selenium* deficiency. It is characterised by stiffness and lameness.

whole farm budgeting a method of budgeting employed when examining possible major changes or the setting up of a new farm. The budget displays the profitability of proposals. Contrast with *partial budgeting.*

wickens see *couch grass.*

Wildlife and Countryside Acts, passed in 1981 and amended in 1985 as an attempt to reconcile the interests of conservationists and farmers and landowners by regulating the circumstances under which certain agricultural developments will be undertaken. It is based on the voluntary cooperation of farmers who are, nevertheless, encouraged to comply with it. Where land of the highest conservation interest is proposed for development (e.g. *drainage* and *cultivation* of wetlands) the *Nature Conservancy Council* (NCC) could offer to buy the land or compensate the owner for conserving it. Farmers are compensated for entering into *management agreements,* with planning authorities or the NCC, in which they agree to forego development. The Act was amended in 1985, particularly with regard to its notification procedures.

wild oats uncultivated forms of *oats* which are *weeds* in *cereal* crops. Plants of Avena strigosa, A. fatua and A. ludoviciana are prolific seeders and can be difficult to eradicate.

wilting loss of turgor in plants due to a reduction in water content. In growing crops this indicates extreme shortage or inaccessibility of water in the soil and yield loss will result. The term is also applied when materials e.g. *grass* and *legume forages* are cut and left to dry out in the field, prior to harvesting as *hay* or *silage.* Rate of water loss depends on relative amounts of rain, sunshine and wind.

Wiltshire Horn a white-faced, horned breed of sheep which is characterised by a short fleece of thick wool and hair.

winnowing a process used to separate the seeds from the *chaff* after *threshing.* The mixture is allowed to fall through a horizontal air stream. The seeds, being more dense, continue to fall vertically whereas the light *chaff* is carried off sideways, thereby affecting separation.

winter feeding a general term for the feeding of livestock, particularly *ruminants,* over the winter months. During this period, with fresh grass unavailable the diet is based upon conserved grass (*hay* or *silage*), other bulk feeds and *concentrates.*

winter wheat the autumn sown form of *wheat.*

wireworms insect pests of cereals and grassland. The natural habitat of wireworms (Agriotes spp.) is grassland. Cereal crops are likely to be damaged when sown on land ploughed out of grass. The pests chew the base of cereal stems below ground level. Control is achieved by the use of *insecticides* especially as a seed treatment.

withers the area between the shoulder blades of an animal.

wool is found on various animals, but the term is usually appled to the fleece of sheep. Wool is a modified type of hair and consists of three types of fibres, kemps, heterotypes and true wool. Kemps and heterotypes are similar in that they are medullated and have the common properties of protection, insulation and water repulsion.   They are coarse and often form the outer coat. The inner wool coat is composed of very fine, true wool fibres which do not possess a medulla. The average annual wool yield varies, depending on breed from 1-8kg/sheep. It is sold to the *British Wool Marketing Board* where it is graded before allocation to the appropriate market.

wool ball a mass of wool and hair, tangled into a ball, which may be found in one of the stomachs of a *lamb*. The wool is accidently swallowed during suckling, accumulates, becomes twisted together and may cause a blockage to the digestive tract.

wool rot a condition of sheep in which a fungus (Dermatophilus dermatonomus) causes irritation to the skin   and the formation of characteristic yellow scabs. As the wool grows the scabs are carried away in the fleece.

working capital the capital required to finance the business through a production cycle. Also known as net current assets, it is defined as current *assets* less current *liabilities*. In other words, it is the proportion of current assets which are funded by long-term capital.

world market price the level of price at which world markets are cleared of supplies. The world market price is often referred to by economists and others in judging the cost of support through *administered prices.* This may be criticised on the grounds that world markets generally handle only a minute share of production, moreover that the prices they determine are very much influenced by the   policies of major producers such as the US and the EC and by the supply situation of major consumers, particularly the Centrally Planned Economies. The world price is a basic determinant of the rates of *variable levy* and *export refund* paid by the EC.

xylem the plant tissue in which the upward movement of water takes place. Xylem tissue consists of a large number of structurally strengthened cells which form an interconnected tubular system from the roots to the shoots.

yearling a term used for an animal between 1 and 2 years of age, which is most commonly applied to cattle.

yellow rust a foliar disease of wheat and barley caused by the fungus Puccinia striiformis. A number of strains exist, each specific to particular varieties. Affected plants show orange/yellow striping on the leaves and infected ears have yellow pustules on the *glumes*. The disease usually becomes apparent in spring in patches: its spread is favoured by changeable weather. Control is achieved by growing *resistant varieties* and *fungicide* treatment of infections.

yield the physical output from an animal or an area of land, e.g. litres of milk per cow, number of eggs per hen and tonnes of grain per hectare. Note that the maximum or highest possible yield, is not always the same as the economic optimum yield. Yield also refers to the rate of return of capital. See *marginality. economic yield* and *biological yield*.

yield components those elements or parts of a crop which combine to produce the yield, e.g. in cereals, tillers/m2, grains/ear, *thousand seed weight*.

yolk 1. The food store of the egg or ovum of animals. In particular, the yellow central part of the egg of birds which is rich in fat and protein. 2. The grease present in wool.

Yorkshire 1. An alternative name for the *large white* breed of pig. 2. An alternative name for the *Durham* breed of cattle from which the various *Shorthorn* breeds originated.

Yorkshire boarding a type of boarding used in livestock housing which consists of vertical wooden timbers which are set apart by gaps, the width of which varies with the location. The purpose is to allow natural ventilation to occur. It is most commonly found in the construction of cattle buildings.

Yorkshire fog (Holcus lanatus) a type of herbage grass often found in long-term *pastures*. It is a fairly unpalatable grass which is tolerant of acid conditions and low fertility.

232

Zebu the Bos indicus *cattle* which are extensively found in tropical regions of the world. Contrast the European, Bos taurus breeds.

zero grazing systems of mechanically harvesting fresh *herbage* or *forage* crops for feeding to enclosed or housed livestock. A technically efficient but expensive and time consuming method of feeding it is not popular in the UK but is more widely practiced in other parts of the world. Contrast *set stocking, paddock grazing, rotational grazing.*

zygote the cell which results from the fusion of the male *gamete* with the female gamete. This will occur when *spermatozoa* come into contact with an *ovum* at *fertilisation.*

STATISTICAL APPENDIX

Table 1 - UK agricultural land use (million ha).

	1976-78	1986
Total* Agricultural Land Use	19.0	18.7
of which:		
Rough Grazing	6.5	6.0
Permanent Grass		
(5 years old and over)	5.1	5.1
Arable	7.0	7.0
of which:		
Cereals	3.7	4.0
Roots	0.4	0.4
Peas and Beans	0.1	0.2
Oilseed Rape	0.1	0.3
Vegetables and Horticulture	0.3	0.2
Total Tillage*	4.9	5.3
Temporary Grass		
(under 5 years old)	2.1	1.7
Other	0.5	0.5

Source: Annual Review of Agriculture, 1988.
*Columns may not sum to totals, due to rounding.

Table 2 - <u>UK livestock numbers (millions).</u>*

	1976-78	1986
Dairy cows	3.3	3.1
Beef cows	1.7	1.3
Heifers in calf	0.9	0.9
Total Cattle and Calves	13.9	12.5
Ewes	11.4	14.3
Shearlings	2.5	3.1
Total Sheep and Lambs	28.8	37.0
Sows	0.7	0.7
Gilts in pig	0.1	0.1
Total Pigs	7.8	7.9
Table fowls	58.0	63.8
Laying fowls	50.1	38.1
Growing pullets	17.4	12.5
Total Poultry	131.7	120.7

Source: Annual Review of Agriculture, 1988.
*Columns may not sum to totals, due to rounding.

235

Table 3 - Percentage distribution of agricultural holdings
by broad type of farm and MAFF region.

	South	S. East/ E. Anglia	Midlands	North + Yorks	Wales	Scot- land	Total
Dairying	32.5	7.2	19.8	26.5	26.5	11.6	20.0
Hill Livestock	4.0	0.0	4.0	13.7	30.6	56.9	13.4
Lowland Cattle and Sheep	37.8	20.3	27.4	21.3	35.4	8.32	7.6
Cropping	12.7	44.7	32.9	23.3	3.3	19.4	24.7
Intensive Livestock	6.7	10.6	6.8	9.1	3.0	1.6	7.5
Horticulture	6.3	17.2	9.1	6.1	1.2	2.2	8.4
Total	100.0	100.0	100.0	100.0	100.0	100.0	100.0

Source: MAFF and DAFS.

Table 4 - <u>Agriculture in the national economy.</u>

	1976-78	1986
Contribution of Gross Domestic product £M (current prices)	3130	5628
per cent of total	2.4	1.8
Consumer Expenditure on Food and alcholic beverages £M (current)	24,906	54,200
Food as per cent of consumers expenditure	21.0	16.1
Share of Gross Fixed Capital Formation £M (current)	765	1,033
per cent of total	2.9	1.6
Manpower - total (thousands)	678	606
- per cent of total	2.8	2.5

Source: Annual Review of Agriculture, 1988.